# GCSE GEOGRAPHY for AVERY HILL

Andy Owen and Colin Lancaster
Editor: Sue Carstairs

Hodder Murray
A MEMBER OF THE HODDER HEADLINE GROUP

## Text acknowledgements

The Publishers would like to thank the following for permission to reproduce copyright material.

### Text extracts and screenshots

**p.47** Table on urban climate, © Crown copyright 2007, data supplied by the Met Office; **p.51** Thomas R. Knutson, U.S. National Oceanographic and Atmospheric Administration/GFDL; **p.58** Marland, G., T.A. Boden, R. J. Andres 2000. Global, Regional, and National $CO_2$ Emissions. In Trends: A Compendium of Data on Global Change. Carbon Dioxide Information Analysis Center, Oak Ridge National Laboratory, U.S. Department of Energy, Oak Ridge, Tenn., U.S.A.; **p.59** University of British Columbia Botanical Garden Website; Extract from Double Blind © Sacha Peter; **p.87** Table of climate data, The South African Weather Service; **p.92** News release, 'Major storm set to batter the UK tonight', 7 January 2005, © Crown copyright 2005, data supplied by the Met Office; **p.114** *l* Screenshot of Holderness coast © Getmapping plc; **p.151** Global Urban Development: "Where the Sidewalks End: How the Poor Combat Poverty Daily", Molly O'Meara Sheehan, November/December 2002 issue of World Watch magazine, reprinted with the permission of the Worldwatch Institute © www.worldwatch.org; **p.174** Lyrics from *Country Life*, 2003, by Show of Hands; **p.201** Daouda Ballo, Bamako Market, 2007. Material is reproduced with the permission of Oxfam GB, Oxfam House, John Smith Drive, Cowley, Oxford OX4 2JY, UK, www.oxfam.org.uk/coolplanet. Oxfam GB does not necessarily endorse any text or activities that accompany the materials.

### We would also like to acknowledge:

**p.20** Weathersys.com © 2007 Cross Media Technologies; **p.31** Sue Greig et al, *Earthrights: Education as if the planet really mattered*, WWF & Kogan Page, 1987; **pp.33, 37** Graph of extinctions and graph of economic benefits of ecosystems, both Millenium Ecosystem Assessment website; **p.39** Robert Lawton, Department of Biological Sciences, University of Alabama, Rainforest Alliance Neotropics Communications Eco-Exchange; **p.55** © Jim Metzner Productions, Inc; **p.59** World View of Global Warming: The Photographic Documentation of Climate Change, Copyright © 2005–2007; **p.121** Viewpoints taken from icWales website © Western Mail & Echo Limited 2007 and BBC Wales website; **p.157** *b* Google search engine © Google 2007; **pp.158, 162** The City of Johannesburg website (www.joburg.org.za); **p.159** Web extract from The United Nations Human Settlements Programme website, UN-HABITAT; **p.167** Table of data from Ghana Living Standard Survey GLSS 4 (1998/99); **p.173** Statistics from Homes for Rural Communities, Commission for Rural Communities 2005; **p.203** *Rural Women in the Sahel and their Access to Agricultural Extension: Overview of Five Country Studies*, 1994, World Bank Report; **p.205** Data from The UK Interdependence Report NEF 2006, Nursing and Midwifery Council 2005; **p.229** Extract from UNICEF website; **p.230** UN Millenium Goals, adapted from The Rough Guide to a Better World, Department for International Development; **p.256** Extract from International Galapagos Tour Operators Association, ©2007 IGTOA.



Orders: please contact Bookpoint Ltd, 130 Milton Park, Abingdon, Oxon OX14 4SB. Telephone: (44) 01235 827720. Fax: (44) 01235 400454. Lines are open 9.00–5.00, Monday to Saturday, with a 24-hour message answering service. Visit our website at www.hoddereducation.co.uk



First published in 2007 by
Hodder Murray, an imprint of Hodder Education,
a member of the Hodder Headline Group,
an Hachette Livre UK Company,
338 Euston Road
London NW1 3BH

Impression number 5 4 3 2 1

Year 2011 2010 2009 2008 2007



Illustrations by Barking Dog Art
Typeset in 11.5pt Times by Cathy May (Endangered Species)
Printed and bound in Italy
A catalogue record for this title is available from the British Library

ISBN-13: 978 0340 906 125

*Dynamic Learning CD-ROM:* ISBN-13: 978 0340 947 814

# Contents

# Introduction

## About this book

### The structure of the book

Your Avery Hill GCSE Geography course is divided into four main units. Each follows a theme. Each unit takes about a term of your two-year course to complete. This book also has four main units: one for each unit of the course.

Each unit in the book is set out in the same way:

Chapter 1: The Big Picture. This chapter introduces you to the main themes or issues of the unit.

Chapters 2 to 7. These chapters cover all of the key ideas that you are expected to know and understand. A key questions box at the beginning of each chapter will help you focus on what's important. These chapters also contain case studies so that the concepts and issues that you read about are always set in the context of real places.

Chapter 8: Problem-solving exercise. This chapter examines an issue from the unit in more detail. At the end of this chapter you are asked to make a plan to solve a problem – this final task is highlighted in red. This chapter is designed to help you with your examination technique in the second paper that you will take at the end of your two-year course.

### The main features of the book

This book includes the following features which have been designed to try to help you make the most of your course and prepare you for your examination.

#### Case studies

A case study is an example of a geographical concept or issue. You will need to learn a few case studies for the first of the two Avery Hill examinations. For a good case study you will need to know:

- the name of the place and where in the world your case study is located
- what this is a good example of
- a few simple facts or figures.

To make you aware of these case studies we have used the above icon. The icon is used at the beginning of the case study.

#### Focus on ... case studies

The examiners have found that if you try to learn too many different case studies you might get them confused with each other! So, we have used some places several times as examples of different aspects of geography. This will allow you to focus on a few places in much more detail, so we have called them Focus on ... case studies. The icon for these (shown above) is used in the same way as the case study icon.

#### Exam technique

The exam technique sections are designed to help you prepare for standard questions that are asked in the examinations. They are spread throughout the book. When you are doing an activity in the book and an exam technique section could give you some help, this table will help you find them easily. The above icon will make them easy to find on the page.

| Exam technique section | Page |
|---|---|
| Describing a climate graph | 11 |
| Describing a location | 120 |
| Describing distributions | 143 |
| Making comparisons | 147 |
| Extending your explanation | 209 |
| Using OS map evidence from extracts | 239 |
| Justifying your plan (useful for the problem-solving exercise) | 256 |

#### Activities

The activities in the book are designed to get you doing a number of things:

- discussing geographical issues
- analysing data in the maps, graphs and photos
- understanding concepts and case studies
- practising examination type questions.

In addition, many activity boxes contain one or more questions which are more time-consuming, more challenging or require some research. These are marked with a red circle behind the question number.

### Internet

The internet is a useful geographical resource. It contains facts that you could use to extend your case study notes. It's also great for finding and explaining people's opinions, which you will find particularly helpful when you are doing your Cross Unit Task. We've used the icon above wherever we think that there is a useful website that could add extra detail to the book. This icon is also used in some internet research boxes. These boxes are designed to maximise your search skills when you are surfing the net for geographical information.

### Going Further

Going Further sections cover some interesting issues that are not essential to your understanding of GCSE Avery Hill Geography, but might lead you into new areas of research. Geography is a popular choice at AS level. Going Further might just get you thinking about this next step.

## Patterns of assessment

Assessment for Avery Hill GCSE Geography includes two pieces of coursework. One of these is the Cross Unit Task which is worth 10 per cent of your total mark.

At the end of your course you will sit two examinations. The first exam (of which Paper 1 is the Foundation tier and Paper 2 is the Higher tier) will test your knowledge and understanding of three of the four units. This paper is commonly called the 'Case Study' paper because the last part of each question asks you to describe case studies that you have learned. The other exam (Paper 3 is the Foundation tier and Paper 4 is the Higher tier) tests your understanding of the other unit. This is the problem-solving paper and the final chapter in each unit of the book will help you prepare for this paper.

The unit which is examined on Papers 3 and 4 varies from one year to the next. The following chart will help you plan your pattern of assessment.

| **Year** | **2007** | | **2008** | | **2009** | | **2010** | |
|---|---|---|---|---|---|---|---|---|
| **Paper** | **1&2** | **3&4** | **1&2** | **3&4** | **1&2** | **3&4** | **1&2** | **3&4** |
| 1 Climate, environment and people | ✓ | | ✓ | | ✓ | | | ✓ |
| 2 Water, landforms and people | ✓ | | | ✓ | ✓ | | ✓ | |
| 3 People and place | | ✓ | ✓ | | ✓ | | ✓ | |
| 4 Work and development | ✓ | | ✓ | | | ✓ | ✓ | |

# Photo acknowledgements

The Publishers would like to thank the following for permission to reproduce copyright material.

**Cover** (from *l* to *r*) © Michael and Patricia Fogden/Corbis, Fernando Bustamante/AP Photo/Empics, Digital Stock, PhotoDisk; **p.7** *t* Still Pictures/Jacques Jangoux, *bl* NASA/Goddard Space Flight Centre, *br* Rex Features; **p.10** Getty Images/photographer's choice; **p.13** NASA/Image Courtesy GOES Project Science Office; **p.14** Space Science and Engineering Center, University of Wisconsin–Madison; **p.16** Andy Owen; **p.18** *tl* Andy Owen, *br* ©Crown copyright 2007, data supplied by the Met Office; **p.20** Getty Images/Stock4b; **p.22** PA Photos; **p.26** *tr* FLPA/Paul Hobson, *all others* Andy Owen; **p.28** *tl* Andy Owen, *tr* Jef Maion/www.maion.com, *b* NHPA/Martin Harvey; **p.30** FLPA/Tui De Roy/Minden Pictures; **p.32** Corbis/Michael & Patricia Fogden; **p.34** NHPA/Jordi Bas Casas; **p.35** FLPA/Gerry Ellis/Minden Pictures; **p.36** Corbis/Wolfgang Kaehler; **p.38** Photolibrary/Peter Weimann; **p.40** NASA/Goddard Space Flight Centre; **p.41** Alamy/Celia Mannings; **p.42** Webb Aviation; **p.43** Andy Owen; **p.44** *t* Still Pictures/L.F. Postl, *b* NHPA/Stephen Dalton; **p.46** The Woodland Trust/BBC; **p.48** *br* WWT London Wetland Centre/picture by BerkeleyHomes *all others* Andy Owen; **p.55** Nature Picture Library/Mats Forsberg; **p.58** Zapiro/Sowetan; **p.60** Rex Features/ James D. Morgan; **p.62** *l* Getty Images/Tim Graham *r* NSWNHPA/A.N.T. Photolibrary; **p.64** *t* Australian Government Bureau of Meteorology, *b* NASA; **p.69** *tl* Science Photo Library/Tom Van Sant/Geosphere Project, Santa Monica, *tr* Still Pictures/Julio Etchart, *bl* ©Greenpeace/Daniel Beltrá; **p.70** *t* Panos Pictures/Crispin Hughes, *b* Corbis/Tony Roberts; **p.72** ©Simon Robinson, 2004; **p.73** *tl* Corbis/Tony Demin, *c* FLPA/Gary K. Smith, *b* University of Illinois Extension; **p.75** Andy Owen; **p.77** Dr Mark Robinson, Centre for Ecology and Hydrology; **p.78** Dr Rudolf Winter; **p.80** *t* Corbis/Yu Xiangquan/Xinhua Press, *b* FLPA/Frans Lanting/Minden Pictures; **p.81** PA Photos/AP/Debra; **p.82** Andy Owen; **p.85** Corbis/Richard T. Nowitz; **p.89** Transformation Resource Centre; **p.91** *t* International Water Management; **p.91** *b* PlayPumps International; **p.94** *t* PA Photos/John Giles, *b* PA Photos/John Giles; **p.97** US Army Corps of Engineers; **p.101** Severn Trent Water; **p.102** *all* Jesse Allen, Earth Observatory/NASA; **p.104** Eye Ubiquitous; **p.106** Colin Lancaster; **p.107** NASA/Goddard Space Flight Centre; **p.108** Colin Lancaster; **p.109** *t* Science Photo Library/M-SAT Ltd., *b* US Army Corps of Engineers; **p.110** *t* Science Photo Library/NASA, *b* WaterAid/Abir Abdullah; **p.112** Andy Owen; **p.113** Andy Owen; **p.114** *r* Scanpix/Kjeld Olesen; **p.115** *all* Andrew Stacey; **p.116** *all* Andy Owen; **p.117** Andrew Stacey; **p.118** *all* ©2007 TerraMetrics, Inc. www.truearth.com; **p.119** Andrew Stacey; **p.120** Brian Harris; **p.123** Alamy/Andrew Palmer; **p.124** Andrew Stacey; **p.126** Robert Seago; **p.131** *t* Rex Features/Sipa Press, *c* Corbis/Arko Datta/Reuters, *l* Getty Images/Simmons Aerofilms; **p.134** *all* Andy Owen; **p.138** Andy Owen; **p.144** Alamy/Tony Vilches; **p.150** Photo by Adam Rogers/UNCDF; **p.154** Getty Images/Touchline; **p.157** *t* Getty Images/Mark Peters; **p.160** Panos Pictures/Sven Torfinn; **p.165** *all* Still Pictures/Jorgen Schytte; **p.168** *l* Corbis/Colin McPherson/Sygma, *r* Peter Bigglestone; **p.169** *l* Getty Images/Maeers/Hulton, *r* Still Pictures/Paul Glendell; **p.172** Andy Owen; **p.174** Andy Owen; **p.175** Peter Bigglestone; **p.176** *t* ©National Land Survey of Iceland, licence number L07050011 Ferdakort 2, Sudurland, 1:250,000 (ISBN number: 9979750375); *b* Andy Owen; **p.177** *all* Andy Owen; **p.179** *t* Science Photo Library/NASA, *b* Corbis/Bob Krist; **p.182** Rex Features/Splashdown Direct; **p.183** Still Pictures/Nick Cobbing; **p.184** Corbis/David Turnley; **p.185** Jeremy Jowell/iAfrika Photos; **p.188** Alamy/Stuart Abraham; **p.191** *tl* Still Pictures/Ron Giling, *tr* Getty Images/Raveendran/AFP, *bl* Getty Images, *br* Corbis/Strauss/Curtis; **p.192** *t* Getty Images/Jo Hale, *b* *Thin Black Lines* (1988), page 36, DEC; **p.194** *tl* Alamy/Jim West, *tr* Alamy/David Pearson, *bl* PA Photos/Thomas Kienzle/AP, *br* PurestockX; **p.197** Corbis/Pierre Vinet/Universal Pictures/ZUMA; **p.198** *t* Image courtesy of The Potteries Museum & Art Gallery, Stoke-on-Trent, *b* Andy Owen; **p.200** *t* Panos Pictures/Dieter Telemans, *bl* Panos Pictures/Crispin Hughes, *br* Getty Images/Seyllou/AFP; **p.201** Alamy/James Hawkins; **p.203** Janet Henshall Momsen (1991) *Women and Development in the Third World*, Routledge, Figure 3.2 page 39; **p.204** PA Photos/Kirsty Wigglesworth; **p.206** *l* Panos Pictures/Christien Jaspars, *r* *Thin Black Lines* (1988), page 24, DEC; **p.209** Panos Pictures/Giacomo Pirozzi; **p.211** Panos Pictures/Alfredo Caliz; **p.214** Corbis/Flip Schulke; **p.216** *tl* Christian Aid/Austin Hargreaves, *tr* Corbis/Reinhard Krause/Reuters, *b* Panos Pictures/Karen Robinson; **p.218** *t* Corbis/Richard Hamilton Smith, *b* Getty Images/Daniel Pepper; **p.220** Christian Aid/Penny Tweedie; **p.221** *l* Oxfam, *r* Greg Williams/Oxfam; **p.222** Panos Pictures/Karen Robinson; **p.225** *t* Fairtrade ® *b* Panos Pictures/Karen Robinson; **p.227** Practical Action/Lucy Stevens; **p.228** Getty Images/Issouf Sanogo/AFP; **p.231** Panos Pictures/Crispin Hughes; **p.234** Corbis/Andreas Gebert/DPA; **p.236** Corbis/Claro Cortes/Reuters; **p.237** Vodacom Lovelife Project; **p.240** Getty Images/Goh Chai Hin/AFP; **p.241** NASA/Goddard Space Flight Center Scientific Visualization Studio; **p.244** *Thin Black Lines* (1988), DEC; **p.248** *t* ©Forests Monitor, *b* ©Forests Monitor; **p.250** Heidi Snell/Visual Escapes; **p.253** Corbis/Stuart Westmorland; **p.254** Photolibrary/Mark Jones; **p.255** Photolibrary/C.C. Lockwood.

*t* = top, *b* = bottom, *l* = left, *r* = right, *c* = centre

Every effort has been made to trace all copyright holders, but if any have been inadvertently overlooked the Publishers will be pleased to make the necessary arrangements at the first opportunity.

# Unit 1 Climate, Environment and People

## Chapter 1 The Big Picture

## Ecosystems are seen as a resource

A key idea in Avery Hill GCSE Geography is that the environment is viewed by people and businesses as a resource; something that can be used for our benefit. Since the Industrial Revolution, a little over 200 years ago, the world's **ecosystems** have been used to supply people with the things they needed:

- Rainforests and coniferous forests have supplied people with timber and other raw materials.
- Land for farming has been created by draining wetlands and destroying forests.
- Ecosystems such as mangroves and coral reefs have increasingly been used as places for tourism development.

### The Millennium Ecosystem Assessment

The Millennium Ecosystem Assessment (MEA) is a scientific report into the state of the environment. Published in 2005, it took five years to write and involved the work of more than 1,360 experts from all parts of the world. The MEA concludes that the world's resources have been used to create a better standard of living for billions of people. Ecosystems have been used to supply people with a range of resources including food, clothing, energy and fresh water. However, it also warns that economic activity has done a great deal of damage to the environment (see Figure 1). One problem identified in the report is that modern fishing methods are unsustainable. More fish are caught each year than are replaced by natural reproduction. This problem was first seen in the Atlantic off the coast of Newfoundland, Canada, as shown in Figure 2.

| | **Millennium Ecosystem Assessment** |
|---|---|
| 1 | Modern fishing techniques do not allow fish stocks to recover. The amount of fish in the seas is decreasing rapidly. |
| 2 | The 2 billion people who live in the world's driest areas are increasingly at risk from drought and poverty. |
| 3 | We are using up fresh water supplies at a rate that is faster than they can be replaced. |
| 4 | **Climate change** will cause massive problems for many ecosystems. |
| 5 | The increasing use of artificial fertilisers and burning of fossil fuels has doubled the amount of nitrogen pollution. This is causing problems in river and marine ecosystems. |
| 6 | The destruction of ecosystems (for example, forests, coral reefs and wetlands) is causing the extinction of many species at a scale that is greater than anything seen in the past. |

**Figure 1** The six main problems identified by the Millennium Ecosystem Assessment

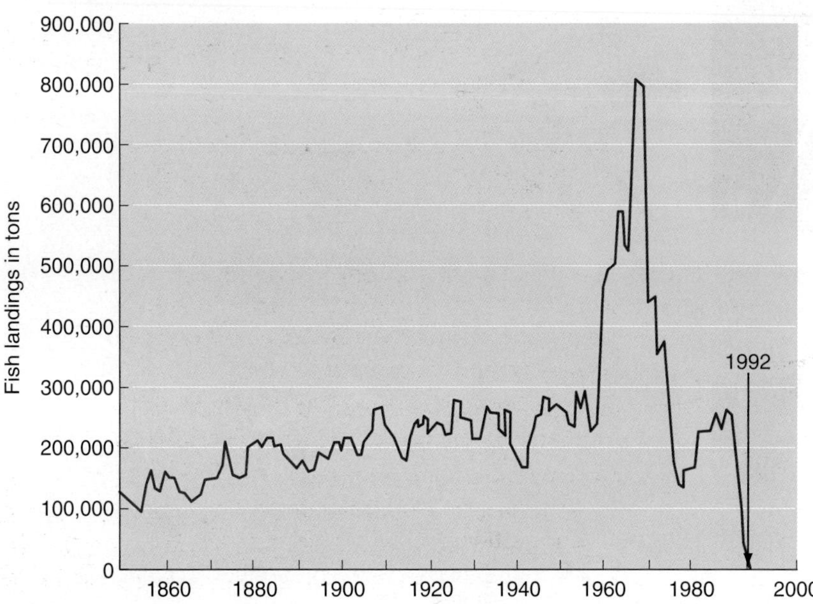


**Figure 2** Overfishing caused the collapse of the Atlantic cod stocks off Newfoundland

| Year | % of catch |
|---|---|
| 1994 | 13 |
| 1995 | 10 |
| 1996 | 11 |
| 1997 | 14 |
| 1998 | 6 |
| 1999 | 8 |
| 2000 | 10 |
| 2001 | 40 |
| 2002 | 8 |
| 2003 | 22 |

**Figure 3** Overfishing by European Union countries. Figures refer to the percentage of the total catch that is considered by scientists to be beyond what is safe for the fish stocks to fully recover (Source: Eurostat, Commission Services)

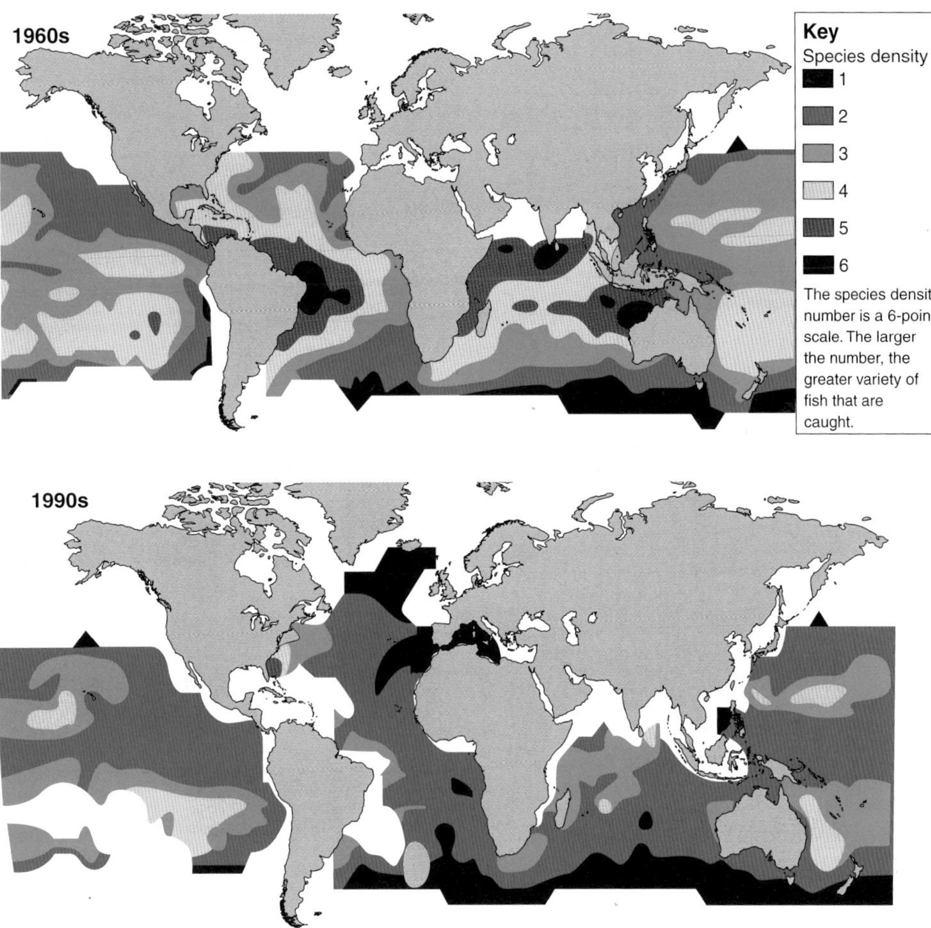


**Figure 4** Changes in average number of species caught by **longline fishing**

## Activity

**1** Study each of the problems listed in Figure 1 by the MEA. Suggest how each of the following economic activities could have contributed to these problems.

| | |
|---|---|
| **Agriculture** | **Fishing** |
| **Mining** | **Timber extraction** |
| **Manufacturing** | **Tourism** |

**2** Study Figure 2.

**a)** Describe the trend of the cod catch:

i) up to 1950

ii) after 1950.

**b)** Explain what happened in the early 1990s and suggest how this affected the local fishing industry.

**3 a)** Choose a suitable graphical method to represent Figure 3.

**b)** What conclusions do you draw from the data in Figures 2 and 3?

**4** Use Figure 4 and an atlas to describe the changing distribution of fish species caught between the 1960s and 1990s.

**5** Conservationists are concerned that fish stocks in the North Sea could crash due to overfishing, just like the Atlantic cod crash off Newfoundland. Suggest:

**a)** two alternative strategies to protect fish stocks in the North Sea from overfishing

**b)** how fishermen, boat repair yards and fishmongers would be affected by your suggestions.

# Chapter 2
# Investigating climate patterns

**KEY QUESTIONS**

- Why are there distinctive types of climate in different parts of the world?
- What's a **pressure system** and how does our atmosphere influence climate patterns?
- How does climate affect the activities of people?

**Figure 1** Crossing central Iceland. How does the Icelandic climate affect people?

## Investigating global patterns of climate

From the icy cold of the Arctic to the tropical heat and intense rainstorms of the Equator, different regions of the world have very different and distinctive climates. Figure 1 shows the special off-road vehicles needed to cross central Iceland. The unsurfaced roads in central Iceland are impassable in winter because of the snow and ice. In summer, the snow melts and the rivers fill with **meltwater**. Iceland, on the edge of the Arctic Circle, has a seasonal climate with cold winters and cool summers. By contrast, the latitudes between the tropics remain hot throughout the year. Figure 2 explains why latitude affects temperature.

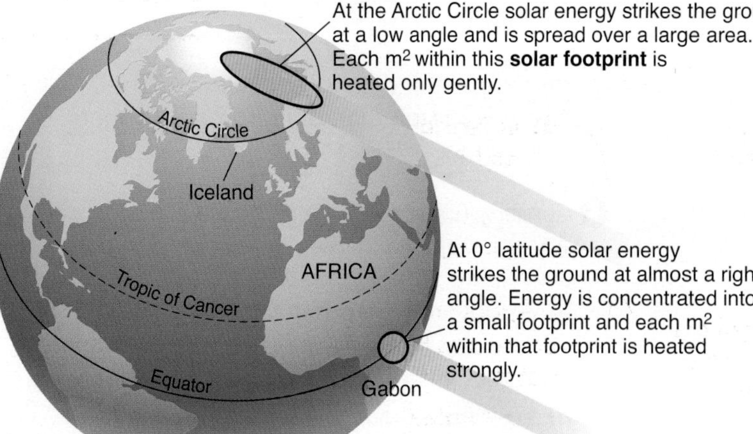


**Figure 2** Solar heating of the Earth varies with latitude

**EXAMTECHNIQUE**

## Describing a climate graph

**Tip 1**

Each climate graph has four features that you need to describe. Study the graph and ask yourself:

1 What is the **total annual rainfall**? This is calculated by adding all of the values for the rainfall bars together.
2 Are there distinctive wet or dry seasons? If so, when are they, and how long does each last?
3 What is the **annual temperature range**? This is the difference in temperature between the hottest and coldest times of the year.
4 Does the temperature show a distinctive seasonal pattern? If so, at what time of year are the hot and cold seasons?

**Tip 2**

You will get higher marks if you can quantify your answer. This means using significant figures from the graph to add quantities to your description.

**Tip 3**

You only need to describe the graph. Don't try to explain the features unless the question has asked you to explain them.

### A model answer: describing the climate of Reykjahlid, Iceland

1 Reykjahlid has a rather dry climate with a total annual rainfall of only around 430 mm.
2 Between December and April the precipitation is very low and, because temperatures are below freezing, would fall as snow. Monthly rainfall in the summer is slightly higher than in winter.
3 The annual temperature range is around 15 °C which is large.
4 The months from June to August are cool, with temperatures just below 10 °C. The months from December to March are cold with temperatures in the range 0 to –4 °C during this winter period.

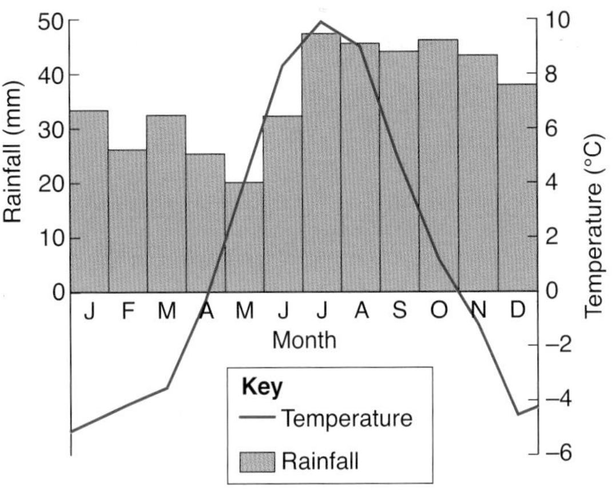


**Figure 3** Climate graph for Reykjahlid in northern-central Iceland

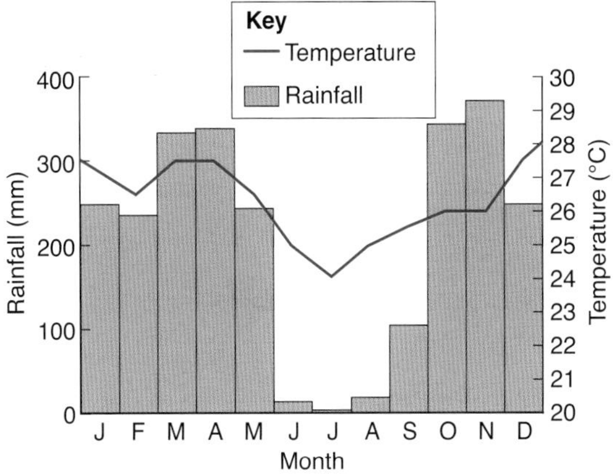


**Figure 4** Climate graph for Gabon, equatorial Africa

## Activity

**1** Study Figure 2 and read the exam technique section on climate graphs before copying and completing the following:

**a)** **Iceland is just south of ........................ whereas Gabon is on the ........................**

**b)** **The Sun strikes the ground in Iceland at ........................ whereas in Gabon this angle is much ........................ This means that the Sun's energy is more ........................ in Gabon.**

**c)** **The annual temperature .......... is the difference between maximum and ............. temperatures.**

**d)** **In Reykjahlid the maximum temp is ....... °C and the minimum is ....... °C.**

**2** Use the exam technique advice to describe the climate pattern in Gabon shown in Figure 4.

**3** Using the following headings, describe the main differences between the climate in Iceland and Gabon.

**Total rainfall**
**Seasonal rainfall pattern**
**Temperature range**

## What are pressure systems and how are they formed?

Our atmosphere is made of tiny molecules of nitrogen, oxygen, carbon dioxide and other rarer gases. Despite their tiny size, these molecules have mass and actually press down on us. This is what we call **air pressure**.

Air pressure is measured in units called millibars. The name comes from the Greek word *baros*, or bar, meaning pressure. A millibar (mb) is one thousandth of a bar. Air pressure varies with altitude, as you can see in Figure 5. Average air pressure at sea level is 1,013.2 mb. Air pressure at sea level varies approximately 80 mb either side of this value. So 970 to 990 mb is **low pressure** while 1,020 to 1,040 millibars is **high pressure**.

**www.noaa.gov** The National Oceanic and Atmospheric Administration website: a fantastic resource of recent and archive satellite images of the Earth and its atmosphere.

Variations in air pressure are usually caused by heating and cooling. In warm air the molecules are further apart than in cold air. Warm air rises, the molecules get further apart and there is less mass pressing down. This causes low air pressure. The opposite is true where air is cool.

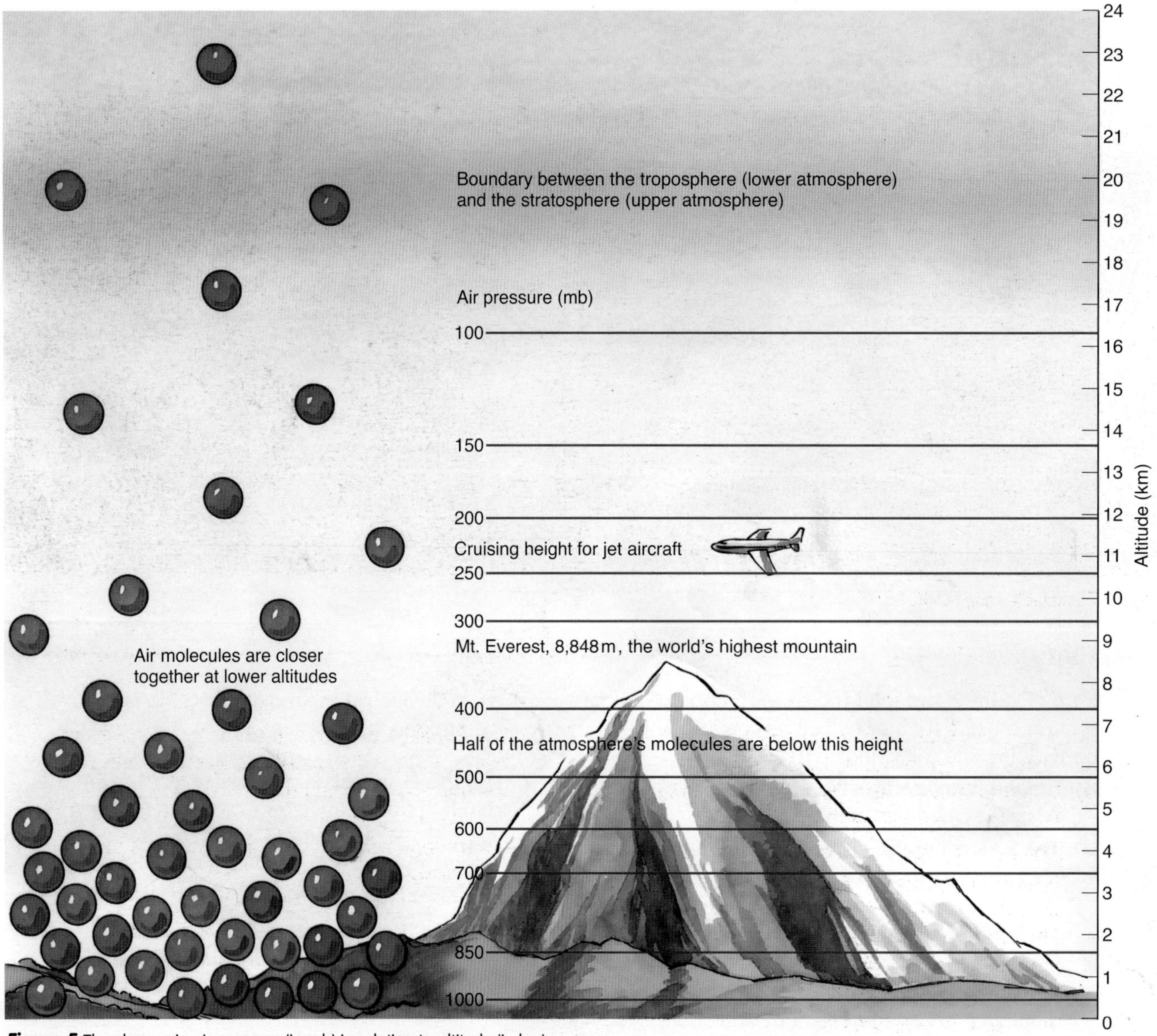

Boundary between the troposphere (lower atmosphere) and the stratosphere (upper atmosphere)

Air pressure (mb)

100
150
200
Cruising height for jet aircraft
250
300
Mt. Everest, 8,848 m, the world's highest mountain
400
Half of the atmosphere's molecules are below this height
500
600
700
850
1000

Air molecules are closer together at lower altitudes

Altitude (km)
24
23
22
21
20
19
18
17
16
15
14
13
12
11
10
9
8
7
6
5
4
3
2
1
0

**Figure 5** The change in air pressure (in mb) in relation to altitude (in km)

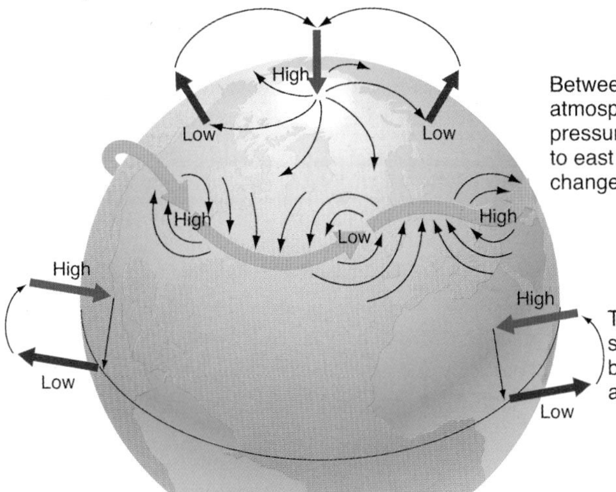


**Figure 6** Pressure systems in the Earth's atmosphere

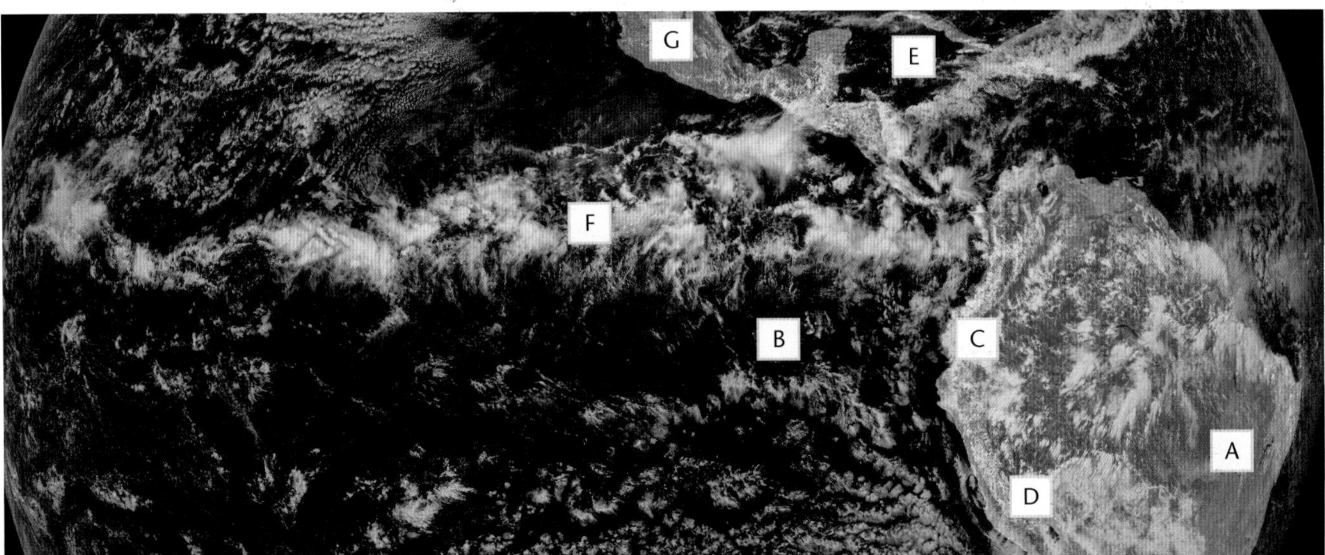


**Figure 7** A satellite image of the Pacific Ocean

## Activity

**4** Study Figures 6 and 7 and an atlas:

**a)** Name the countries A, B, C, D and E.

**b)** Working in pairs, match the following labels to letters F and G:

- The atmosphere is warmed by the hot region below. Warm air rises, creating clouds and an area of low pressure.
- Sinking air creates high pressure and cloudless skies.

**c)** Explain why the clouds on Figure 7 indicate areas of low pressure.

**5** Use Figure 6 and your understanding of solar heating of the Earth (Figure 2) to explain why:

**a)** the polar regions generally have high pressure

**b)** the equatorial region generally has low pressure.

**6** Explain why the weather between latitudes 35 °N–65 °N is so changeable.

## High pressure systems and the continental climate

Around the edge of the Arctic region, between 60 °N and 70 °N, are large parts of the North American, European and Asian land masses. The climate here is characterised by severe winters and relatively short, cool summers. The most extreme temperatures are experienced in places far from the sea such as Norilsk in Russia. Here, the average winter temperature is -32 °C whereas summer temperatures reach a comparatively high 15 °C. This enormous temperature range (of 47 °C) is due to the fact that continents heat up and cool down very quickly. This fcaturc of thc climatc of largc land masses is known as **continentality**.

During the winter, temperatures in Russia and Canada can fall to -20 °C and below. The extremely cold ground chills the air above it. The cold air sinks, pressing down on the ground creating a high pressure system known as an **anticyclone**. Anticyclones are characterised by clear, cloudless skies. Any heat given to the ground by the weak winter sunshine is quickly lost in the cloudless night sky.

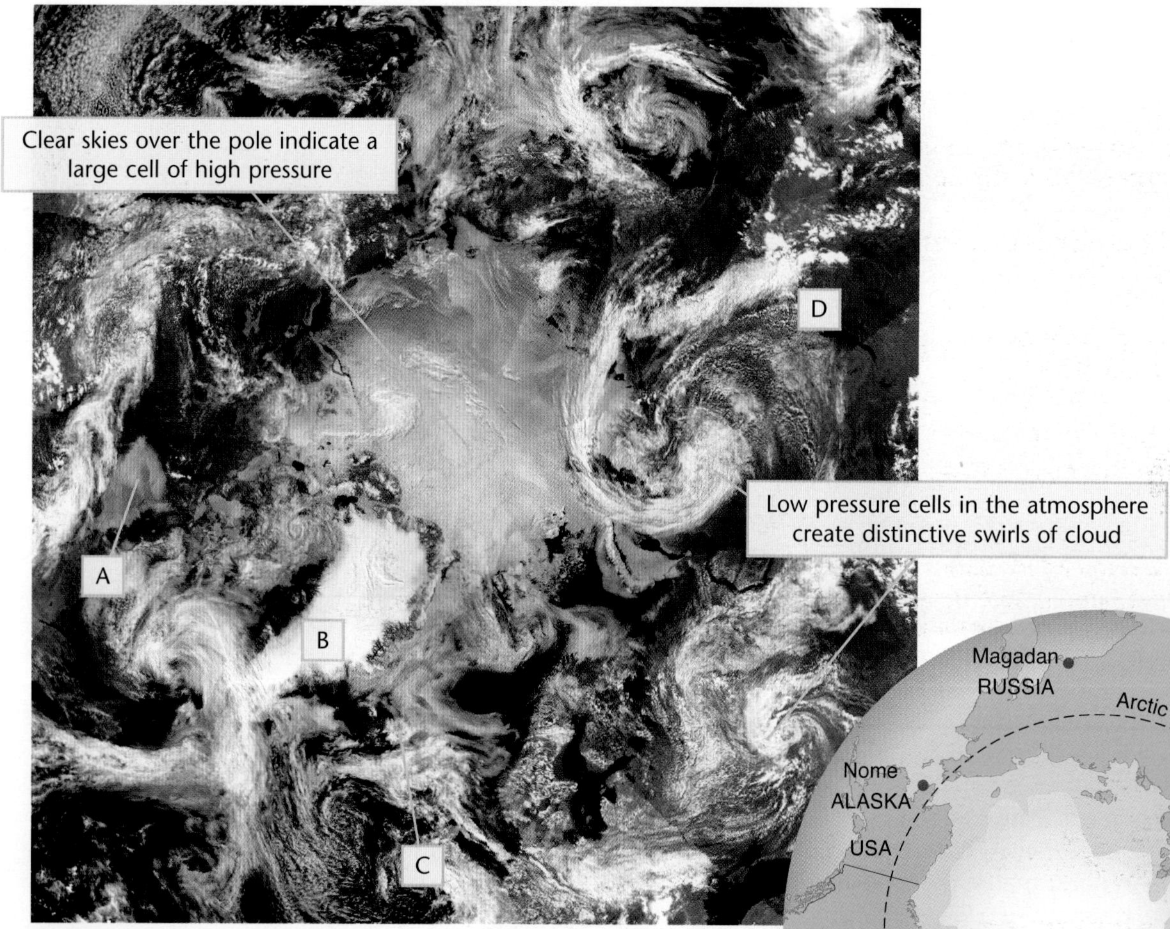

Clear skies over the pole indicate a large cell of high pressure

Low pressure cells in the atmosphere create distinctive swirls of cloud

**Figure 8** A satellite image of the Arctic

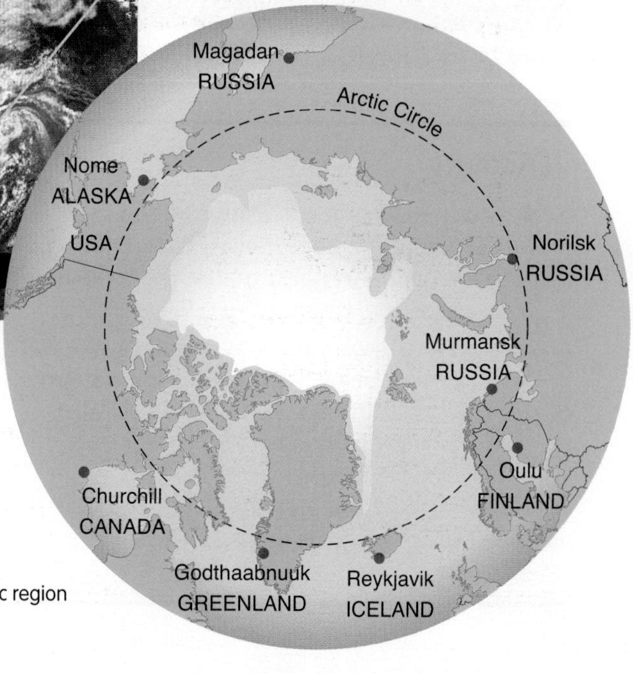

Magadan RUSSIA

Arctic Circle

Nome ALASKA USA

Norilsk RUSSIA

Murmansk RUSSIA

Oulu FINLAND

Churchill CANADA

Godthaabnuuk GREENLAND

Reykjavik ICELAND

**Figure 9** The Arctic region

| Station | Latitude/ Longitude | Min temp (°C) | Max temp (°C) | Temp range |
|---|---|---|---|---|
| Reykjavik, Iceland | 64 °13'N 21°90'W | –1 | 11 | 12 |
| Oulu, Finland | 64 °93'N 25 °36'E | | 16 | 26 |
| Murmansk, Russia | 68 °96'N 33 °5'E | –12 | | 24 |
| Norilsk, Russia | 69 °33'N 88 °10'E | –32 | 15 | |
| Magadan, Russia | 59 °58'N 150 °78'E | –18 | 12 | |
| Nome, Alaska | 64 °30'N 165 °25'W | –16 | 11 | |
| Churchill, Canada | 58 °75'N 94 °6'W | | 12 | 38 |
| Godthaabnuuk, Greenland | 64 °16'N 51 °75'W | –10 | | 16 |

**Figure 10** Climate data for selected climate stations between 58 °N and 70 °N

## Activity

**7** Use Figure 9 to name five countries that have territory north of the Arctic Circle.

**8** Use Figure 9 to name countries A, B, C and D on Figure 8.

**9** Explain why the skies over the polar region of Figure 8 are cloudless.

**10** Make a copy of Figure 10:

**a)** Calculate the missing value for each climate station.

**b)** Which station has the:

i) coldest minimum temperature

ii) largest temperature range?

**c)** Suggest reasons for the wide variation in temperature ranges at these climate stations.

**11 a)** Suggest a hypothesis you could investigate using climate data that links the following variables:

**minimum temperature**
**latitude**
**distance from the sea.**

**b)** Predict the likely outcome of your enquiry and explain why you expect this outcome.

**c)** Compare the minimum temperatures in Iceland and Greenland. Do these temperatures follow your expected outcome?

## Going Further

### Permafrost

**Permafrost** is soil or rock that has remained frozen for at least two consecutive years. Approximately 26 per cent of the Earth's land area is affected by permafrost. The climate of permafrost regions reaches temperatures above 0 °C during the summer so, although the ground at depth remains frozen, a thin layer of soil at the surface thaws. This surface layer is known as the active layer. When water in the soil freezes, and when lenses of ice form in the soil, the ground surface is lifted: a process known as frost heave. In the late spring, when the active layer thaws, the ground surface subsides. This combination of heaving and collapsing can cause subsidence problems in roads and buildings. Scientists predict that global warming will increase the effect of subsidence problems on buildings and roads in Arctic regions.

**12** Use the web link below to research the likely effects of global warming on permafrost. Prepare a three-minute presentation to give to the class.

**www.acia.uaf.edu**
For access to some excellent graphics, satellite images and maps describing the impact of climate change on the Arctic region.

Iceland

## Investigating the effect of the sea: a case study of Iceland's climate

**Figure 11** Despite the Gulf Stream, Iceland has a cold and challenging winter climate. Europe's largest ice cap, Vatnajökull, and a number of smaller ice caps (like the one shown here) and glaciers cover around eleven per cent of the island

**www.vedur.is/english/**
The English homepage of the official website of the Icelandic Met Office. Use the link to find climate data or whether Iceland's roads are blocked with snow.

We have seen how the land masses of Canada and Russia quickly lose their heat in the Arctic winter. By comparison, oceans cool down very slowly. So ocean currents are able to transfer heat from warm latitudes to cooler ones. Iceland's coastline is kept warm by one such current of warm water, the Gulf Stream. This brings warm water across the Atlantic from the tropics. This warm water heats the air above it and gives Iceland's coastal regions a **maritime climate** which is warmer and wetter than other places at similar latitudes.

### How does Iceland's climate affect its people?

Iceland's climate has always been a challenge to the Icelandic people. Snow in the winter closes many roads and some are not passable until May. However, the Gulf Stream prevents ice forming in coastal waters so fishing boats can leave port throughout the year. Figure 15 summarises some of the impacts of Iceland's climate on the country's economy and its people.

| | **Vestmannaeyjar Islands** | | **Akureyri** | |
|---|---|---|---|---|
| Month | °C | Precipitation (mm) | °C | Precipitation (mm) |
| Jan | 1.3 | 158 | –2.2 | 52 |
| Feb | 2.0 | 139 | –1.5 | 43 |
| Mar | 1.7 | 141 | –1.3 | 43 |
| Apr | 3.4 | 117 | 1.6 | 29 |
| May | 5.8 | 105 | 5.5 | 19 |
| Jun | 8.0 | 102 | 9.1 | 28 |
| Jul | 9.6 | 95 | 10.5 | 33 |
| Aug | 9.6 | 140 | 10.0 | 34 |
| Sep | 7.4 | 131 | 6.3 | 39 |
| Oct | 5.0 | 161 | 3.0 | 58 |
| Nov | 2.4 | 154 | –0.4 | 54 |
| Dec | 1.4 | 193 | –1.9 | 53 |
| | 4.8 av. | 1588.6 total | 3.2 av. | 489.5 total |

**Figure 12** Climate data for selected climate stations in Iceland

### Activity

**13** Use Figure 12 to draw climate graphs for each weather station.

**14** Using the exam technique box 'Describing a climate graph' on page 11 to help you, describe the features of each of the climate graphs.

**15** Draw an outline map of Iceland and a cross-section diagram like Figure 14. Use the additional labels to add extra annotations to your map and cross-section.

**16** Use Figures 13 and 14 to explain why:
- **a)** winters in Akureyri are colder than in Reykjavik
- **b)** rainfall totals are relatively low in Akureyri but high in southern Iceland.

**17** Look at Figure 15. Write a paragraph explaining how Iceland's climate affects its people.

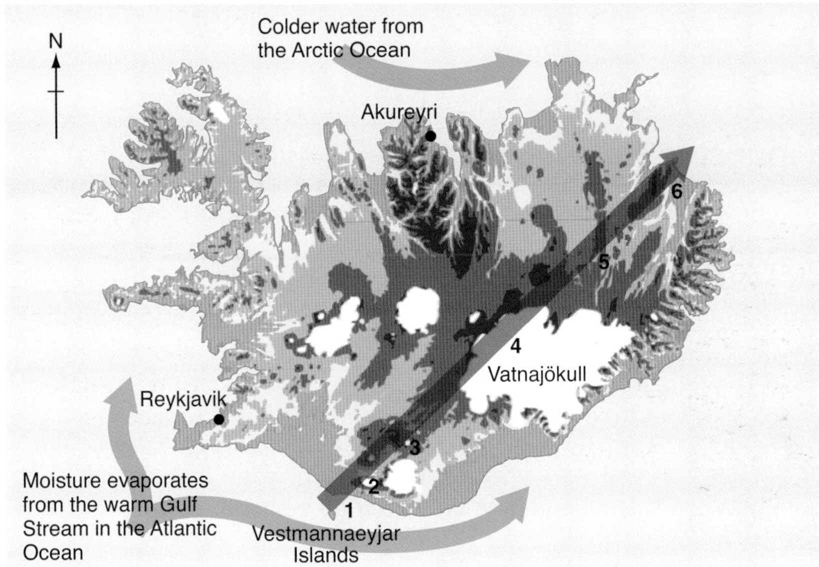


**Figure 13** The factors that influence Iceland's regional patterns of climate

**Additional labels for Figure 14**

Air rises over the highlands of south Iceland.

An area of rain shadow where it seldom rains.

The wind often blows in from the south-west. This is the **prevailing wind** direction.

Some precipitation falls as snow on Vatnajökull, adding to the ice cap.

After crossing the highlands and ice cap, the air sinks and warms.

As the air rises it cools and water vapour condenses forming cloud and precipitation.

**Figure 14** Relief rainfall: the reason for Iceland's regional pattern of rain

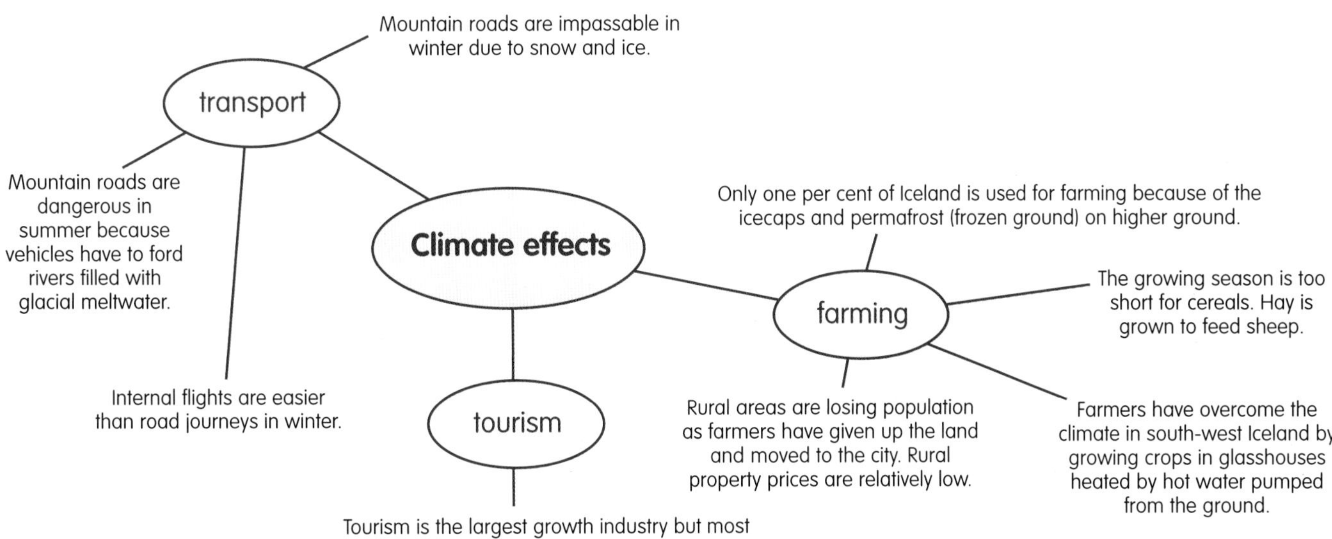


**Figure 15** How Iceland's climate affects people

# Chapter 3 Weather

**KEY QUESTIONS**

- How and why is the weather measured, recorded and presented?
- What is the difference between weather and climate?
- How can the weather affect business and our daily lives?
- How and why do **weather hazards** have severe impacts on people's lives?

## Why do we measure the weather?

The weather influences many aspects of our lives. Whether the weather is wet or dry, hot or cold, affects many decisions that we take every day, especially in countries like the UK where the weather can be very changeable:

- What clothes should we wear?
- Will it be safe to travel if it is snowing, foggy or very windy?
- Will the cricket or tennis match be cancelled?

We therefore measure aspects of the weather such as temperature, **precipitation** and atmospheric pressure so that we can make forecasts of what the weather will do next. More and more of this data is now collected by **remote sensing** equipment, as shown in Figure 1.

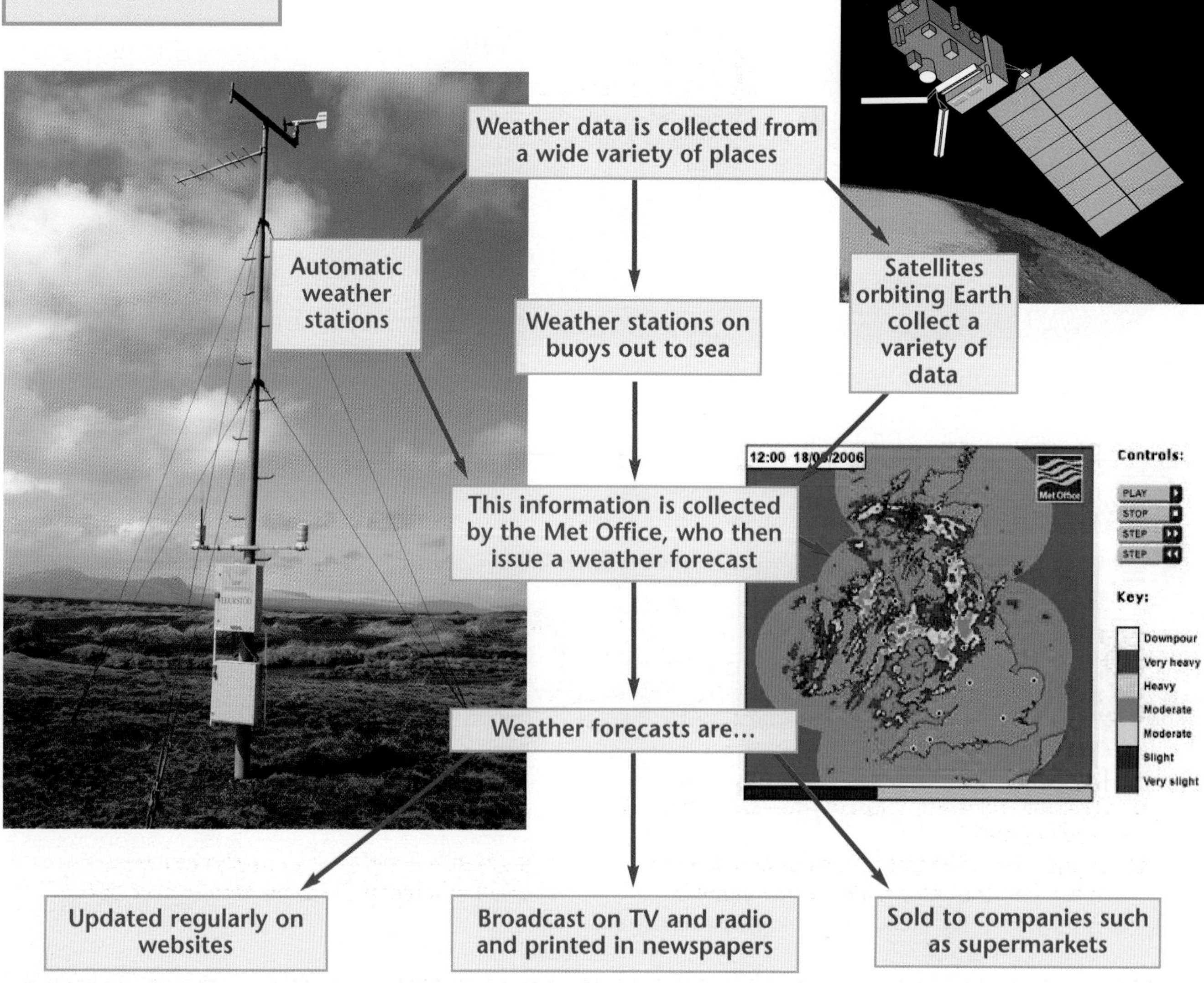


**Figure 1** How weather forecasts are created

### Satellite technology

At the heart of this remote sensing system are a number of satellites. The European Space Agency provides data to weather forecasters from a combination of two types of satellite:

1 MeteoStat is a geostationary system in orbit 36,000 km above the Earth. It keeps pace with the Earth's rotation, so it is always above the same point and able to take images of Europe and the Atlantic. This is important because most of the high and low pressure systems that affect Europe come from the Atlantic.

2 MetOp is a new series of satellites first launched in 2006. This system is in a polar orbit 800 km above the Earth. This means it takes much more detailed readings, and of the whole Earth's surface. This allows scientists to:

- make more accurate medium- and long-term weather forecasts. This should give people more warning of extreme weather events and help to reduce the risk to people from weather hazards.
- take readings over long periods of time to allow them to look for trends that might show that the climate is changing.

**www.metoffice.gov.uk/weather/europe/uk/radar/** will take you to part of the UK Met Office site, where you can play an animation of the latest rainfall radar images.

**www.esa.int/esaCP/index.html** is the home page of the European Space Agency. Follow the multimedia gallery link to find video and animations of the MetOp programme.

## Activity

**1** List five other different aspects of weather, apart from temperature and rainfall, that we can measure.

**2** Study the Met Office radar image in Figure 1.
- **a)** Describe the location of the very heavy rainfall.
- **b)** Describe the distribution of the moderately heavy rainfall.
- **c)** Suggest five different groups of people who might find this information very helpful in March.

**3** Describe the two main aims of using satellite technology to collect weather data.

**4** Describe the kind of weather conditions that might disrupt:
- **a)** sporting events
- **b)** transport
- **c)** energy supplies.

**5** Suggest two different examples of how a weather forecast could be used to save lives.

## Why studying and predicting the weather is big business

Having an accurate weather forecast is particularly important to many businesses. Farmers, fishermen, the construction industry, airlines and airports all need to know what the weather will do next as it may influence safety or productivity. Retailers are also affected by the weather. The changing weather has a major impact on consumer behaviour, for example, sales of salad vegetables, lagers and meat products that can be cooked on a barbecue all increase dramatically during periods of hot weather. Supermarkets such as Tesco pay for detailed weather forecasts so that they can meet customer demand for these types of products. Store managers use the weather forecast so that they can move the right quantity of stock from the warehouses to the supermarket shelves. This can maximise sales of, for example, ice cream during periods of hot weather. It can also help reduce waste, for example, less salad vegetables will be ordered and brought into the store during a spell of cool or wet summer weather.

**Figure 3** Sales of ice cream are higher during spells of hot weather

> Weather plays a large part in Tesco's retail business and that is why we use Weather Commerce products. The ability to plan fourteen days ahead means we can reduce waste, maximise sales, and have the right products at the right time. Longer-range forecasts and historical data allow us to further enhance our planning strategies.
>
> **Brian Judge – Tesco**

> Having a fourteen-day rolling forecast allows Northern Ireland Electricity to consider the potential impact of severe weather and make appropriate plans. With more notice of severe gales, ice accretion or thunderstorms this gives incident managers time to adequately prepare and ensure the availability of key staff.
>
> **Michael Skelton – Northern Ireland Electricity**

**Figure 2** Extracts from the Weather Commerce website. Weather Commerce is a weather forecasting company that provides a forecast service to many UK companies

### Activity

**6** Use Figure 2 to explain why each of the following businesses pay for weather forecasts:

**a)** supermarkets
**b)** energy suppliers.

## Investigating the demand for ice cream

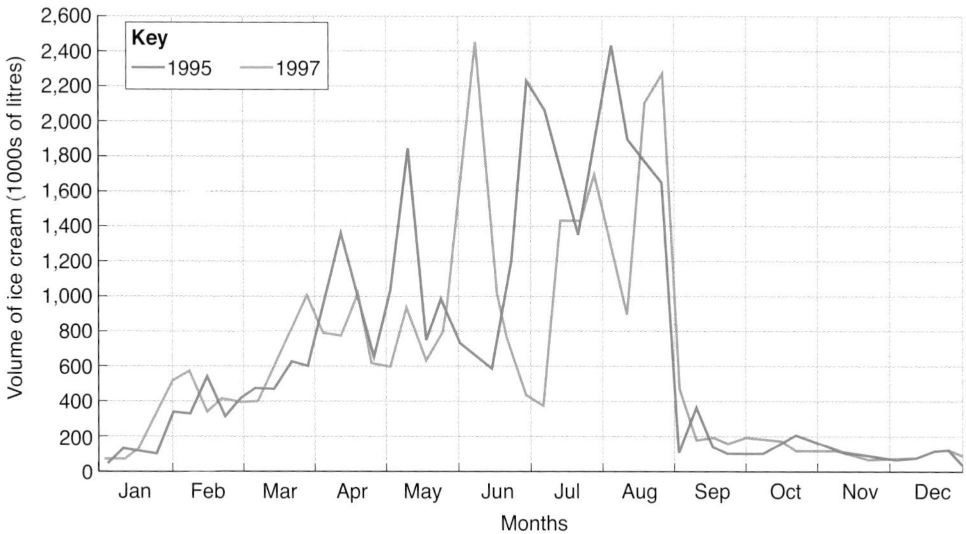


**Figure 4** Weekly sales of ice creams 1995 and 1997 (*Birds Eye Walls ice cream)

### Activity

**7 a)** Suggest a hypothesis that links sales of ice creams to weather conditions.

**b)** Using Figure 4, describe the peak sales periods for ice cream in 1995 and 1997.

**c)** Use the data in Figure 5 to draw a pair of line graphs to show average maximum temperatures in 1995 and 1997.

**d)** Compare the graphs you have drawn to Figure 4. Can you prove your hypothesis?

**e)** Evaluate your investigation. What other factors, apart from weather, might influence ice cream sales? What other information would you need to know to make your investigation more successful?

| Date | Max (°C) 1995 | Max (°C) 1997 |
|---|---|---|
| 26 Mar | 12 | 15 |
| 02 Apr | 17 | 16 |
| 09 Apr | 18 | 18 |
| 16 Apr | 11 | 13 |
| 23 Apr | 13 | 14 |
| 30 Apr | 26 | 19 |
| 07 May | 17 | 12 |
| 14 May | 12 | 18 |
| 21 May | 18 | 17 |
| 28 May | 18 | 22 |
| 04 Jun | 17 | 23 |
| 11 Jun | 18 | 21 |
| 18 Jun | 23 | 16 |
| 25 Jun | 28 | 22 |
| 02 Jul | 23 | 24 |
| 09 Jul | 25 | 24 |
| 16 Jul | 27 | 24 |
| 23 Jul | 28 | 25 |
| 30 Jul | 32 | 22 |
| 06 Aug | 26 | 28 |
| 13 Aug | 29 | 27 |
| 20 Aug | 25 | 25 |
| 27 Aug | 21 | 21 |
| 03 Sep | 20 | 21 |

**Figure 5** Weekly average maximum temperatures in southern England 1995 and 1997

## The impact of weather on transport businesses

We all know that the weather has an impact on travel and transport:

- A sunny bank holiday can cause traffic jams to build up on the roads.
- A heavy fall of snow can cause the closure of schools.

However, the weather can also have a major impact on transport businesses such as train and ferry companies, airlines and airport authorities. One such example occurred between 20 and 22 December 2006. An area of high pressure settled over the UK. This trapped and prevented cool air over the UK from rising. Moisture in the air condensed forming thick fog. Several airlines had to cancel flights and compensate their passengers or find them alternative transport arrangements by train or coach. For example, on 22 December a total of 411 flights were cancelled from UK airports, including 350 from Heathrow. At least 40,000 people were affected by the travel chaos: this should have been the busiest day of the Christmas holiday.

British Airways was probably the company worst affected by the three days of fog. During the three months including December 2006 their earnings fell by £40 million. However, the company was also hit by the added cost of extra security measures at UK airports during this period, as well as the effect of the fog.

# Heatwave 2003

## What's the difference between weather and climate?

One simple answer is that climate is what we expect but weather is what we get! **Weather** is our day-to-day experience of temperature, wind, precipitation and sunshine. **Climate** is about taking weather readings over long periods of time, and then working out averages, patterns and trends. A simple way to show the difference between weather and climate is to compare the weather in two different years.

**Figure 6** An intense rainstorm caused severe floods in Boscastle, Cornwall, in August 2004

## Comparing the UK weather in August 2003 with August 2004

The hottest ever day in the UK was recorded in Faversham, Kent, on 10 August 2003. It came during a long period of very hot, dry weather. By comparison, August 2004 was cooler and much wetter. On the afternoon of 16 August, Boscastle, in Cornwall, was hit by a freak rainstorm that caused disastrous floods. In just four hours 200 mm of rain fell, causing the local river to burst its banks. Normally, the high ground to the south of Boscastle gets 100 to 120 mm of rainfall during the whole of August.

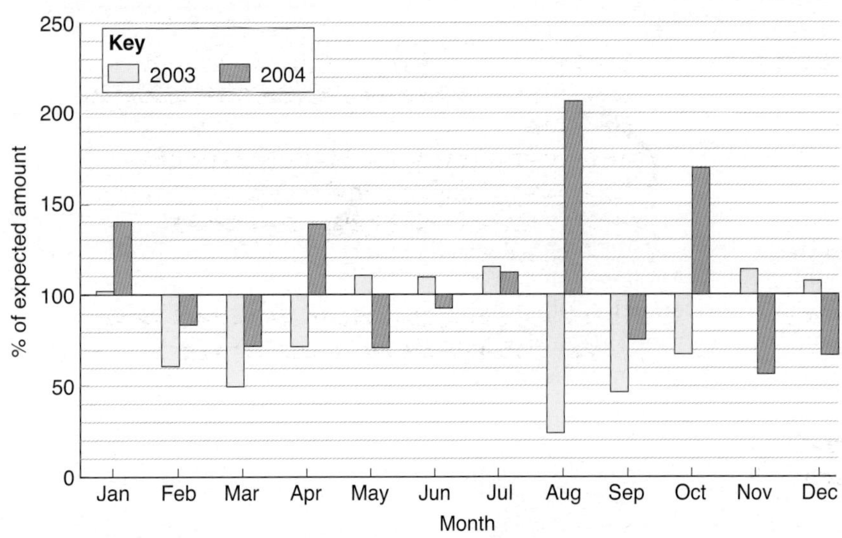


**Figure 7** Rainfall in England in 2003 and 2004. Each month is shown as a percentage of the amount normally expected for that month (based on averages for 1961 to 1990)

| | 2003 mean temp. anomaly (°C) | 2004 mean temp. anomaly (°C) |
|---|---|---|
| Jan | 0.8 | 1.5 |
| Feb | 0.3 | 1.7 |
| Mar | 2.0 | 1.0 |
| Apr | 1.9 | 1.8 |
| May | 1.2 | 1.2 |
| Jun | 2.0 | 1.5 |
| Jul | 1.7 | 0.0 |
| Aug | 2.5 | 1.9 |
| Sep | 0.9 | 1.3 |
| Oct | −1.3 | 0.2 |
| Nov | 1.8 | 1.3 |
| Dec | 0.5 | 0.9 |

**Figure 8** Temperature anomalies in England for 2003 and 2004. Figures are the temperature (°C) above or below the monthly average (1961 to 1990)

## When extreme weather is a hazard

The extreme heat of August 2003 caused suffering and discomfort for millions of people across Europe. The heat caused heatstroke and dehydration, especially among elderly people. It is estimated that 30,000 people died in the extreme heat. France was worst hit. French doctors estimate that the heatwave caused 14,000 deaths. On a normal August day about 50 people are admitted to hospital suffering from heat exhaustion. In August 2003 that number rose to 500. The hospitals struggled to cope. In addition, the heatwave also caused several forest fires in southern Europe. All in all, the extreme heat is estimated to have caused €1 billion of damage.

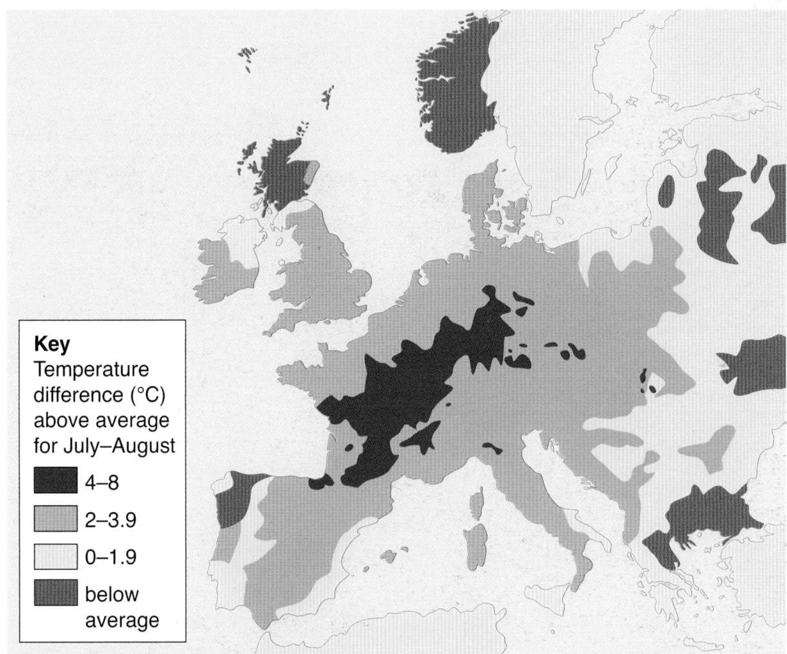


**Figure 9** Temperature anomalies in Europe in August 2003

### Activity

**8** Use Figure 7 to describe the pattern of rainfall in 2003. In which months was the rainfall:
- **a)** above average
- **b)** average
- **c)** below average?

**9 a)** Use the data in Figure 8 to draw a graph similar to Figure 7.
**b)** Pick out one similarity and one difference between the temperatures of 2003 and 2004.

**10** Use Figure 9 and an atlas to list five countries where temperatures were at least 4 °C above average in 2003.

**11** Use Figures 6, 7, 8 and 9. Describe how these two summers might have affected the following businesses:
- **a)** supermarket sales at Tesco and Sainsbury
- **b)** bed and breakfasts in Cornwall
- **c)** accident and emergency departments in France.

**12** Describe and explain how the extreme weather in one of these summers caused a hazard.

## Why does the UK have such changeable weather conditions?

We saw in Chapter 2 (page 13) that the latitude of the UK is within a belt that gets a mixture of high and low pressure. These pressure systems come across the UK from the Atlantic and bring with them very changeable patterns of weather.

### High pressure: anticyclones

Areas of high pressure are also known as anticyclones. Anticyclones bring dry, settled periods of weather. The long period of hot, dry weather in July and August 2003 was due to an anticyclone that stayed over Europe for several weeks. If an anticyclone becomes fixed over the UK in winter the weather is sunny and dry but cold, and especially cold at night.

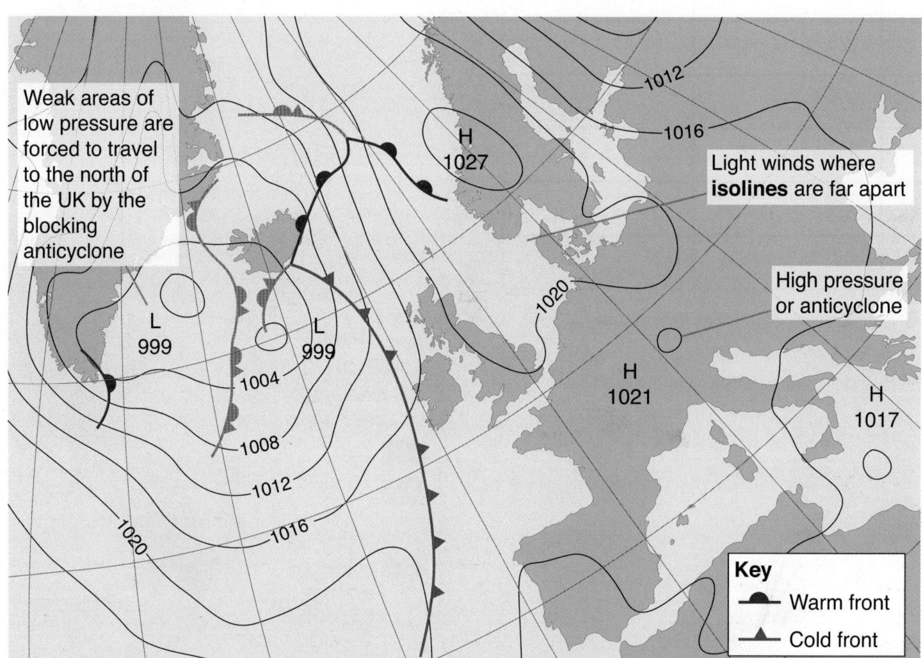


**Figure 10** A weather map showing an anticyclone

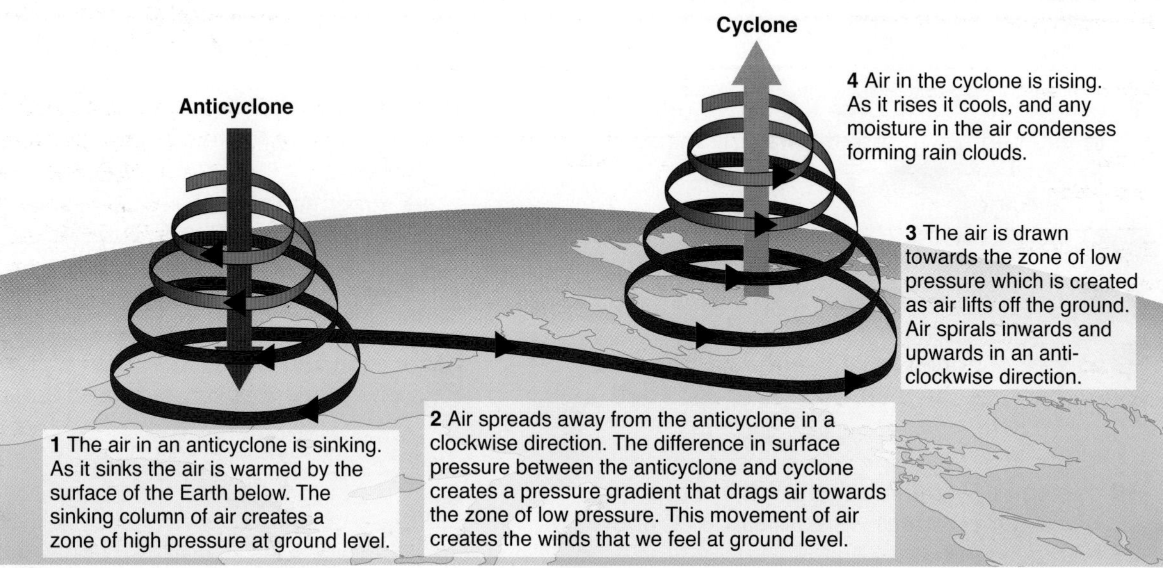


**Figure 11** The movement of air from areas of high pressure to areas of low pressure

### Low pressure: cyclones

Regions of low pressure, also known as **cyclones**, bring changeable weather. Low pressure brings cloud and rain and gusty or strong winds. The weather in July and August 2003 was due to several regions of low pressure that brought cloud, wind and unusual amounts of rain across the UK. If the air pressure is very low a storm with much stronger gusts of wind will develop. Severe tropical storms also have very low air pressure and strong winds and are also known as cyclones or **hurricanes**. However, they are formed in a way different from the regions of low pressure that commonly affect the UK.

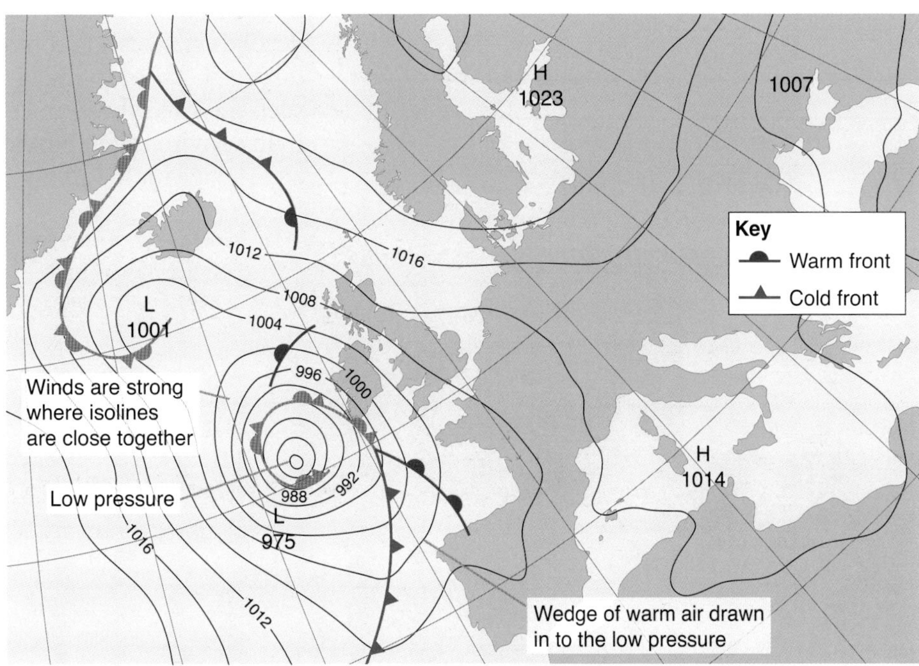


**Figure 12** Weather map showing a cyclone

| Feature | Cyclones | Anticyclones |
|---|---|---|
| Air pressure | | High, usually above 1010 mb (millibars) |
| Air movement | Rising | |
| Wind strength | Strong | |
| Wind circulation | | Clockwise |
| Typical winter weather | | Cold and dry. Clear skies in the daytime. Frost at night. |
| Typical summer weather | Mild and wet. Cloudy with periods of heavy rain separated by showers. | |

**Figure 13** Comparing cyclones and anticyclones

### Activity

**13** Make a large copy of the table in Figure 13 and complete the blank spaces using information from Figures 10, 11 and 12.

**14** Use an atlas and Figures 11 and 12.

**a)** Describe the location of the zones of high and low pressure.

**b)** One map shows the pressure systems for 9 August 2003, the other is for 8 August 2004. Use the information on these pages to state which is which.

**c)** Give reasons for your choice.

**15** Write a report which uses Figures 11 and 12 to explain the different weather experienced in the summers of 2003 and 2004.

# Chapter 4
# Ecosystems

## KEY QUESTIONS

- What is an ecosystem?
- How do the living and non-living parts of an ecosystem interact?
- How do climate conditions affect plant growth and the functioning of ecosystems?

## What are ecosystems?

An **ecosystem** is a community of plants and animals and the environment in which they live. Ecosystems contain both living and non-living parts. The living part includes such things as plants, insects and birds, which depend on each other for food. Plants may also depend on insects and birds for pollination and seed dispersal. The non-living part of an ecosystem includes such things as the climate, soils and rocks. This non-living environment provides nutrients, warmth, water and shelter for the living parts of the ecosystem.

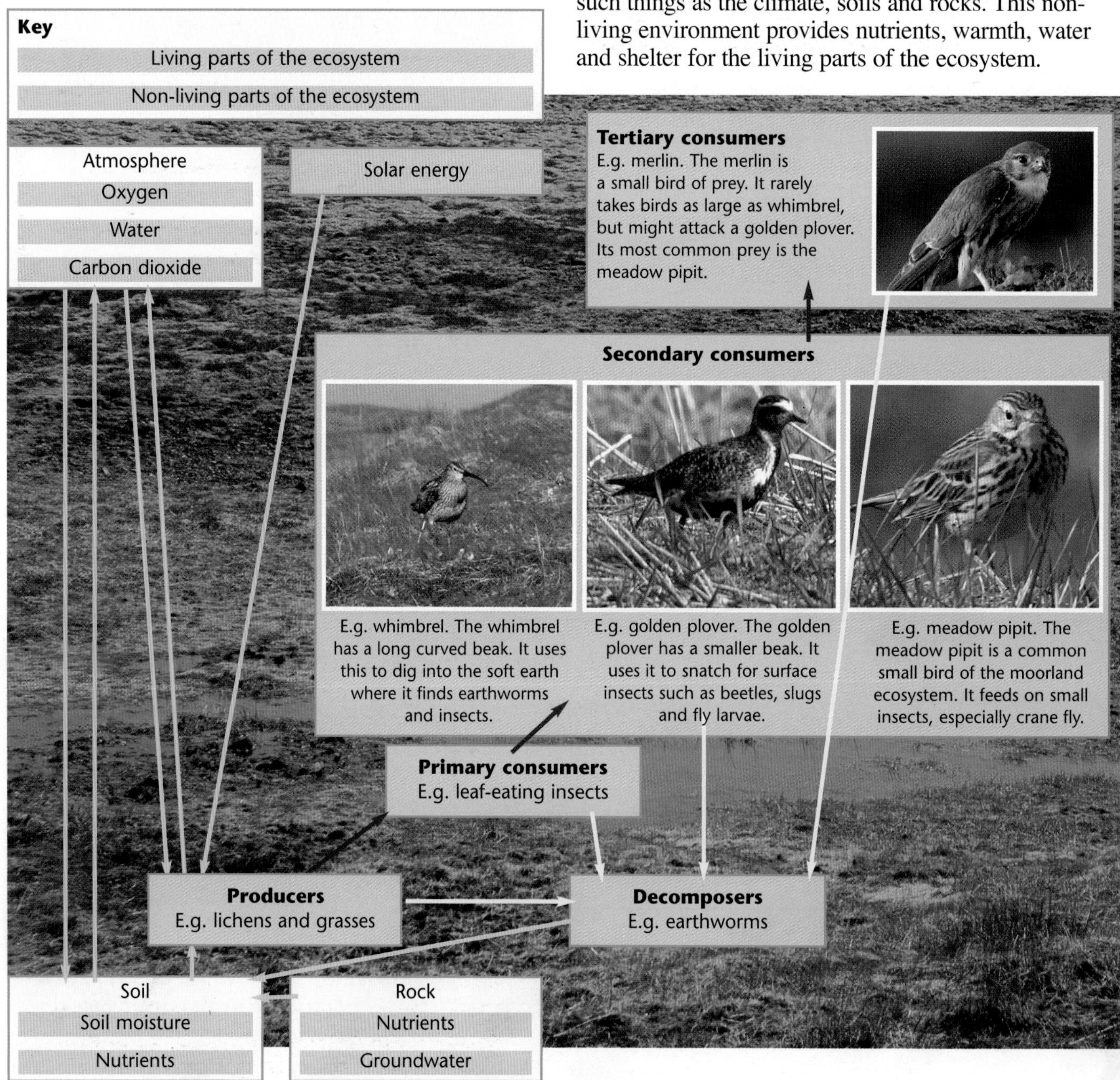


**Figure 1** The living and non-living parts (or components) of the treeless moorland ecosystem in Iceland: an example of **tundra**

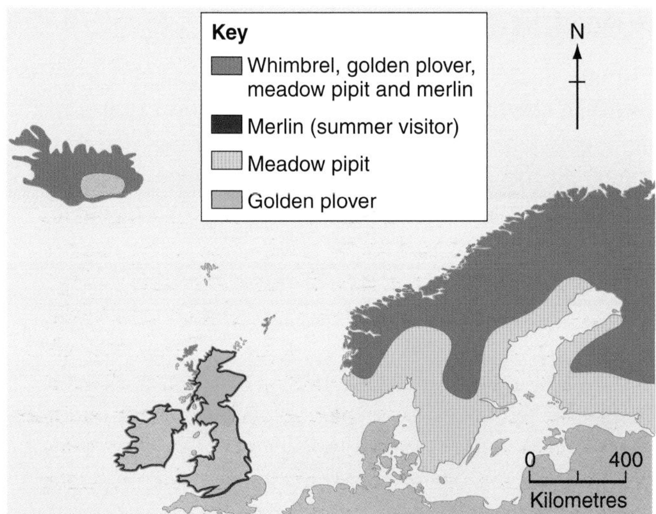


## Ecosystems exist at different scales

Ecosystems exist at a variety of scales. The largest, such as tropical rainforests or desert ecosystems, cover large parts of the Earth and are known as **biomes**. But ecosystems also exist at much smaller scales, for example salt marshes and sand dunes may cover only a few hectares while a garden pond is an ecosystem that is only a few metres across.

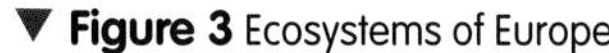

◀ **Figure 2** The distribution of the four moorland birds shown in Figure 1

▼ **Figure 3** Ecosystems of Europe

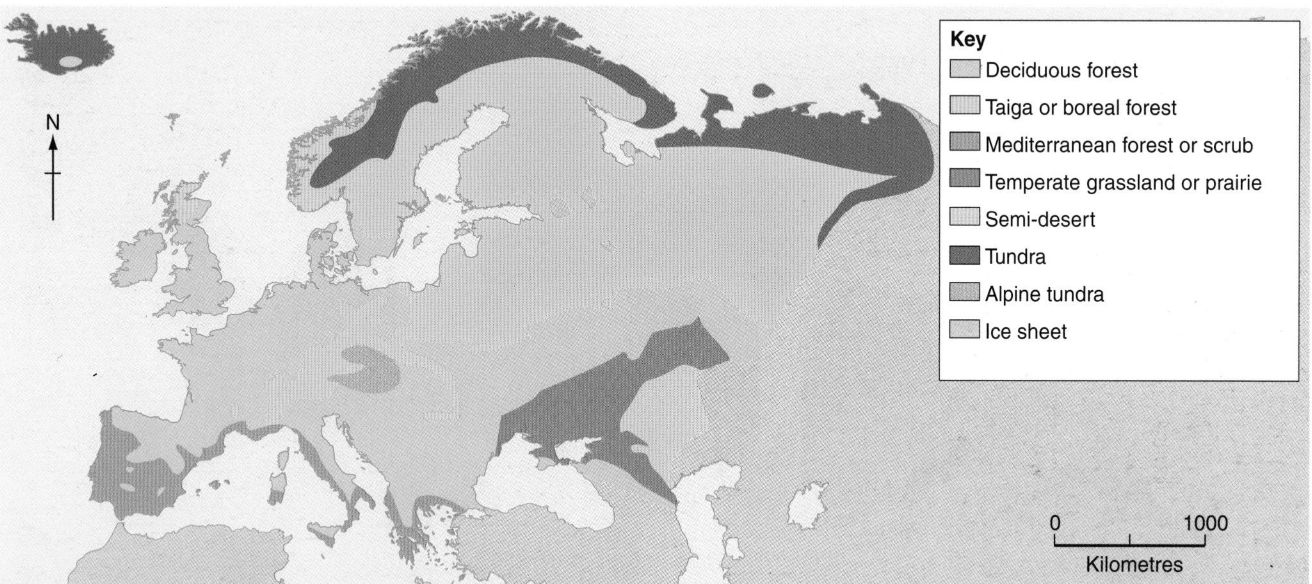


## Activity

**1 a)** Use Figure 1 to draw a food chain that includes the meadow pipit.

**b)** What would happen to the merlin if the population of meadow pipit fell for some reason (perhaps because a new predator was introduced to Iceland)?

**2** Study Figures 2 and 3 with an atlas.

**a)** Copy and complete the following:

**The tundra moorlands are found mainly in ...................... Europe in countries such as ........ and ........ The boreal (coniferous) forests are found further ........ and ........ in countries such as ........ and ........**

**b)** Describe the distribution of the whimbrel and golden plover.

**c)** Explain why the whimbrel and golden plover are more at risk from loss of the moorland ecosystem than the meadow pipit or merlin.

**3** Work in pairs. Using the text and diagrams on these pages discuss as many links as you can think of between:

**a)** animals and plants

**b)** wildlife and climate

**c)** people and wildlife.

**4** Still working in your pairs, use your discussion to draw a spider diagram or concept map to show how people fit into an ecosystem as shown in Figure 1.

## Investigating the relationship between climate and ecosystems

Climate is such an important factor in influencing the natural vegetation and wildlife of a region that large-scale ecosystems broadly match the world's climate zones. At the global scale these large ecosystems are known as biomes. Each biome has its own climate and vegetation, soils and wildlife.

**Figure 5** Boreal forest, Finland

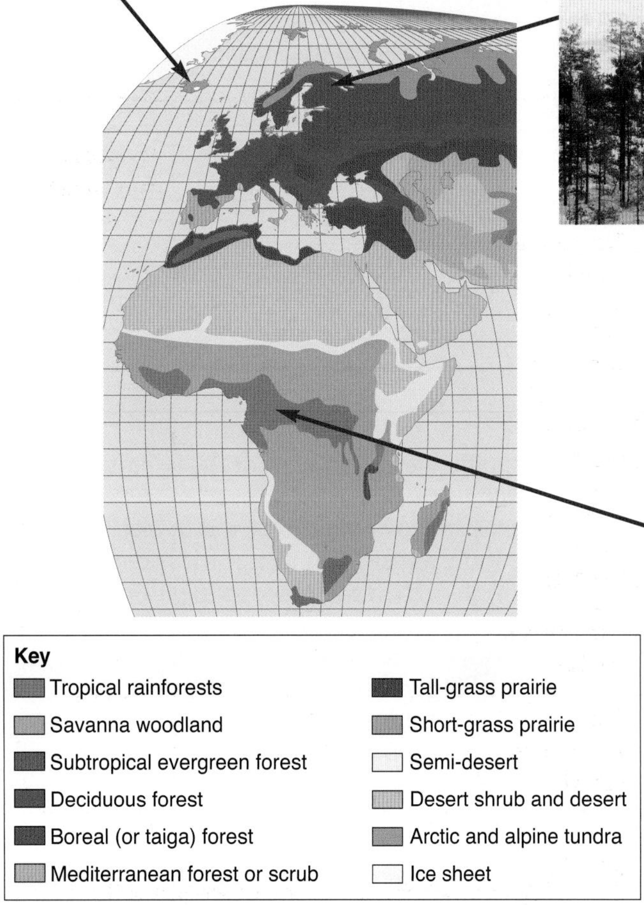

**Figure 4** Tundra moorland, Iceland

Key
- Tropical rainforests
- Savanna woodland
- Subtropical evergreen forest
- Deciduous forest
- Boreal (or taiga) forest
- Mediterranean forest or scrub
- Tall-grass prairie
- Short-grass prairie
- Semi-desert
- Desert shrub and desert
- Arctic and alpine tundra
- Ice sheet

**Figure 6** Biomes of Africa and Europe

**Figure 7** Tropical rainforest, Gabon

| | Tundra moorland 64° N, Iceland | | Boreal forest 62° N, Finland | | Tropical rainforest 0° N, Gabon | |
|---|---|---|---|---|---|---|
| Month | Temperature (°C) | Precipitation (mm) | Temperature (°C) | Precipitation (mm) | Temperature (°C) | Precipitation (mm) |
| Jan | –0.5 | 145 | –8.0 | 38 | 27.0 | 249 |
| Feb | 0.4 | 130 | –7.5 | 30 | 26.5 | 236 |
| Mar | 0.5 | 115 | –4.5 | 25 | 27.5 | 335 |
| Apr | 2.9 | 117 | 2.5 | 35 | 27.5 | 340 |
| May | 6.3 | 131 | 8.5 | 42 | 26.5 | 244 |
| Jun | 9.0 | 120 | 14.0 | 48 | 25.0 | 13 |
| Jul | 10.6 | 158 | 17.0 | 76 | 24.0 | 3 |
| Aug | 10.3 | 141 | 15.5 | 75 | 25.0 | 18 |
| Sep | 7.4 | 184 | 10.5 | 57 | 25.5 | 104 |
| Oct | 4.4 | 184 | 5.5 | 57 | 26.0 | 345 |
| Nov | 1.1 | 137 | 0 | 49 | 26.0 | 373 |
| Dec | –0.2 | 133 | –4.0 | 41 | 27.5 | 249 |

**Figure 8** Climate data for three climate stations

## Activity

**5** Use figure 6. Describe the distribution of:
**a)** tropical rainforests **b)** boreal forests.

**6** Use the climate data in Figure 8 to complete your own copy of the table on the right.

**7** Suggest how the differences in climate might affect plant growth in the two forest systems.

**8** Use Figures 4, 5 and 7 to outline the main characteristics of each biome. Comment on the height of plants; the variety of plants; and the structure of the ecosystem (space between plants and their relationship to each other).

**9** Using Google Earth, 'fly' over the tropical rainforest of Gabon to the tundra of Iceland. Search for these places in your flight:

- Gabon
- Cano, Nigeria
- Akasjokisuu, Finland
- Isafjordur, Iceland.

Focus on the following questions:
**a)** In which direction are you flying?
**b)** How is the vegetation changing?
**c)** How might the changing climate patterns be affecting the conditions needed for plants to grow?

| | Tundra moorland | Boreal forest | Tropical rainforest |
|---|---|---|---|
| Temperature range | | | |
| Months above 10 °C (length of growing season) | | | |
| Months below freezing | | | |
| Total annual rainfall | | | |
| Seasonal variation in rainfall | | | |

**www.earth.google.com**
On Google Earth, you can view any part of the Earth's surface, from any angle and from any height. It allows you to go on a 'virtual fieldtrip' and see anywhere in the world. Tip: An altitude of 800 to 1000 metres is best for viewing ecosystems.

## How do climate patterns influence biomes?

Some biomes, such as the tropical rainforest, have climatic conditions that promote rapid plant growth. Rainforest trees grow quickly and can reach heights of 40 m or more. Other biomes, like the tundra, have very slow-growing plants that never grow more than a few centimetres high. The rate of plant growth depends on a number of factors. These include: amount of sunlight; length of day; warmth; and amount of water. These factors all depend on either climate or latitude. For example, most plants need the temperature to be above 10 °C in order for them to grow. When temperatures are below 10 °C, as they are for many months in the boreal forest, plants are dormant. But in equatorial regions, where temperatures are constantly above 25 °C, plants can grow all year.

## Nutrient cycles also depend on climate

Plants need minerals containing nitrogen and phosphates. These **nutrients** exist in rocks, water and atmosphere. The plants take them from the soil, releasing them back into the soil when the plant dies. This process forms a continuous **cycle**.

Figure 9 represents nutrient stores and flows in the rainforest ecosystem. The circles represent **nutrient stores**. The size of each circle is in proportion to the amount of nutrients kept in that part of the ecosystem. The arrows represent **nutrient flows** as minerals move from one store to another. The thickness of each arrow is in proportion to the size of the flow, so large flows of nutrients are shown with thick arrows while smaller flows are shown with narrow arrows.

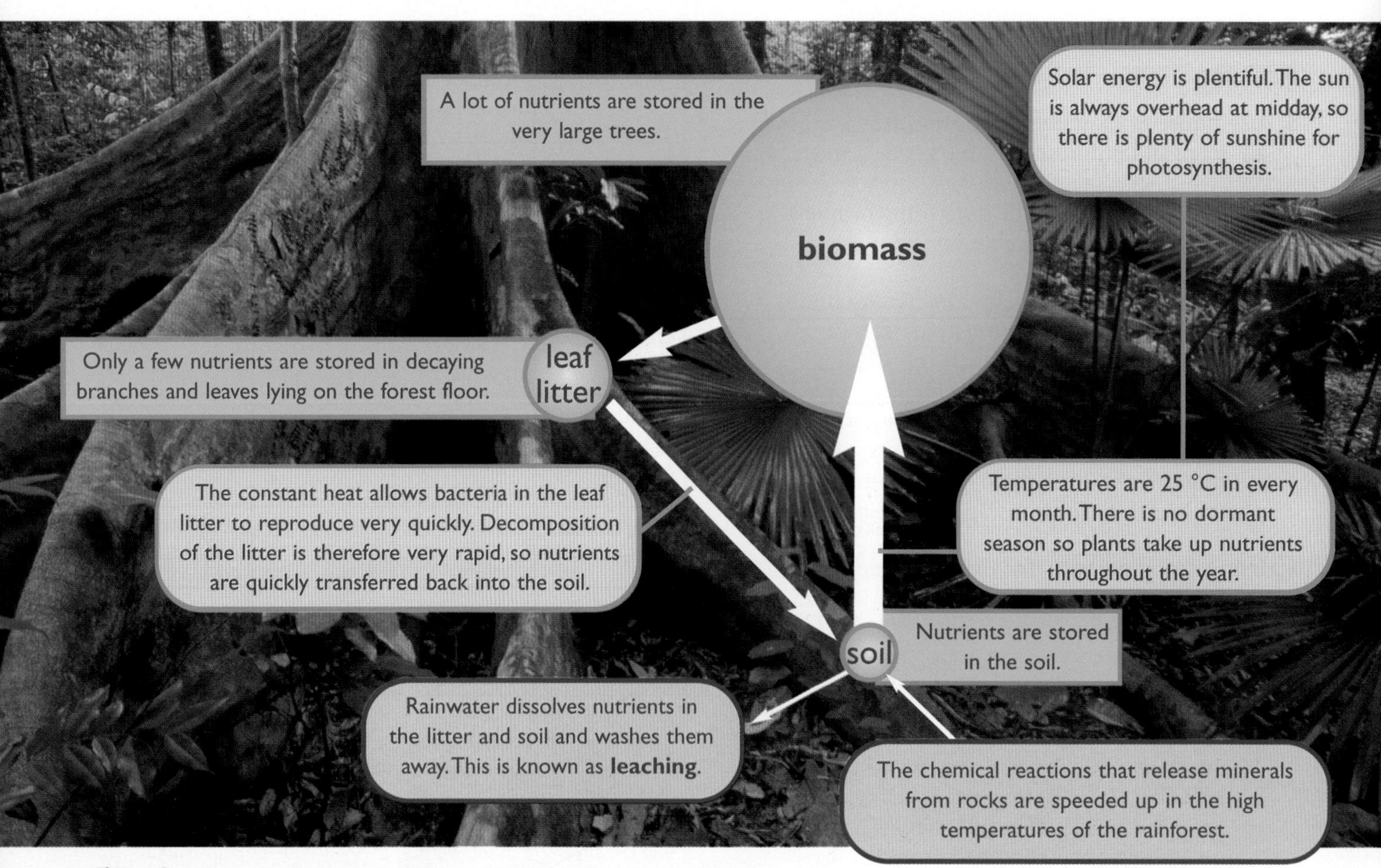


**Figure 9** How climate affects stores and flows of nutrients in the tropical rainforest

## Activity

**10** Define what is meant by nutrient stores and nutrient flows.

**11** Describe three places where nutrients are stored in an ecosystem.

**12** Study Figure 9.
- **a)** Describe two ways that nutrients can enter the soil.
- **b)** Explain why these two nutrient flows are rapid in the rainforest.
- **c)** Explain why these nutrient flows are likely to be much slower in the boreal forest and tundra.

**13** Study Figure 9. Explain why nutrient cycle diagrams for the tundra and boreal forest would have:
- **a)** a larger circle for leaf litter than in the rainforest
- **b)** a thinner arrow for leaching
- **c)** a thinner arrow showing nutrient flows into the biomass.

## Going Further

### Stewardship

**Stewardship** is a key ethical concept in conservation. As stewards we accept that we have a responsibility to care for the environment. People have different reasons for supporting the concept of stewardship:

**A** Wildlife and the Earth have equal rights to people. We have a responsibility to protect those rights.

**C** Ecosystems provide a number of key services such as regulation of oxygen and carbon dioxide in the atmosphere. We should conserve the environment to help protect ourselves from natural disaster.

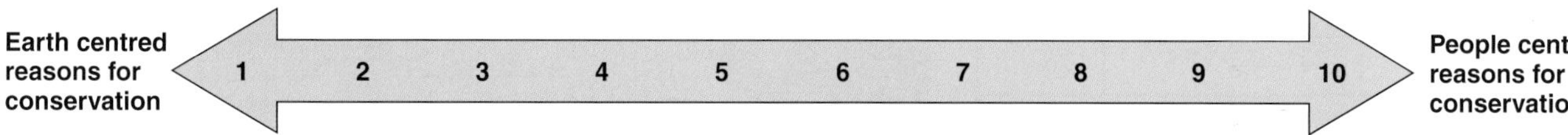


**B** Future generations of people have a right to enjoy the natural environment. We have a responsibility to protect the environment for their sake.

**Figure 10** Reasons for supporting the concept of stewardship fall on a continuum

> 'Whatever befalls the Earth befalls the sons of the Earth. If men spit upon the ground, they spit on themselves. This we know – the Earth does not belong to man, man belongs to the Earth. All things are connected like the blood which unites one family. Whatever befalls the Earth befalls the sons of the Earth. Man did not weave the web of life; he is merely a strand in it. Whatever he does to the web he does to himself.'

**Figure 11** Quote from Chief Seattle (native North American tribal leader, 1855). Taken from *Earthrights: Education as if the Planet really mattered* (WWF and Kogan Page)

**14** Work in a group of four. Study Figure 10. On the scale of one to ten, where would you place each of the statements (A to C)?

**15** Work in a group of four. Read Figure 11 and then discuss it.
- **a)** This quotation is full of puzzling and challenging ideas. It raises lots of questions. Write down a list of questions raised during your discussion.
- **b)** Share your questions with the rest of the class.
- **c)** As a class choose one question from your list that you would like to discuss further. You should all agree with the choice.
- **d)** Discuss your question in more detail. Listen carefully to each other. What interesting ideas / points of view do you have?

**16** Working on your own:
- **a)** Try to write down how you think Chief Seattle felt about the Earth (in Figure 11).
- **b)** Where on Figure 10 would you place Chief Seattle?
- **c)** Where on Figure 10 do you place yourself?

# Chapter 5
# Human impact on forest ecosystems

**KEY QUESTIONS**

- How are ecosystems and climate linked at the regional scale?
- In what ways are ecosystems seen to be a resource?
- How can rainforest ecosystems be managed and conserved?

| | Guatemala City | | Belize City | |
|---|---|---|---|---|
| Month | Temp (°C) | Rainfall (mm) | Temp (°C) | Rainfall (mm) |
| Jan | 17.5 | 8 | 23.0 | 137 |
| Feb | 18.5 | 3 | 24.5 | 61 |
| Mar | 21.0 | 13 | 25.5 | 38 |
| Apr | 21.0 | 5 | 26.5 | 56 |
| May | 22.5 | 152 | 27.5 | 109 |
| Jun | 21.5 | 274 | 27.5 | 196 |
| Jul | 21.0 | 203 | 27.5 | 163 |
| Aug | 21.0 | 198 | 27.5 | 170 |
| Sep | 21.0 | 231 | 27.0 | 244 |
| Oct | 20.0 | 173 | 26.0 | 305 |
| Nov | 18.5 | 23 | 24.0 | 226 |
| Dec | 17.5 | 8 | 23.5 | 185 |

**Figure 1** Climate data for Guatemala City and Belize City

## Regional patterns of climate and vegetation in Central America

In Chapter 4 we examined the close link between climate and **ecosystems** at the global scale. This chapter will focus on the ecosystems of Central America (also known as Mesoamerica) and look at how climate and ecosystems function at the regional scale. The tropical rainforest biome contains a number of distinctive types of forest: ecosystems that exist at the regional scale. For example, within South and Central America, the rainforest biome can be divided into several ecosystems which include:

- lowland rainforest such as most of the Amazonian rainforest
- **cloud forests** that grow in more mountainous areas
- **mangrove forests** that grow in coastal areas.

**Figure 2** The golden toad of Costa Rica

**Figure 3** Distribution of cloud forest and mangrove forest in Central America

## Cloud forests

Cloud forests are cooler than lowland rainforests and, because they are in mountain regions, they are often blanketed in cloud or mist. They are home to many species of frog and toad that rely on the moisture in the atmosphere. In the 1970s, a scientist studying a 30 km$^2$ area of the Monteverde cloud forest in Costa Rica identified 50 different species of frog and toad. Since 1970, twenty species have disappeared, including the beautiful golden toad in Figure 2. The golden toad was known to live only in this one small area of forest, so it is now assumed to be extinct. Did human actions cause the golden toad's extinction? We will find out later in the chapter.

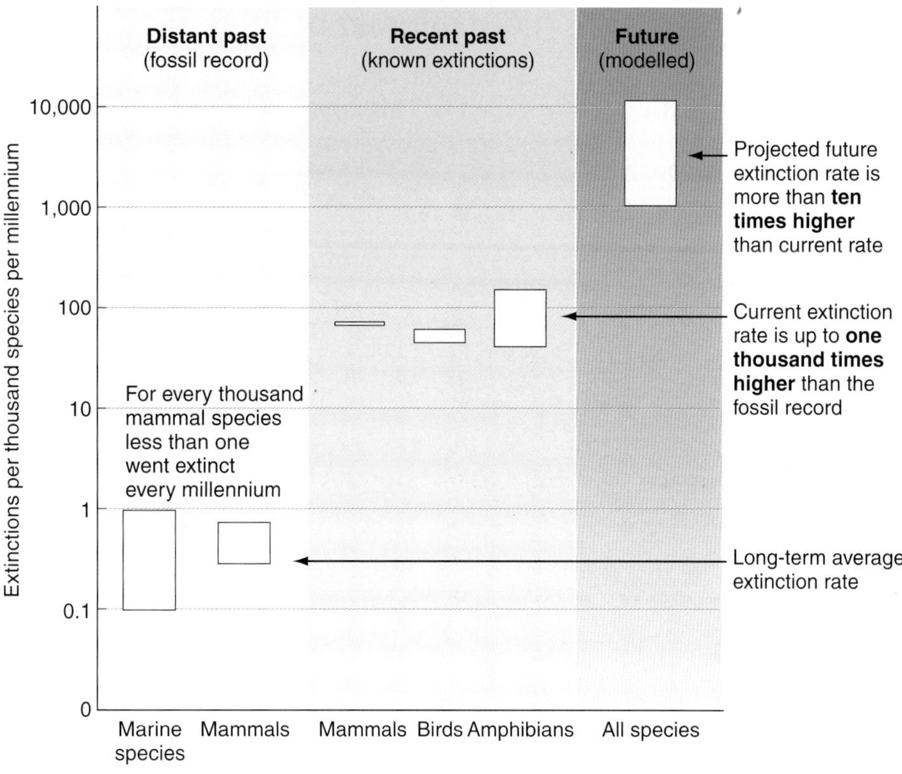


**Figure 4** Past, current and future rates of extinction

## Activity

**1** Use Figure 3 to copy and complete the following sentences.

**All areas of mangrove forest are found in coastal areas. Most are along the coastline of the ............. . In addition, some mangrove grows on the Pacific coast in countries like ............... By contrast the cloud forests only grow in the mountainous regions of Central America. They stretch from the area around Oaxaca in ......... in the north of Central America to Panama in the ........ of the region.**

**2** Describe the location of:

**a)** Belize City

**b)** Guatemala City.

**3 a)** Use Figure 1 to draw climate graphs for Belize City and Guatemala City.

**b)** Compare the climate of these two Central American cities.

**c)** Suggest why the mangrove and rainforest in Belize grow well all through the year. Use evidence from your graphs.

**4** Use Figure 4.

**a)** For every thousand mammal species, how many species went extinct every thousand years:

i) in the fossil record

ii) in the recent past?

**b)** Which animal group experienced most extinctions in the recent past?

**c)** Describe what is expected to happen to the extinction rate in the near future.

**d)** Suggest reasons for this prediction.

## The rainforest canopy and its effects on regional climate

Viewed from above, a tropical rainforest is an unbroken **canopy** of green vegetation. This continuous canopy is a characteristic part of the structure of the rainforest ecosystem and it plays an essential role in:

- regulating the regional water cycle
- preventing soil erosion
- preventing river floods.

The rainforest is said to provide **key services** in protecting the water supply and safety of people who live in the forest and in the wider region. How does it do this?

### How does the structure of the rainforest regulate water supply?

Figure 6 shows how rainforests play an essential role in the regional **water cycle** of tropical areas. The forest acts as a **store** for water in between rainfall events.

After a rainstorm it is thought that about 80 per cent of the rainfall is transferred back to the atmosphere by **evaporation** and **transpiration**. So, rainforests are a source of moisture for future rainfall events.

At least 200 million people live in the world's tropical rainforests. This includes the tribal groups, or **indigenous peoples**, of the rainforest. Many more people live downstream of the rivers that leave these forests. The forest maintains a constant and even supply of water to these rivers. If the rainforest water cycle were to be broken, the water supply of many millions of people could be put at risk. The total amount of water flowing in the rivers would be reduced and the supply would become more uneven with periods of low water supply punctuated by sudden flooding.

**Emergent** trees such as brazil nut and caypock grow through the canopy.

The continuous canopy is formed by the crowns of individual trees growing next to each other.

**Figure 5** Structure of the tropical rainforest

### Activity

**5** Define what is meant by stores and flows in the water cycle.

**6** Using Figure 6:

**a)** List the places where water is stored in the rainforest.

**b)** Explain how water flows from the atmosphere to the forest and back again.

**7** Describe and explain why:

**a)** areas of rainforest maintain a steady supply of water for local communities

**b)** damaging the structure of the rainforest could affect local people, as well as people in the wider region.

**8** Make a copy of Figure 7. Add the following labels to appropriate places on your diagram:

| | |
|---|---|
| **evaporation** | **warm air rising** |
| **condensation** | **precipitation** |

**9** Explain why the cloud forest climate is cooler and wetter than the lowland forest.

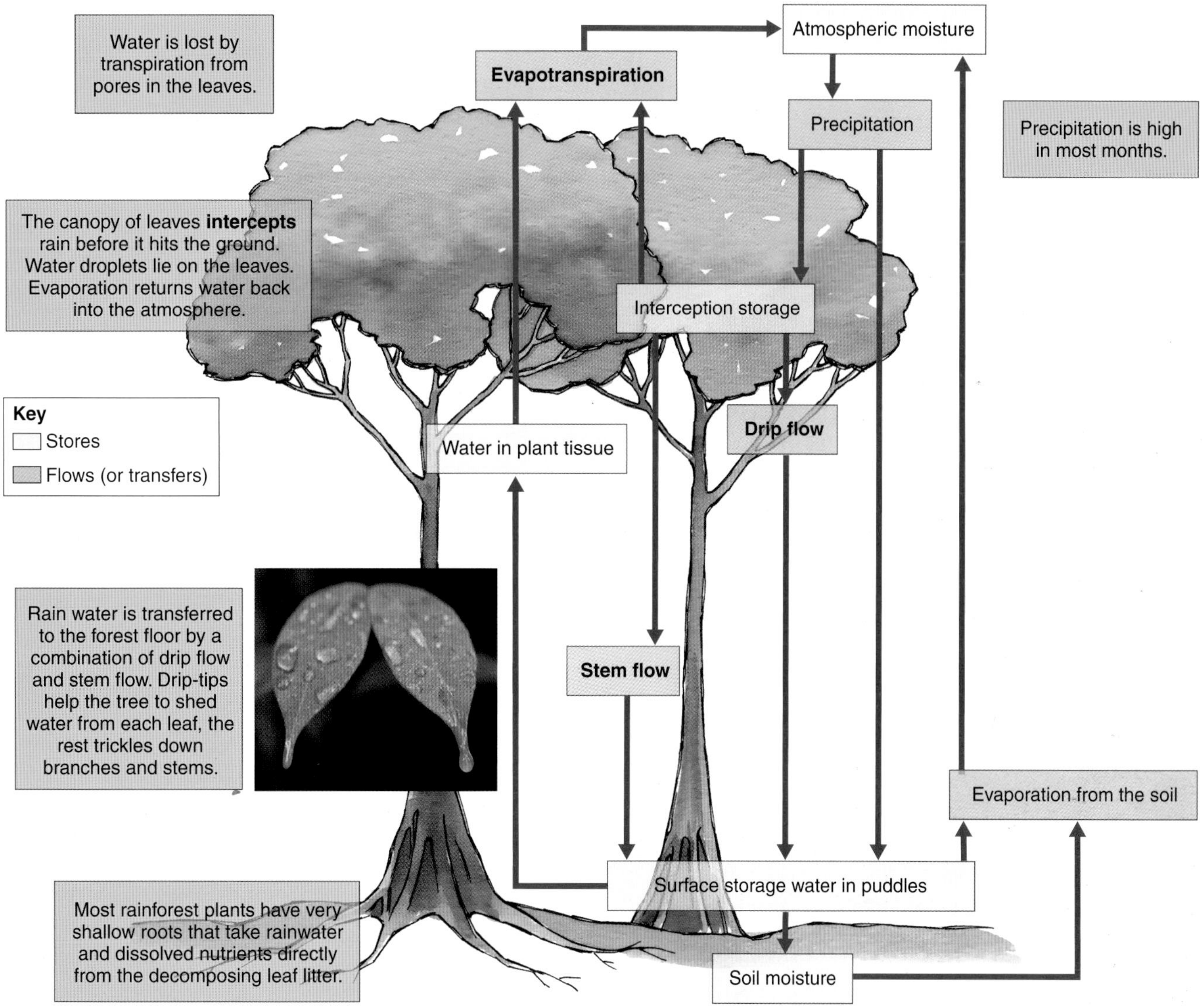

Water is lost by transpiration from pores in the leaves.
Evapotranspiration
Atmospheric moisture
Precipitation
Precipitation is high in most months.
The canopy of leaves **intercepts** rain before it hits the ground. Water droplets lie on the leaves. Evaporation returns water back into the atmosphere.
Interception storage
Key
Stores
Flows (or transfers)
Water in plant tissue
Drip flow
Rain water is transferred to the forest floor by a combination of drip flow and stem flow. Drip-tips help the tree to shed water from each leaf, the rest trickles down branches and stems.
Stem flow
Evaporation from the soil
Surface storage water in puddles
Most rainforest plants have very shallow roots that take rainwater and dissolved nutrients directly from the decomposing leaf litter.
Soil moisture

**Figure 6** The water cycle in the tropical rainforest

Mid-afternoon
5. The tops of the cumulus clouds are now 2,500 m to 3,500 m high. Water droplets join, become larger and heavier until a rainstorm begins.
Midday
4. The air is so full of water vapour that condensation occurs at a low level, so cumulus clouds begin to form between 600 m and 800 m.
Mid-morning
1. Sunshine heats the ground, which heats the air above it.
2. A bubble of warm air full of water vapour from the forest begins to rise.
3. The rising bubble of air is fed by more warm air from below. This column of air is known as a **thermal**.
Lowland forest
Cloud forest
6. This mountain range forces the warm moist air to rise. Clouds cover the slopes in the afternoon. This is cloud forest.

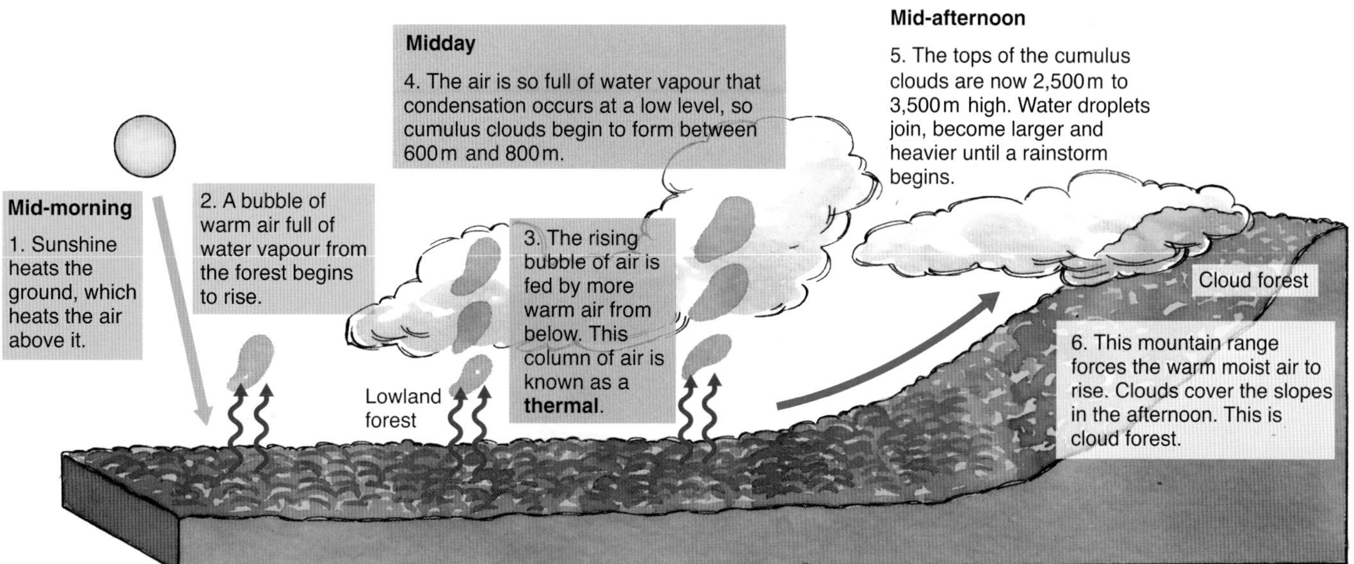

**Figure 7** Convectional rainfall over lowland rainforest and cloud forest

## How does the structure of the rainforest prevent soil erosion and flooding?

The canopy of the rainforest acts rather like an umbrella: intercepting rainfall and preventing much of it from falling directly to the ground. Raindrops from a tropical storm hit the ground with great force, causing soil erosion. But drip and stem flow have much less force, so a continuous canopy prevents soil erosion.

Most tribal people of the rainforest who plant crops do so by creating small clearings in the forest. The canopy is broken, but soil erosion is minimised because the stumps of the trees are left in the ground and the roots help to bind the soil together. Soil erosion is a much bigger problem when large areas of rainforest are cleared by commercial loggers.

| Forest type | Location of study | Percentage intercepted and evaporated from canopy |
|---|---|---|
| Sitka spruce (conifer) | Scotland | 28 |
| Douglas fir (conifer) | Oregon (USA) | 19 |
| Beech (deciduous) | England | 15 |
| Tropical rainforest | Indonesia | 21 |
| Tropical rainforest | Dominica | 27 |
| Tropical rainforest | West Malaysia | 27 |

**Figure 8** Interception and evaporation of water from different forests' canopies

**Figure 9** A small plot of land that has been cleared in the Amazon

**Figure 10** The consequences of **deforestation**

## Activity

**10 a)** Choose a suitable method to graph the data in Figure 8.

**b)** Calculate average interception rates for coniferous forest, deciduous forest and tropical rainforest.

**c)** Explain why the deciduous forest has significantly lower figures.

**11** Explain how the canopy of the rainforest reduces the risk of soil erosion.

**12** Explain how tribal people are able to minimise soil erosion from their farms.

**13** Using Figure 10 as a starting point, create a flow chart or spider diagram to explain the links between deforestation, soil erosion, silt deposition in rivers, and river floods.

**14** Research a rainforest tribe using the website of Survival International (see below). Make notes that cover the location, lifestyle and threats facing your chosen tribe.

**www.survival-international.org** is the website of a Non-Governmental Organisation (NGO) that campaigns on behalf of indigenous peoples.

**15** What is Survival International trying to achieve? What rights do tribal people have? Discuss how these rights compare to the right of a nation such as Brazil to exploit its resources and generate wealth for its people.

## Going Further

### Tropical rainforests provide key services

Over the last 60 years tropical rainforests have been exploited for their timber and cleared away to make new farmland. Scientists believe that this has had a catastrophic effect on a number of **key services** that are provided by forests. These key services include:

- maintaining a steady supply of clean water to rivers
- preventing soil erosion
- reducing the risk of river floods
- providing natural materials such as timber for building, or plants for medicinal use. Seventy-five per cent of the world's population still rely on plant extracts to provide them with medication
- providing foodstuffs such as honey, fruit and nuts.

Conservationists argue that we need to place a greater value on these key services rather than the value of the tropical timber alone. The benefit of a clean and regular water supply can be measured in financial terms. Rebuilding homes after a river flood can also be measured financially. They argue that these key services are more valuable over the long term than the short-term profits gained from logging.

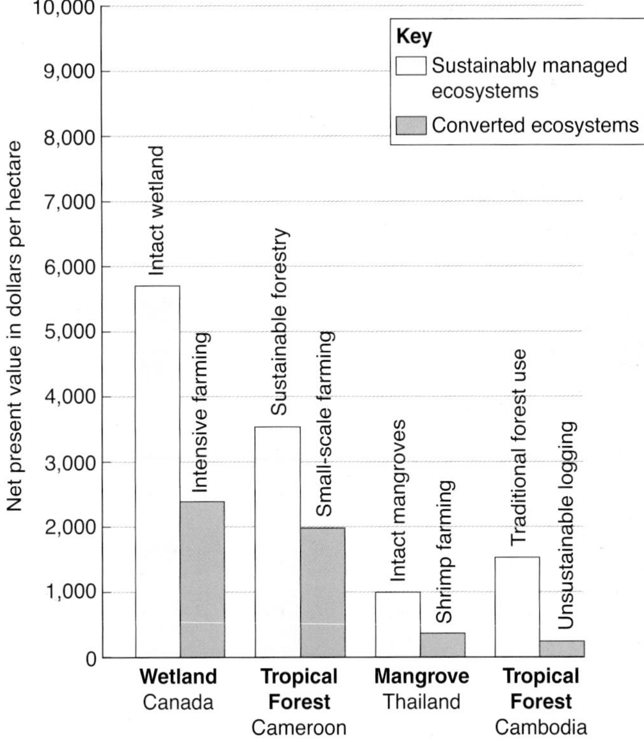


**Figure 11** The economic benefits of sustainable management of an ecosystem compared with the benefits of converting the ecosystem to farmland or timber

**16** Write a letter campaigning for the conservation of Central America's cloud forest or mangrove forest. Use information from Figure 11 to provide evidence of the real value of these key services.

## Regional effects of deforestation: a case study of climate change in Costa Rica

**Figure 12** The location of the cloud forest in Costa Rica

The cloud forest of Monteverde, Costa Rica, is an international tourist attraction, famous for the wide **biodiversity** of plants and animals that live here. However, this delicate ecosystem is being damaged. Since the 1970s, twenty species of frog and toad have disappeared from Monteverde, including the beautiful golden toad pictured in Figure 2 (see page 32). Meteorologists have noticed that mist in the forest is a less frequent event than it used to be and that the base height of the clouds is now higher than it was. This could explain the extinction of the frogs and toads. But why is the climate changing?

At first the scientists thought that the drier climate in the cloud forest might be evidence of global climate change. However, it now seems that these changes are due to deforestation in the region. As we have seen (see page 34), rainforests recycle approximately 80 per cent of their moisture back into the atmosphere by evapotranspiration. The lowlands around Monteverde used to be covered in lowland rainforest. These forests would have provided a lot of moisture which, on rising over the mountains of Monteverde, would have condensed and produced low-level cloud and mist.

**Figure 13** Deforestation of the lowland areas to the west of Monteverde has left a grassland environment

However, over the last few decades, deforestation has reduced the lowland forest to just a few isolated patches. The deforested land, which can be seen in Figure 13, is now largely used for cattle grazing. This vegetation produces much less water by evaporation and transpiration than forested areas, so the clouds that should be forming over Monteverde no longer have a source.

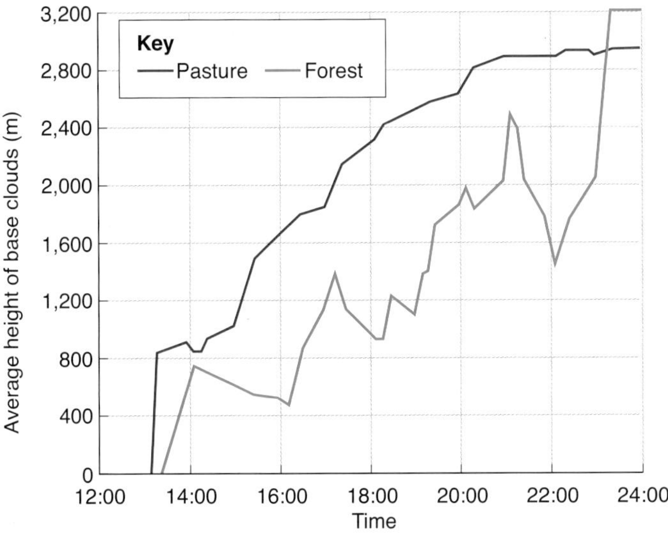


**Figure 14** A computer simulation for the height of the cloud base over pasture and forest

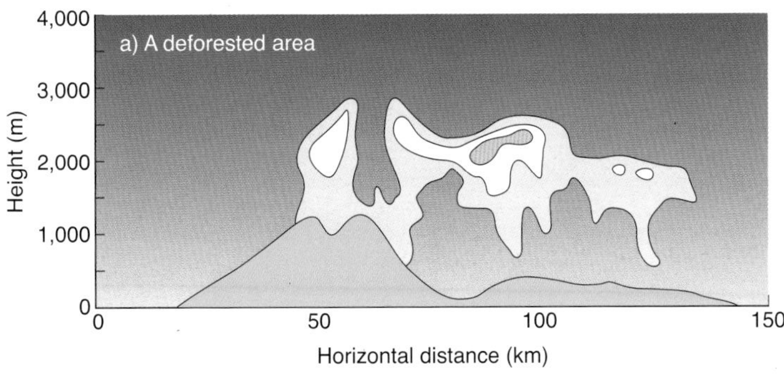


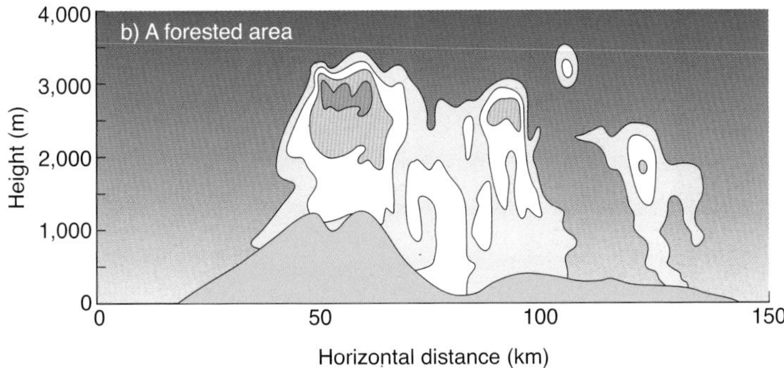


**Figure 15** A computer simulation showing the expected cloud cover at midday for a) a deforested area, and b) a forested area

From our point of view, there are a number of reasons to worry about the cloudiness of mountain forests. One involves just the conservation implications. These cloud forests are communities of organisms adapted to cloud forest conditions. Take away the cloudy conditions, and we might expect to see all sorts of changes. How many cloud forest organisms could go the way of the golden toad?

The other interesting problem is that cloud forests are such important components of many mountain watersheds that provide either drinking water supplies or the water for hydroelectric facilities. Monteverde's forests feed the Lake Arenal hydroelectric project. So one of the serious questions is to what extent cloud input is important to the water budgets of watersheds like Arenal. If it is really important, then there are big economic reasons – in addition to conservation reasons – to care about cloud forests.

**Robert Lawton, Department of Biological Sciences, University of Alabama**

**Figure 16** The view of Robert Lawton, a scientist studying the effects of climate change in Monteverde

## Activity

**17** Describe the location of the Monteverde cloud forest.

**18 a)** Use Figure 14 to describe the height of the cloud base at 2pm, 4pm and 6pm over the forest and pasture.
**b)** Use Figure 15 to explain how cloud height affects the frequency of mists in the cloud forests of Monteverde.

**19 a)** Draw a diagram to show how the lowland forest used to supply moisture to the cloud forest. Show stores (such as the lowland forest) and transfers (such as evaporation) on your diagram.
**b)** Draw a second diagram to show how deforestation has affected the water cycle at a regional scale.

**20 a)** Read Figure 16. Use it to identify three regional consequences of deforestation in Costa Rica.
**b)** Explain how this research might make conservation of the remaining forest easier to achieve.

## What is being done to protect Costa Rica's environment?

Despite the problems in Monteverde, Costa Rica has a relatively good record for conservation work. The government has established a large number of National Parks and Forest Reserves. It is also co-operating with neighbouring countries in an ambitious project to create a continuous **wildlife corridor** through the length of Central America. Deforestation creates a major problem for wildlife: the forest becomes fragmented. As clearings get bigger the wildlife is restricted to isolated fragments of forest that are separated by farmland. By planting strips of forest to connect the remaining fragments together, conservationists create wildlife corridors. The seven governments of Central America, and Mexico, are working jointly on a project called the Mesoamerican Biological Corridor (known by its Spanish initials, CBM). This project aims to connect and conserve all the protected lands that stretch through Central America (Mesoamerica). This region is a **biodiversity hotspot**. It amounts to only one per cent of the world's land surface, but it is estimated to contain seven per cent of the world's terrestrial (land-based) species.

**Figure 17A** Satellite image of Mesoamerican Biological Corridor (CBM). The red dots indicate where forest fires are burning

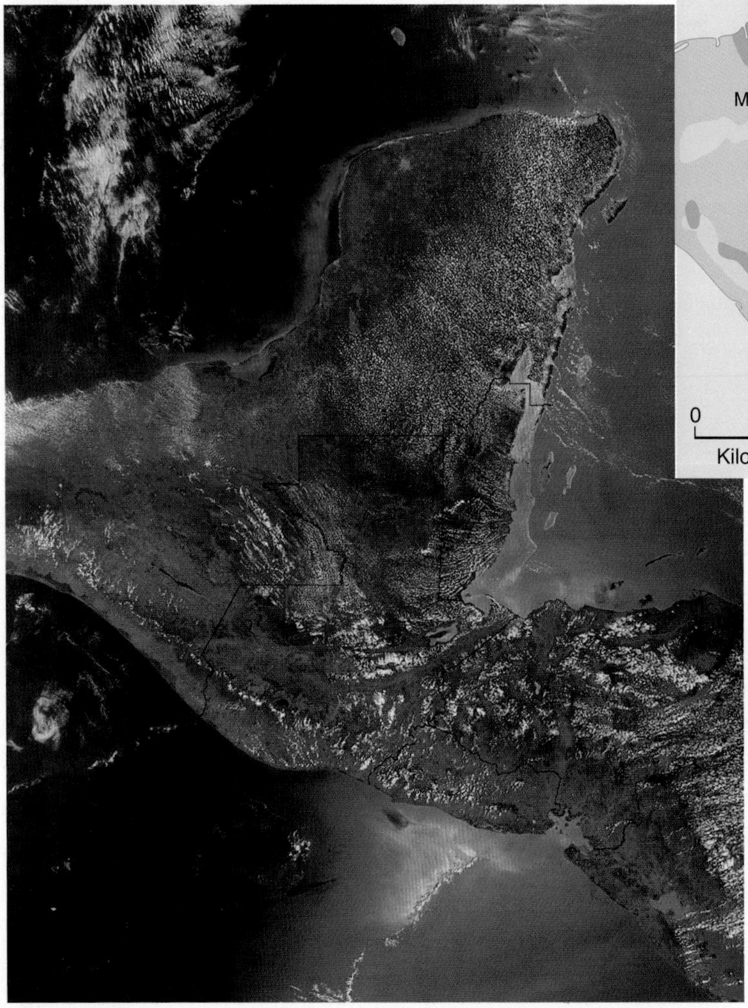

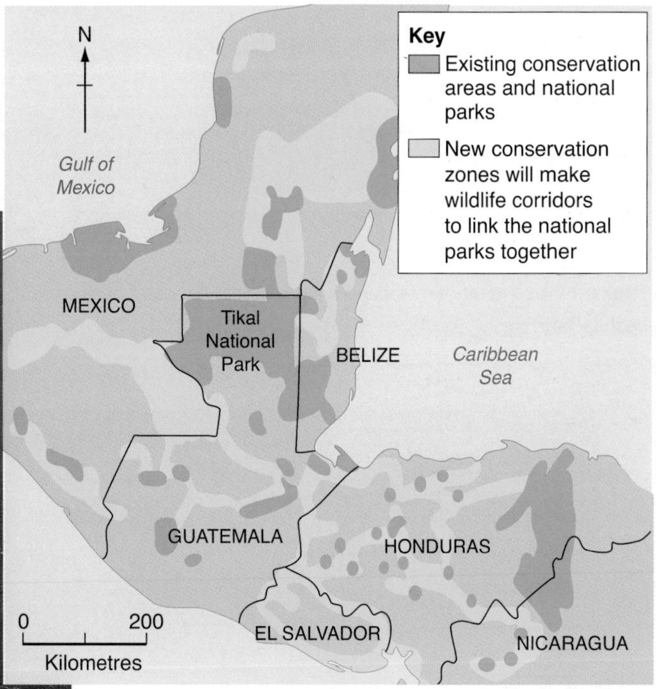

**Figure 17B** The structure of the CBM project

The government and businesses in Costa Rica have also encouraged the growth of **ecotourism**: small-scale tourist projects that create money for conservation as well as creating local jobs. It is estimated that 70 per cent of Costa Rica's tourists visit the protected environments. In 2000 Costa Rica earned $1.25 billion from ecotourism. One successful example is the creation of a canopy walkway through a small, privately owned part of the Monteverde reserve (see Figure 19). Tourists are charged $45 to climb up into the canopy and walk along rope bridges, the longest of which is 300 m long.

| Country | Protected land as % of total area |
|---|---|
| Belize | 47.5 |
| Costa Rica | 23.4 |
| El Salvador | 2.0 |
| Guatemala | 25.3 |
| Honduras | 20.8 |
| Mexico | 5.0 |
| Nicaragua | 21.8 |
| Panama | 19.5 |

**Figure 18** Protected areas (including forest reserves) in Central America and Mexico (Source: Earthlands)

**Figure 19** The canopy walkway allows visitors to see the birds and other wildlife that live in the canopy of the cloud forest

## Activity

**21** Study the satellite image and map in Figure 17 A and B.

**a)** Estimate the percentage of Guatemala that is conserved as national park.

**b)** Suggest how the new conservation zones will help wildlife.

**22** Study Figure 18.

**a)** Calculate the average amount of land that is protected in Central America and Mexico.

**b)** Graph the data, and include a bar for the average.

**c)** How good is Costa Rica's record on conservation compared with its neighbours?

**23** Draw a spider diagram which shows how fragmentation of the rainforest affects wildlife. Consider the likely impacts of fragmentation on:

- food chains
- success of mating
- predator/prey relationships
- pollination and seed dispersal.

**24** For an ecosystem you have studied:

**a)** name and locate the case study

**b)** describe the main features of the ecosystem

**c)** describe and explain how it is being managed by people.

# Chapter 6
# Getting up close to nature: investigating microclimates and small-scale ecosystems

**KEY QUESTIONS**

- What are the features of small-scale ecosystems?
- How can ecosystems be restored and managed?
- How do urban areas affect patterns of climate at the micro scale?

## Investigating ecosystems in your back garden: urban ecosystems

We tend to think that ecosystems and their wildlife are all in distant places and that there is little we can do to save or conserve them. However, there is an important ecosystem that is literally on your doorstep. Recent scientific studies have highlighted the importance of the UK's gardens as a wildlife habitat. Gardens contain an important variety of small ecosystems.

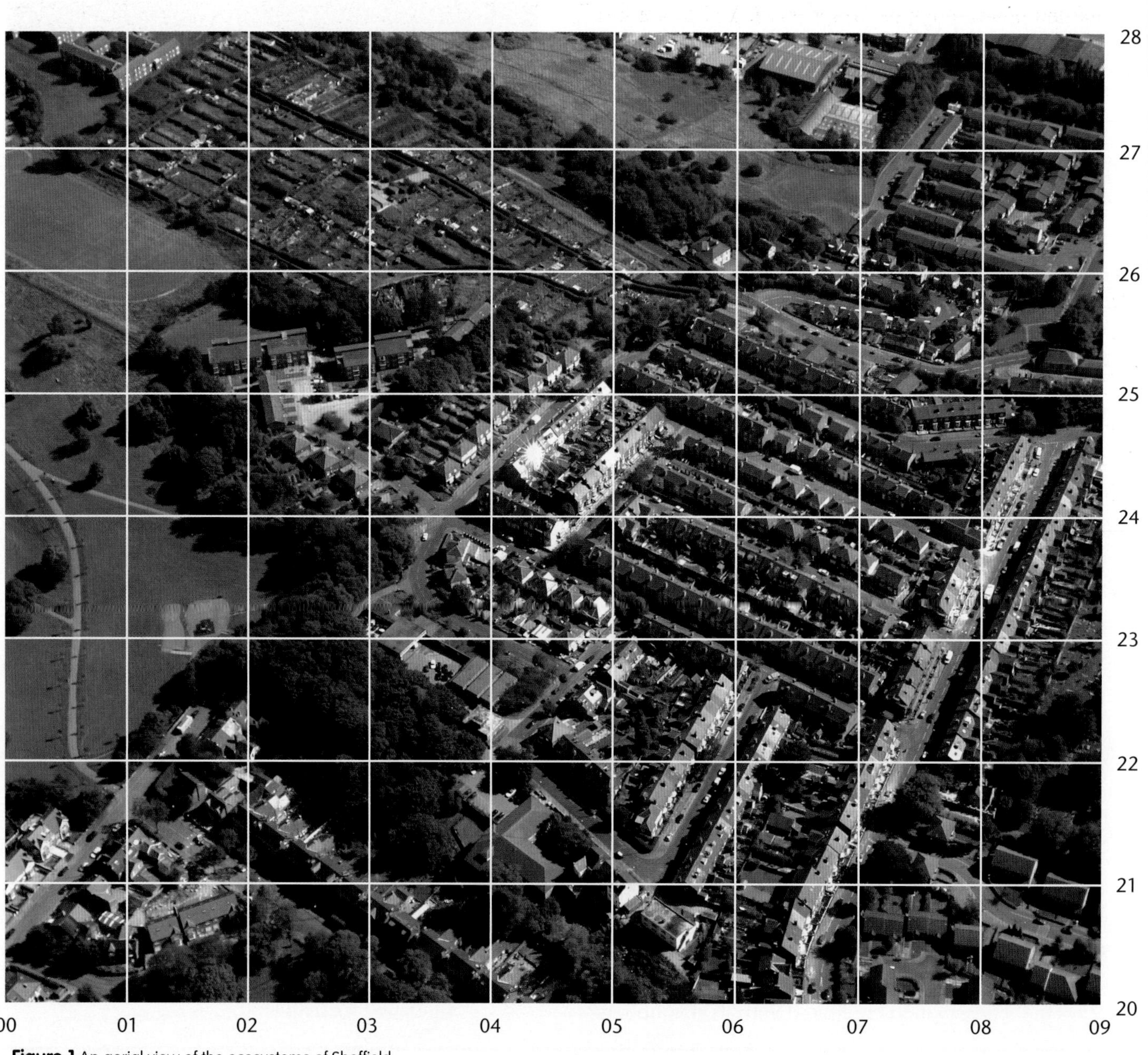


**Figure 1** An aerial view of the ecosystems of Sheffield

From above, like the aerial photo in Figure 1, the average town or city in the UK can be seen to be a patchwork of gardens, parks, golf courses and small woodlands. A detailed study of the wildlife in Sheffield discovered that 33 km$^2$, almost one-quarter of the city, was covered in gardens. These green areas are connected by hundreds of kilometres of hedgerows planted along many garden boundaries. The hedgerows are important wildlife corridors; they allow birds and mammals such as hedgehogs and foxes to move safely from one garden to another without being spotted by predators such as cats or birds of prey. So, the urban ecosystem is woodland with a discontinuous canopy: scattered trees and shrubs linked by dense hedgerows. Within this ecosystem are a number of much smaller ecosystems: garden ponds, compost heaps and log piles are just three examples of miniature ecosystems found within many gardens. Each of these small-scale ecosystems has its own distinctive set of interactions between the non-living environment and a specialised community of wildlife.

Sheffield has an estimated:

- 25,200 ponds
- 45,500 nest boxes
- 50,750 compost heaps
- 360,000 trees taller than 2 m

**Figure 2** The findings of the Biodiversity in Urban Gardens in Sheffield (BUGS) project carried out by Sheffield University

**www.shef.ac.uk/uni/projects/bugs**
for a description of the BUGS project in Sheffield.

**Figure 3** Insects are an essential living part of the urban ecosystem. They pollinate plants and provide food for birds. Red mason bees are particularly useful because they pollinate fruit trees. They lay their eggs in tubes. You can encourage them to use your garden as a nest site by providing a bee box like this one. It should be sited high on a post or in a tree in direct sunlight

## Activity

1 Outline the different land uses you can see in Figure 1.

2 Give at least three examples of urban ecosystems that are at different scales.

3 You are going to sample the land use in Figure 1.
   **a)** Choose five grid lines (vertical or horizontal) across Figure 1.
   **b)** Measure the total length of the five lines in millimetres.
   **c)** Measure the length of each of the following land uses along each line:
   - gardens
   - housing
   - roads
   - parks
   - other.

   **d)** Calculate the total length of each land use, and then calculate these as percentages of the whole.

4 Explain how you could improve the accuracy of your estimate of the percentage land use in Sheffield.

## How can people help the wildlife in the UK's cities?

Gardeners can encourage wildlife by being a little less tidy around their garden. By mowing the grass less frequently and allowing some areas of grass to grow long you will encourage more insects as well as voles. Rather than burning or shredding branches that have been pruned from the tree, why not make a log pile? A small pile of decaying wood is a miniature ecosystem. The rotting wood provides a habitat for fungi. Wood-boring insects such as stag beetle grubs (Figure 4) and woodlice burrow through the decaying wood. The crevices between the sticks provide a place for insects such as bumblebees to overwinter.

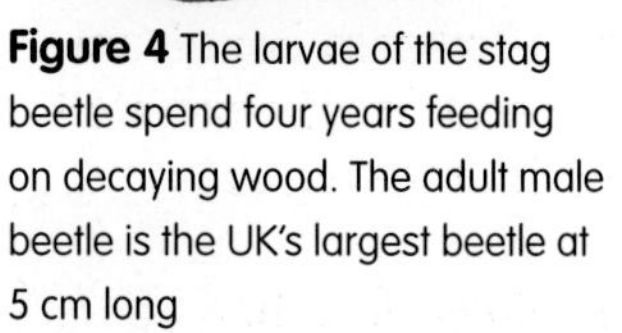

**Figure 4** The larvae of the stag beetle spend four years feeding on decaying wood. The adult male beetle is the UK's largest beetle at 5 cm long

Another great way to increase the biodiversity of your garden is to create a pond. Bigger pools are better than smaller ones, but any pool should be stocked by 'seeding' it with water from an established pond in a neighbouring garden. This encourages the population of insects and larvae to populate the new pond.

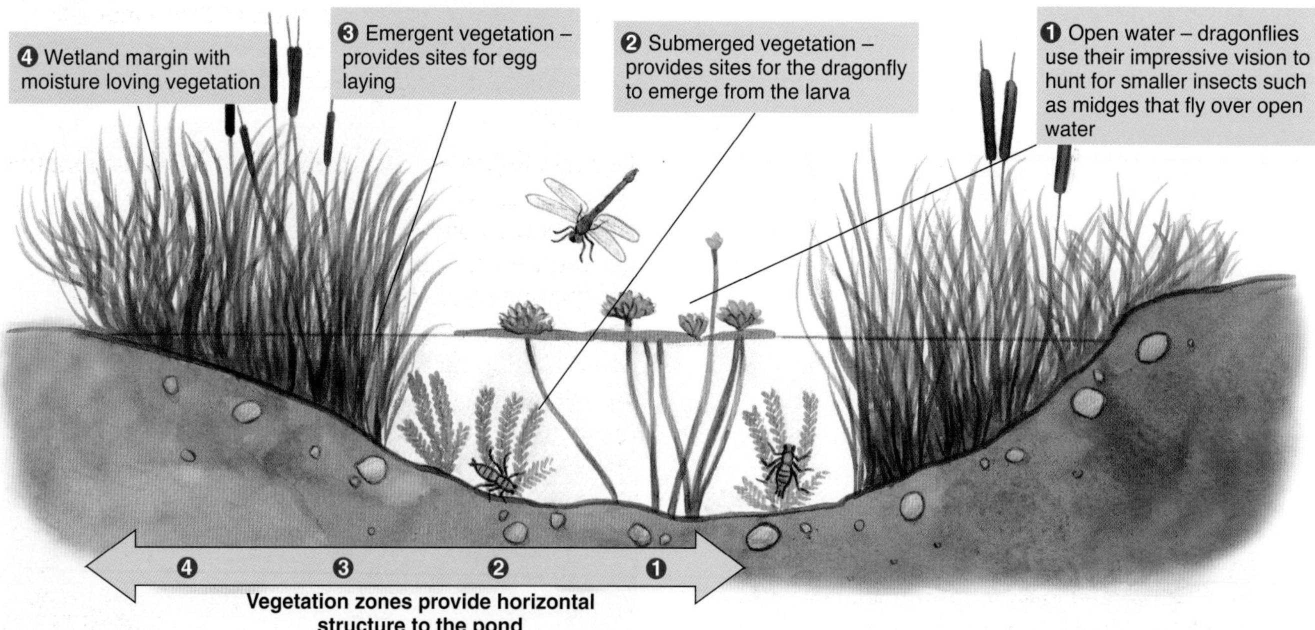


▲ **Figure 5** Structure of a garden pond, and the life cycle of the dragonfly

The BUGS project in Sheffield proved that small gardens can be just as useful to wildlife as larger gardens. What made the biggest difference to biodiversity of the gardens were:

- The aspect of the garden. Gardens on a south-facing slope were the best.
- The amount of canopy. The best gardens for wildlife had at least one small tree/large shrub with a canopy 2 m off the ground.
- Most wildlife is found in gardens that have plenty of vegetation in and around the garden.

Planners and developers can help by designing new estates that have plenty of space for gardens that are big enough for people to plant trees and create ponds and compost heaps. If the government tries to tackle the shortage of affordable starter homes by building high-density housing developments then there may not be enough room for wildlife.

**Figure 6** The emperor dragonfly is commonly seen at ponds in the UK

## Activity

**5** **a)** Make a copy of Figure 5.
**b)** Describe the structure of this ecosystem.

**6** Explain how the structure of this ecosystem provides a variety of habitats for insects such as dragonflies.

**7** Design a garden, no more than 10 m by 10 m, that would be attractive to wildlife. Include at least three different miniature ecosystems in your design.

**8** Discuss how the environment of your school grounds could be improved for wildlife. If you have a college council, make a poster which shows your plans and present it to them.

## The urban microclimate

Just as urban areas have their own small-scale ecosystems, they also have their own climate. The buildings and traffic in a large city influence the local climate, an effect known as **urban microclimate**. One of the main impacts of a city on the local climate is to create temperatures that are warmer than in the surrounding rural area. This is known as the **urban heat island**. Basically the city acts rather like a huge storage heater, transferring heat from buildings and cars to the dome of air that covers the city:

- Concrete, brick and tarmac all absorb heat from the sun during the day. This heat is then radiated into the atmosphere during the evening and at night.
- Buildings that are badly insulated lose heat energy, especially through roofs and windows. Heat is also created in cars and factories and this heat is also lost to the air from exhausts and chimneys.

During the heatwave of August 2003 the temperature in central London was 9 °C higher than the surrounding countryside. This caused severe discomfort for many people. In July 2001 an underground train broke down, trapping 4,000 people. The temperature rose to 40 °C and 600 people had to be treated for heat exhaustion. If climate change results in warmer temperatures, planners will have to find ways of reducing the urban heat island effect, especially on the underground.

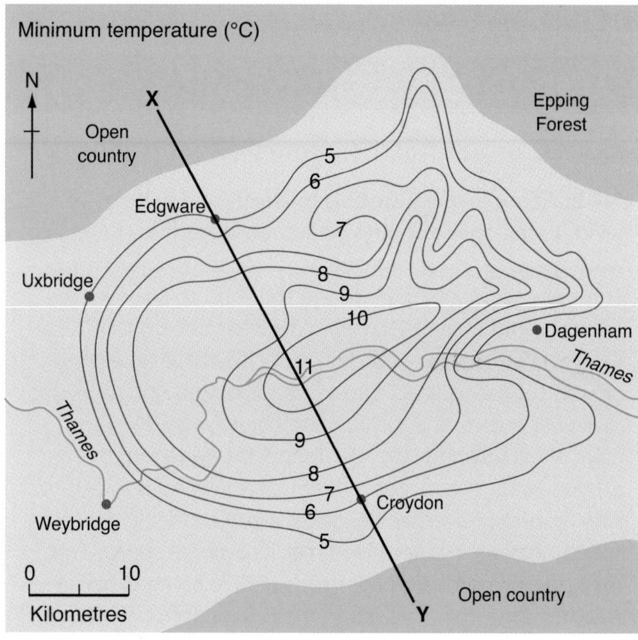


**Figure 7** London's urban heat island, night time temperatures in mid-May

## Activity

**9** Use Figure 7.
**a)** Describe the location of the area of highest temperatures in London.
**b)** Describe the distribution of places with lower temperatures.
**c)** Suggest reasons for the pattern shown on the map.

**10** Use Figure 7 to draw a cross-section of London's urban heat island along the line x–y.

**11** Predict how the urban heat islands of the following cities would compare with one another:
**a)** Two cities in the UK, one large, the other with a much smaller population.
**b)** Two cities of similar size, one in the tropics, the other in higher latitudes (e.g. Moscow).

## How do microclimates affect ecosystems?

The urban heat island has a number of effects. There are fewer frosts and less ice on the roads in the winter. Spring starts earlier than in surrounding rural areas and the growing season for vegetation is longer. Summers are hotter and there may be more days when people may suffer the effects of heat stress. Figure 8 is taken from the BBC Springwatch website. It illustrates that frogspawn, which is an indicator of the arrival of spring, arrives earlier in urban areas.

### Activity

**12** Use Figure 8.

**a)** Describe the distribution of sightings of frogspawn on the map.

**b)** Explain why there may have been more sightings in some parts of the UK than others.

**13** The graph in Figure 8 shows the total number of sightings each day between 24 November 2004 and 16 April 2005.

**a)** Describe the pattern shown on the graph.

**b)** Suggest why the graph has this distinctive shape.

**c)** Explain how you could investigate the actual reason for the shape of this graph.

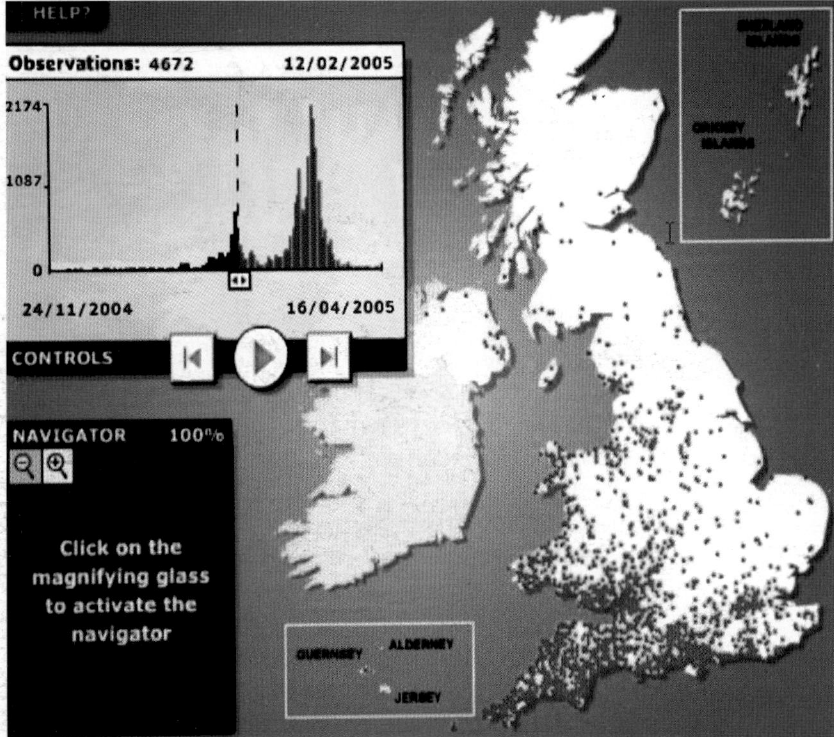


**Figure 8** Map of the first sightings of frogspawn up until 12 February 2005 from the BBC Springwatch website

## Going Further

### How do urban microclimates affect patterns of wind and rainfall?

Tall buildings in a city are able to affect local patterns of wind. In the open countryside farmers plant trees to reduce wind speeds and the damage wind can do to their crops. The trees act as a barrier, forcing the wind to rise over the tree tops and therefore creating a shelter belt on the **leeward side**. The tall buildings in cities have an even greater sheltering effect and so average wind speeds in cities are lower than in the surrounding countryside. However, rows of tall buildings can also funnel the wind into the canyon-like streets between them. As the wind is forced to flow around or over tall buildings, it can suddenly gust at speeds that are two to three times its average speed. This may cause hazards for pedestrians and, in some extreme weather conditions, has led to the collapse of scaffolding.

A large city may even affect local patterns of rainfall. During the summer months, the extra heat due to the urban heat island can cause more frequent convectional rainstorms over the city and the neighbouring rural area. Urban air has ten times more dust particles in it than the air in rural areas. The dust comes from car exhausts, heating systems in people's homes, industry and building sites, and it is another reason for slightly higher cloud cover and rainfall. When water vapour condenses in the air to form water droplets it does so by attaching itself to a dust particle. Without the dust, less condensation would be possible. In this way the atmosphere is self-cleaning: rainfall helps to remove pollution from the urban atmosphere.

## Going Further continued

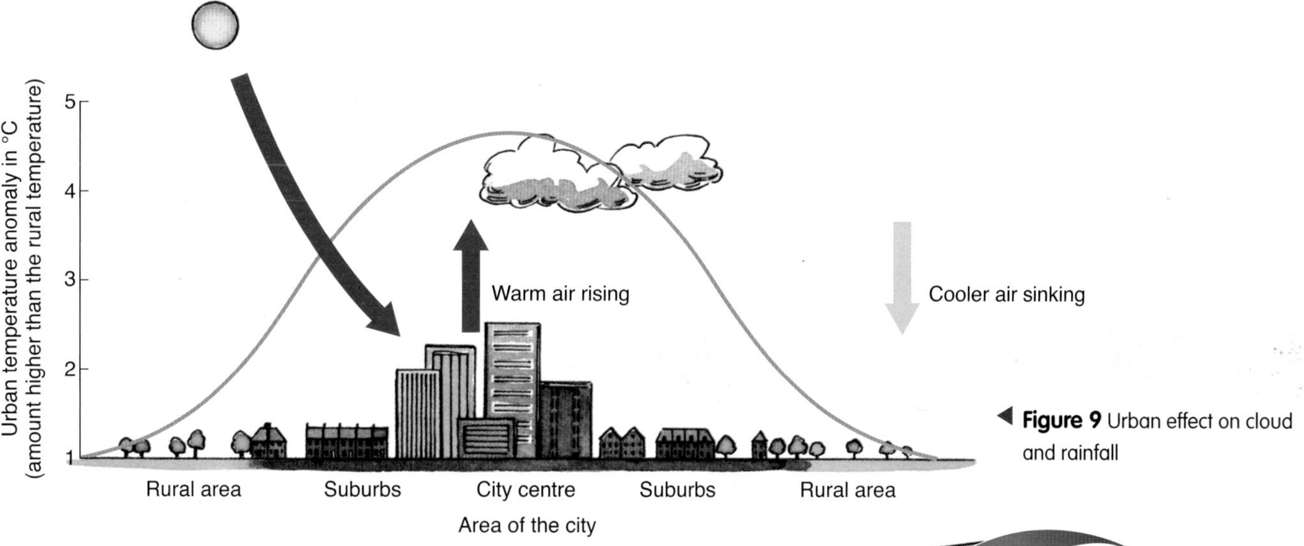


Figure 9 Urban effect on cloud and rainfall

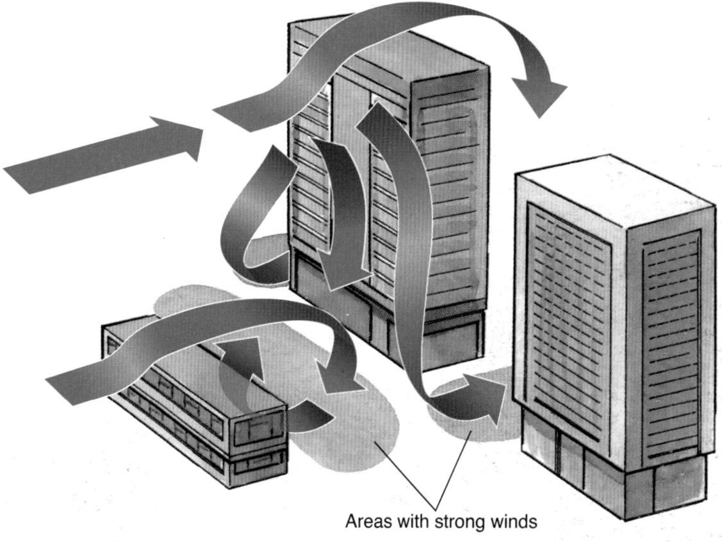


Figure 10 Urban wind patterns

**Additional labels for Figures 9 and 10**

Wind is funnelled by tall buildings

Prevailing wind

Decreased air pressure

Increased air pressure

Sun's energy is absorbed by building materials

Gusty winds may be two to three times stronger than average

Cumulus clouds form where rising warm air meets colder air

**14** Make copies of Figures 9 and 10. Sort the 'additional' labels and add them to appropriate places on your diagrams.

**15** Study Figure 11. Outline the advantages and disadvantages of the urban microclimate for the people who live in cities.

**16** Suggest how the creation of more parks, woodlands and lakes in our cities might:
**a)** affect the urban microclimate
**b)** make urban areas more sustainable in the future.

**www.atmosphere.mpg.de/enid/wb.html** has a good explanation for urban heat islands with animations of wind movement through the city.

| Sunshine duration | 5–15% less |
|---|---|
| Annual mean temperature | 1–2 °C warmer |
| Temperatures on sunny days | 2–6 °C warmer |
| Occurrence of frosts | 2–3 weeks fewer |
| Total precipitation | 5–30% more |
| Number of rain days | 10% more |
| Number of days with snow | 14% fewer |
| Cloud cover | 5–10% more |
| Occurrence of fog in winter | 100% more |
| Amount of condensation nuclei | 10 times more |

Figure 11 The effects of the urban climate in the UK

London

## The London Wetland Centre

The London **Wetland** Centre in Barnes, South London, provides a case study of the conservation and management of a small-scale ecosystem. It also shows the way in which people see the environment as a resource, and how the use of that resource is changing.

The London Wetland Centre has been created on the site of four disused Victorian water storage reservoirs. The reservoirs had been designated as a Site of Special Scientific Interest (SSSI) in 1975 because of the large numbers of waterfowl who used the reservoirs. The reservoirs were no longer needed, so, in 1995, a huge reclamation project began to convert the reservoirs into a 40-hectare wetland ecosystem that would benefit a wide biodiversity.

**www.wwt.org.uk** is the official website of the Wildfowl and Wetlands Trust and has information about all nine WWT visitor centres in the UK. Why not see if there is one near you?

The reclamation project had three partners:

- The Wildfowl and Wetlands Trust: a charity which manages nine sites around the UK. Its aim is to conserve wetland birds and their habitats.
- Thames Water: the water company which owned the reservoirs.
- Berkeley Homes: a property developer which helped to finance the project by building and selling houses on part of the site.

**Grazing marsh**
This wildflower meadow is flooded in winter so that grass seed is washed into the water where it can be eaten by ducks. It is drained in the spring to provide nesting sites.

**Reedbeds**
The water's edge is planted with common reed, which provides cover for small songbirds such as reed buntings and sedge warblers.

**Sheltered lagoon**
The sheltered areas provided by vegetation around this shallow lake are preferred by breeding and roosting birds.

**Wader scrape**
This flat area is flooded in winter. The water is then lowered in the spring to expose mud banks. This mud provides feeding areas for long-billed waders such as redshank.

**Figure 12** Wetland habitats created at the London Wetland Centre

Figure 13 An Ordnance Survey extract featuring the London Wetland Centre Scale 1:25,000 Sheet 161

### London Wetland Centre facts and figures

- The site contains more than 30 different wetlands.
- There are 600 m of boardwalk and 3.4 km of pathway.
- More than 130 species of wild bird are recorded annually.
- 24 species of butterfly and 260 moth species are recorded annually.
- Eighteen dragon and damselfly species are recorded annually.
- Four species of amphibian are recorded annually.

Figure 14 An aerial view of the London Wetland Centre

## Activity

**17** Use Figure 13.

**a)** Describe the location of the Wetland Centre.

**b)** Give six-figure grid references for:
i) Hammersmith Bridge
ii) Barnes Station.

**c)** Give directions, including distances, for a visitor approaching the Wetlands Visitor Centre (at 226767) on foot from:
i) Hammersmith Bridge
ii) Barnes Station.

**d)** What is the approximate area of the Wetlands Centre?
i) a little less than 1 $km^2$
ii) a little more than 1 $km^2$
iii) 2 $km^2$

**18** Use Figure 12 to describe the living and non-living parts of this ecosystem.

**19** Make notes on the London Wetland Centre. Include:

**a)** location and scale of the ecosystem

**b)** main features and structure of the ecosystem

**c)** how different groups of people have helped to manage this ecosystem.

# Chapter 7 Climate change

**KEY QUESTIONS**

- Are our actions responsible for an increasing number of extreme weather events?
- Can human activities change climate patterns?
- Why is climate change an issue of international concern?

## Is the weather getting more extreme?

Extreme weather events such as the floods in Boscastle in 2004 (see page 22) are very unusual. But a growing number of very unusual weather events have been reported in recent years, so are extreme weather events becoming more frequent?

### Are more frequent hurricanes evidence of climate change?

The islands of the Caribbean and Florida (USA), had record-breaking weather in August and September 2004. This region often has severe tropical storms, known in the USA as hurricanes, at this time of year. But in a period of just five weeks from 12 August to 18 September the region experienced four massive hurricanes which killed more than 1,500 people between them. Hurricanes are formed when sea water is heated to above 27 °C. The warm water heats the air above it, causing it to rise and creating a large zone of low air pressure.

In the summer of 2005, the region was hit by another four category-5 hurricanes, the strongest category of hurricane with wind speeds greater than 250 km per hour. These included:

- Wilma: the strongest hurricane ever recorded in the region.
- Katrina: the most expensive hurricane in recorded history, which created at least $80m of damage. Katrina was also the deadliest storm to hit the United States since 1926 as it killed at least 1,300 people.

Scientists believe that one effect of **global warming** is that tropical regions are likely to suffer from more frequent or more violent hurricanes. To some people in the media, the exceptional occurrence of so many record-breaking hurricanes over two seasons constituted evidence of global warming.

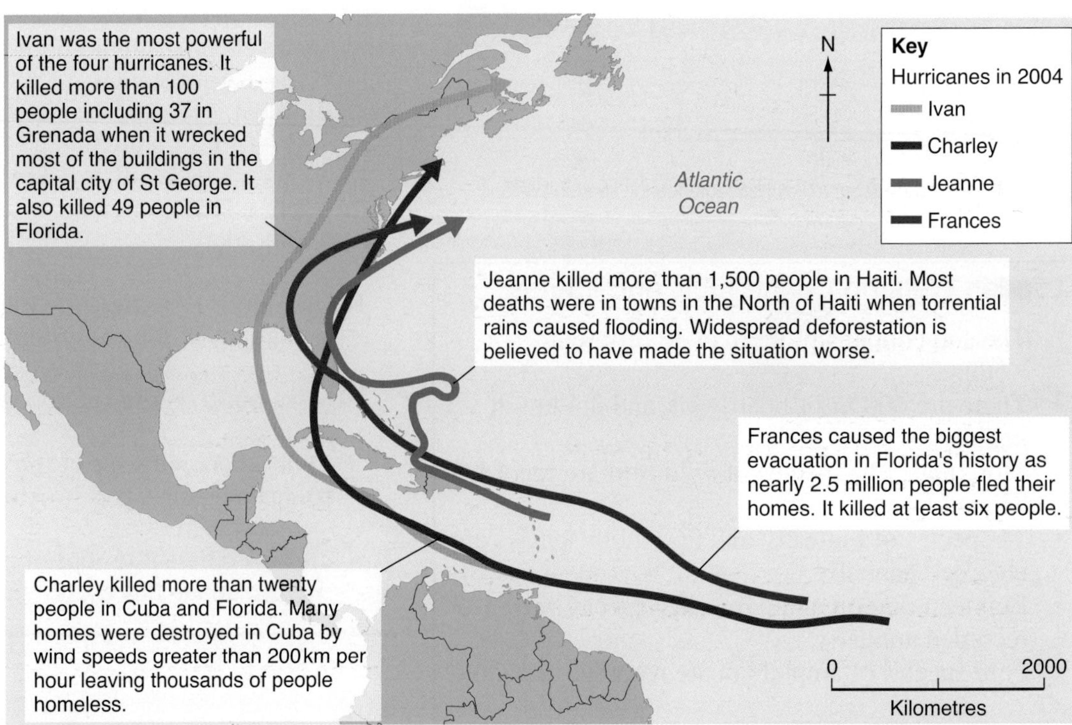


**Figure 1** The paths taken across the Caribbean by the four hurricanes of 2004

**Category 5:** Over 250 kph. Complete failure of some smaller buildings. Failure of the roofs of large industrial buildings. Extensive coastal flooding damages the ground floor of many buildings.

**Category 4:** 211–250 kph. Complete destruction of the roofs of smaller buildings and more extensive damage to the walls. All signs and trees are blown down. Flooding of coastal areas 3 to 5 hours before the arrival of the storm may cut off escape routes.

**Category 3:** 178–210 kph. Severe damage to the roofs of small buildings. Some structural damage to walls. Mobile homes destroyed. Poorly constructed road signs destroyed. Large trees blown down.

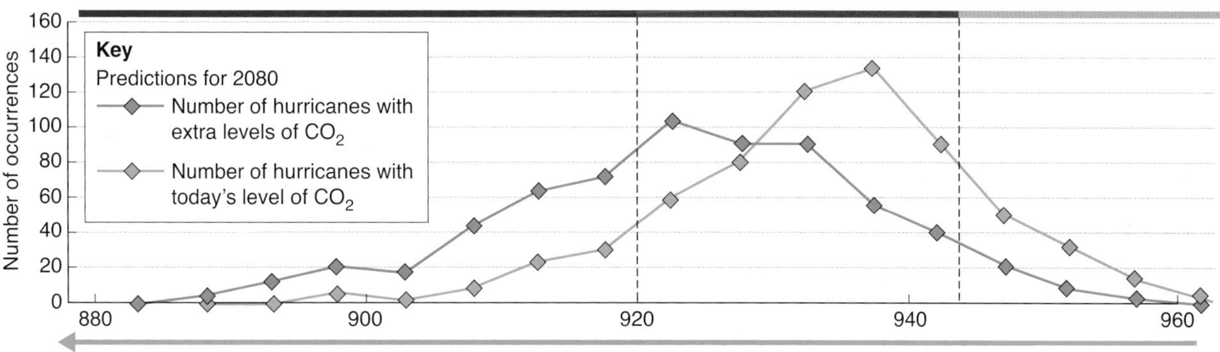


The strongest hurricanes in the present climate may be upstaged by even more intense hurricanes over the next century as the Earth's climate is warmed by increasing levels of greenhouse gases in the atmosphere. Although we cannot say at present whether more or fewer hurricanes will occur in the future with global warming, the hurricanes that do occur near the end of the 21st century are expected to be stronger and have significantly more intense rainfall than under present-day climate conditions.

**Figure 2** The National Oceanic and Atmosphere Administration (NOAA) has used computer models to predict frequency of hurricanes in 2080

## Activity

**1** Study Figure 1. Describe the main effects of each of the hurricanes.

**2** Consider each of the following factors. Explain how it might influence the size of the death toll during a hurricane:

**wind speed**
**intensity of rainfall**
**population density close to the coast**
**poverty or wealth of the area**
**deforestation**

**3** Study Figure 2. Describe how the frequency and violence of hurricanes are expected to change.

**4** Use evidence from pages 50–51 to explain why global warming is an 'issue of international concern'.

**5** Explain why you think there were more deaths in Haiti than in Florida during the hurricanes of 2004. Do you consider these deaths to be due to a natural disaster or poverty? Justify your reasoning.

**6** Explain why planting trees in Haiti could save lives.

## How global warming is affecting global patterns of climate

We have seen that some extreme weather events are being blamed on global warming. The theory is that pollution is causing heat to be trapped in our atmosphere. This extra heat energy may be causing:

- more violent storms such as hurricane Katrina
- more heatwaves, like the one in Europe in 2003 (see pages 22–23).

In addition, global warming is likely to affect global patterns of climate. Desert regions may become drier. The wet tropical regions which contain our rainforests may also receive less annual rainfall. That's why the media often refers to global warming as climate change. One region where there is evidence that the climate is already changing is the Arctic.

## A case study of climate change in the Arctic

The polar bear is the world's largest land predator. There are about 20,000 polar bears living in the wild, but their numbers are falling. Why is this happening?

There are 1,200 polar bears living in the region of Hudson Bay, Canada. Their population has been monitored by the Canadian Wildlife Service (CWS) for more than 40 years. The results show that the polar bears are under threat: many bears are under weight; female bears are less fertile; and the survival rate of pups is falling.

The CWS has considered many possible explanations for the decline of the polar bear population. One is chemical pollution. Bears are at the top of the Arctic food chain and can accumulate poisons in their bodies that they have taken in from their numerous prey. However, the CWS has come to the conclusion that the bears are under threat as a result of climate change.

CWS studies show that the ice now melts three weeks earlier than it did when studies began in the early 1970s. This is direct evidence of climate change. For each week that the thaw comes early, the bears have less chance to feed, and come on shore 10 kg lighter. The consequences of further climate change are worrying:

- more young bears and pups will starve over the longer summer.
- females will be less fertile
- hungry bears are more likely to forage for food in towns where they come into conflict with people.

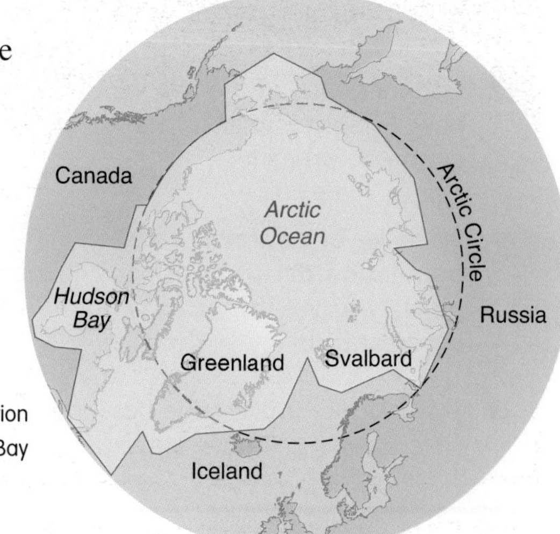


**Figure 3** Distribution of polar bears and location of Hudson Bay

▼ **Figure 4** The Arctic food web

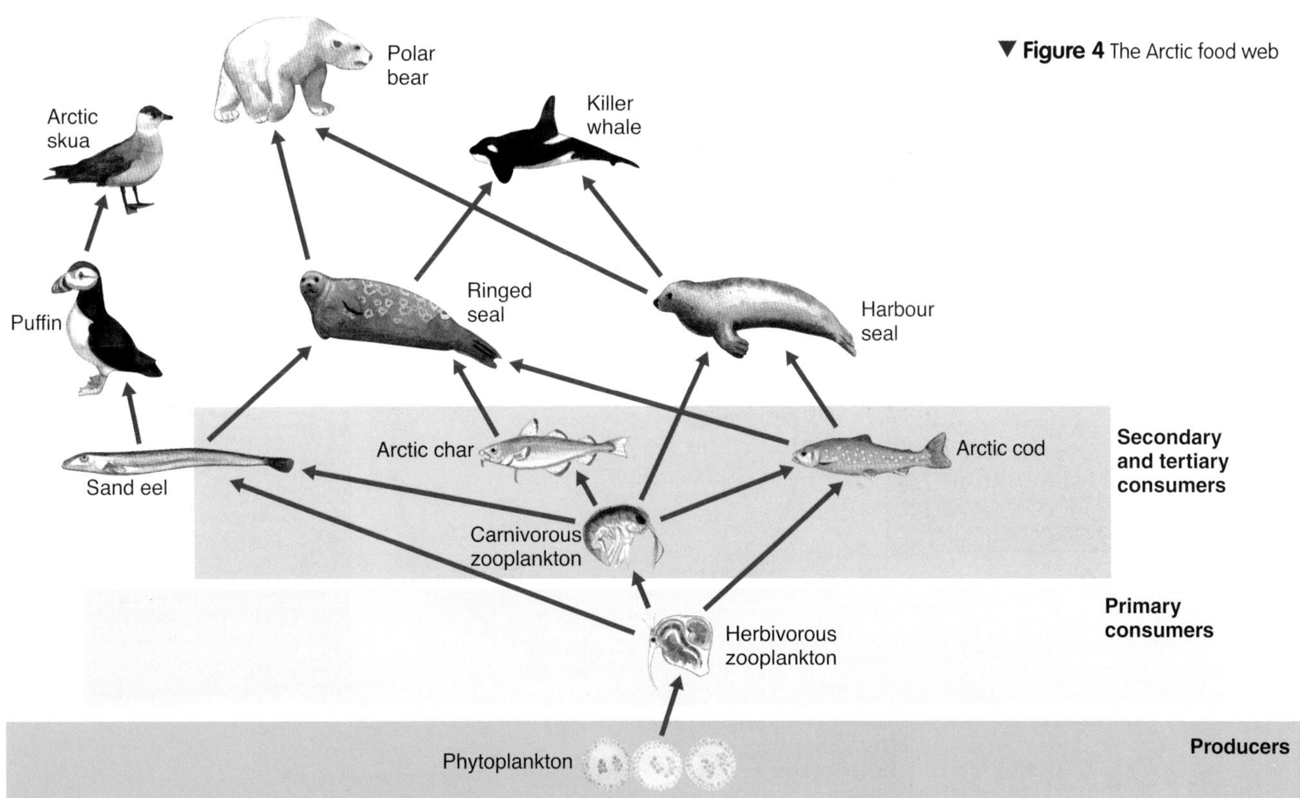


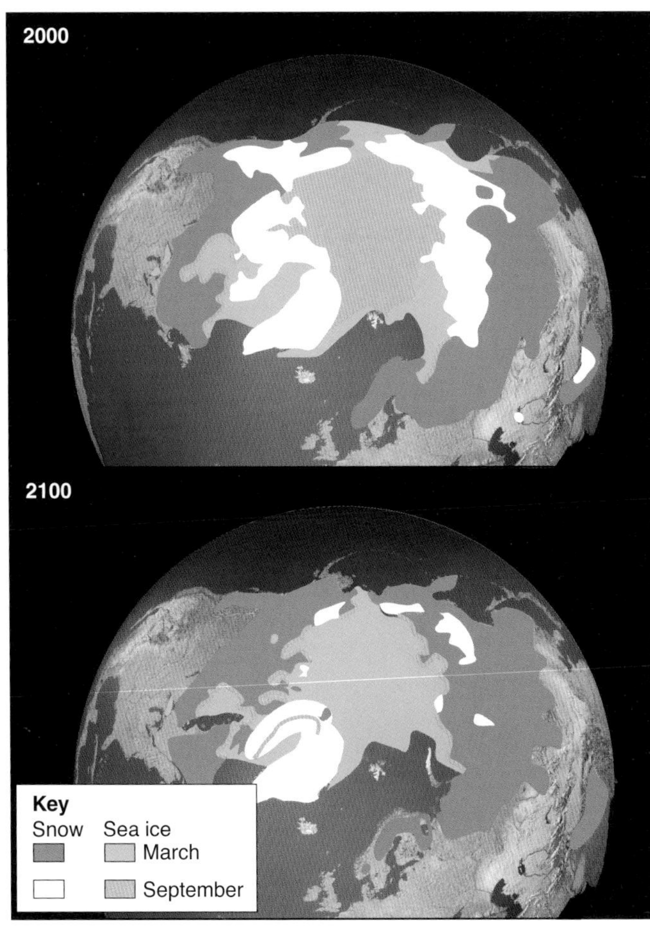


**Figure 5** The extent of sea ice in 2000 compared with the predicted extent in 2100

## Activity

**7** Study Figure 3.

**a)** Describe the location of Hudson Bay.

**b)** Describe the distribution of polar bears.

**8** **a)** Use Figure 4 to draw a food chain which includes the polar bear.

**b)** Explain what will happen to this food web if the polar bears are unable to catch enough ringed seals to survive the summer.

**9** Look at Figures 3 and 5.

**a)** Compare the distribution of polar bears to the sea ice in March 2000.

**b)** Describe what is predicted to happen to the sea ice in March 2100.

**c)** Compare the distribution of September sea ice in 2000 to 2100.

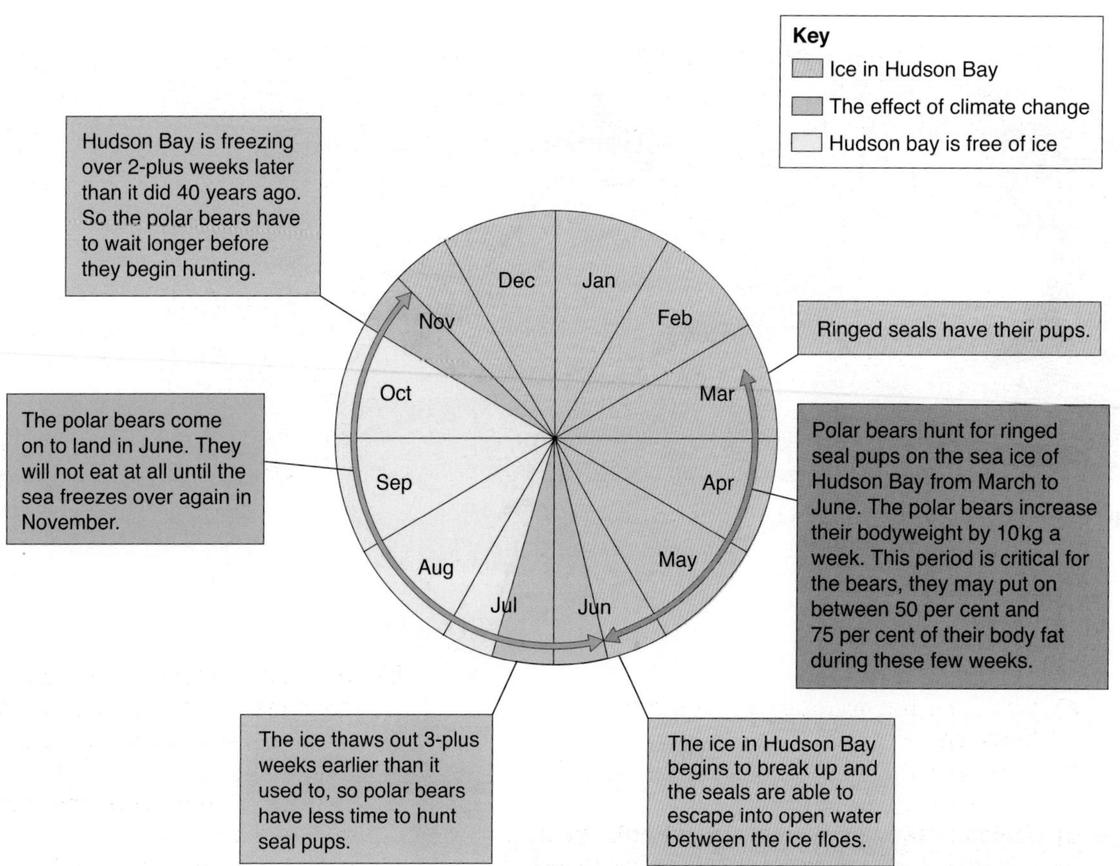


**Figure 6** How the earlier spring thaw is affecting the Arctic food chain

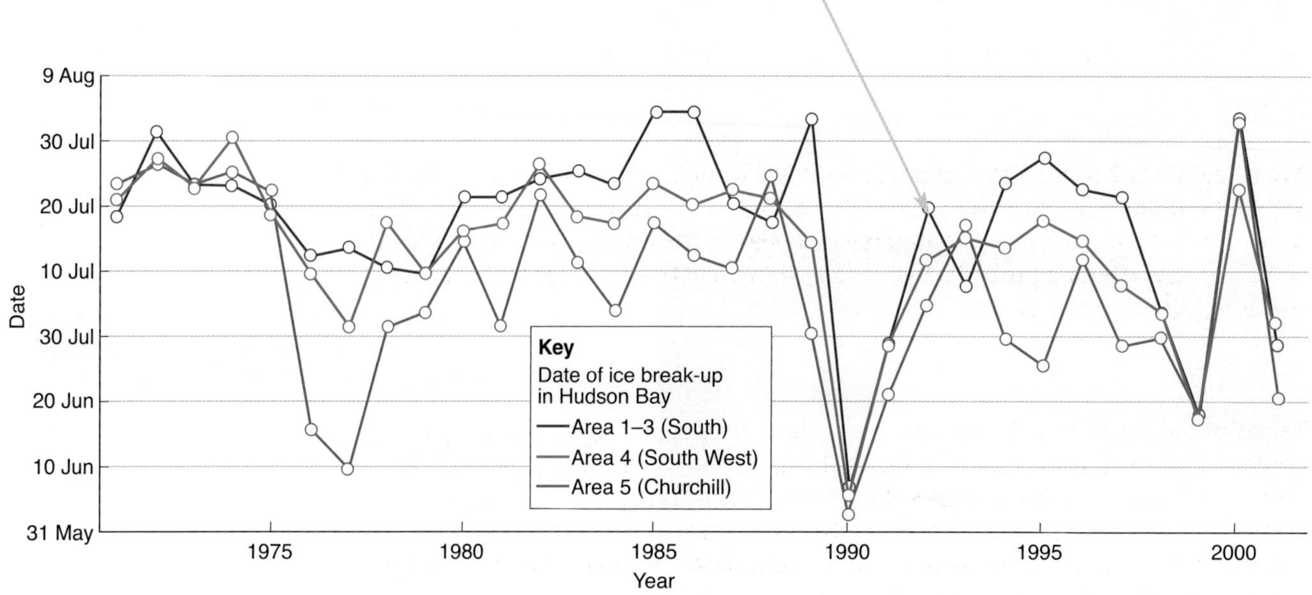


**Figure 7** The average date of ice break-up in Hudson Bay

Figure 8 Polar bears in Hudson Bay are the most studied group of polar bears in the world

The potential for fairly significant rises in temperature in Arctic regions seems to be quite high. And should that happen, especially over a time scale of decades, the possibility of marine mammals being able to adapt rapidly enough is very low.

**Figure 9** The opinion of Dr Malcolm Ramsay, Professor of Biology at the University of Saskatchewan in Canada

### Activity

**10** Study Figure 7.

**a)** What was the average date of the thaw between 1971 and 1975?

**b)** What was the average date of the thaw in 1999 and 2001?

**c)** Which of the two populations of polar bears will be more threatened by an earlier thaw? Explain your choice.

**11 a)** Use Figure 6 to help you explain why polar bears are unable to adapt to climate change.

**b)** Does it matter that polar bears might be threatened with extinction in the next few decades? Explain your point of view.

**12 a)** Use Figure 7 to describe the thaw in the years from 1990 to 1993.

**b)** Explain why this happened and the effect it had on the bears.

**c)** Explain how this evidence supports the view that global warming is having a direct effect on polar bear populations.

**13** Draw a flow chart to show how climate change is affecting the polar bears.

## What is causing climate change?

Most scientists believe that human actions are to blame for climate change. They say that the emission of certain gases, such as carbon dioxide, methane, CFCs, nitrous oxides and ozone, is trapping extra heat in the atmosphere. These are the so-called **greenhouse gases (GGs)**. Many human activities release these gases, including the burning of fossil fuels for energy.

### The carbon cycle

Three of the main greenhouse gases – carbon dioxide, methane and CFCs – contain carbon. Carbon exists in many different forms and many parts of the environment act as carbon **stores**. It is stored in all living things; in simple compounds such as carbon dioxide in the atmosphere and oceans; and in much more complex compounds such as the hydrocarbon compounds that make up fossil fuels such as oil, coal and gas.

Carbon is mobile in the environment: it is able to **flow**, or be transferred from one store to another through a series of processes such as **respiration** or solution. The flow of carbon between various stores is shown in the **carbon cycle** diagram in Figure 10. It is important to understand that some parts of the environment store carbon only for short periods of time. Others, such as fossil fuels, are able to store the carbon over much longer periods of time. These are known as **carbon sinks**.

## The enhanced greenhouse effect

The greenhouse effect is a natural process of our atmosphere. Without it, the average surface temperature of the Earth would be –17 °C rather than the 15 °C we currently experience. However, human activities over the last 200 years have significantly increased the concentration of greenhouse gases in the atmosphere. Emissions of greenhouse gases throw the global carbon cycle out of balance, transferring carbon from sinks such as forests and reserves of coal into the atmosphere. With larger concentrations of greenhouse gases in the atmosphere able to absorb and trap heat, the greenhouse effect has become stronger. This is what we call the **enhanced greenhouse effect**.

### Activity

**14** Study Figure 10.

**a)** Describe all the human actions that release carbon dioxide into the atmosphere.

**b)** Give two reasons why the burning of tropical rainforests will increase the amount of carbon dioxide in the atmosphere.

**15 a)** Describe the difference in the speed of transfer of carbon in the natural part of the cycle compared to the part of the cycle affected by human action.

**b)** Explain what difference this makes to the amount of carbon stored in the atmosphere compared with the long-lasting carbon sinks. Explain why this is alarming.

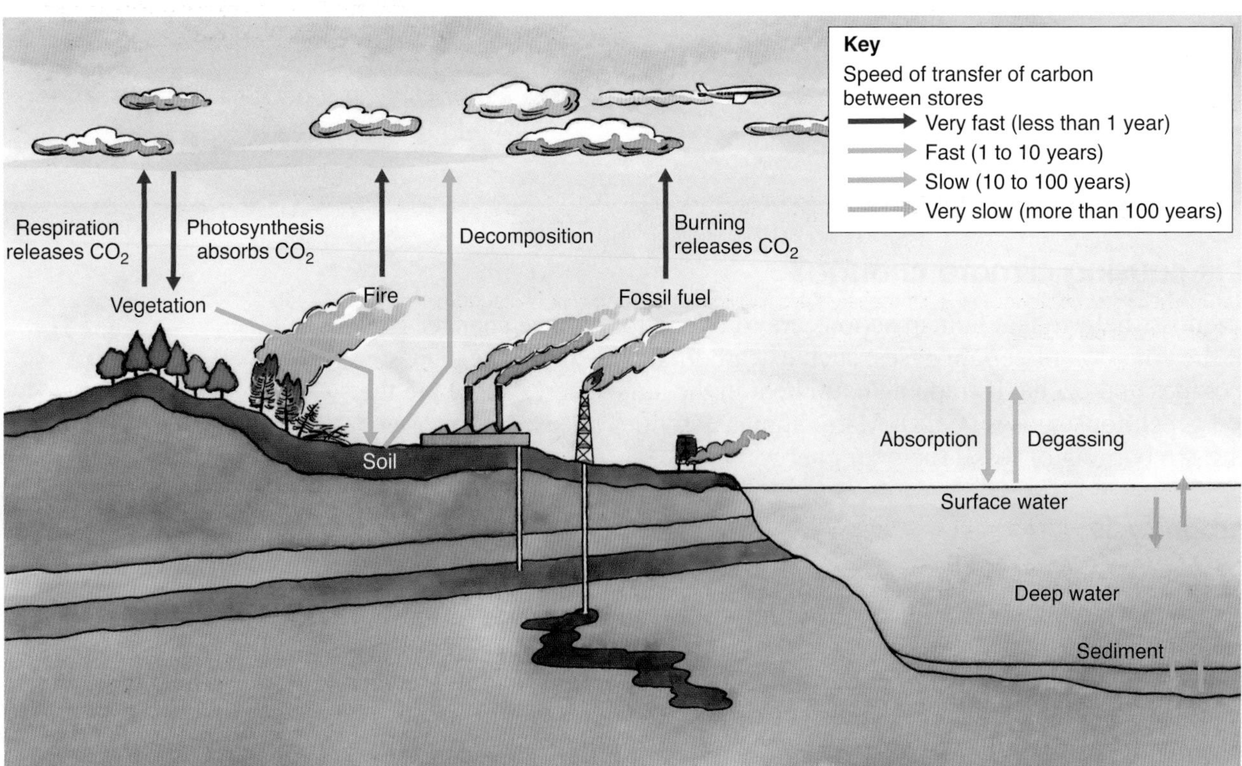


**Figure 10** The carbon cycle, showing fast and slow transfers

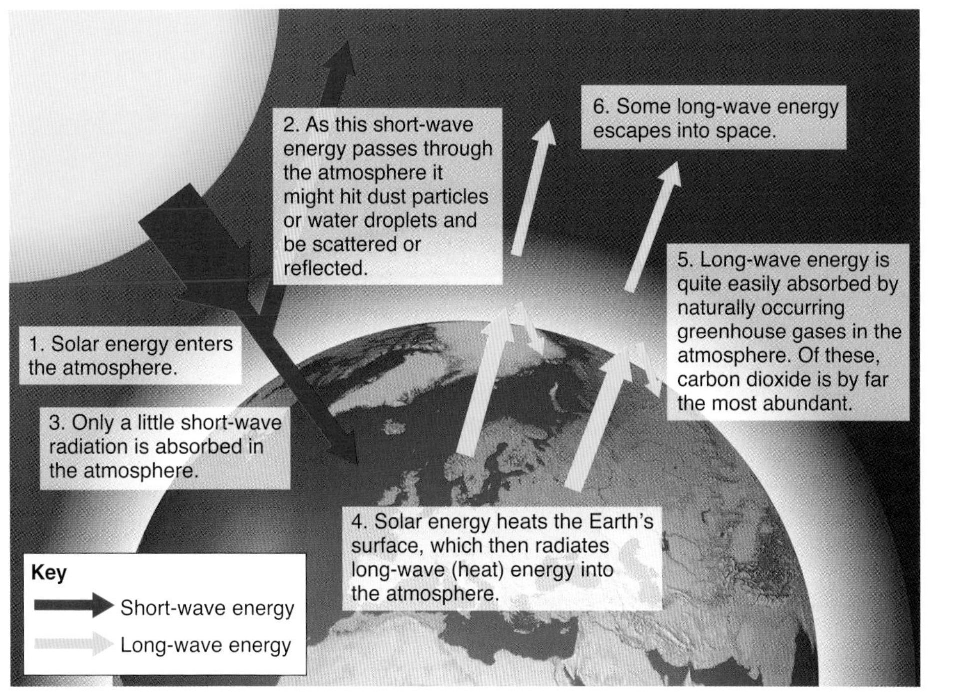


**Figure 11** The greenhouse effect

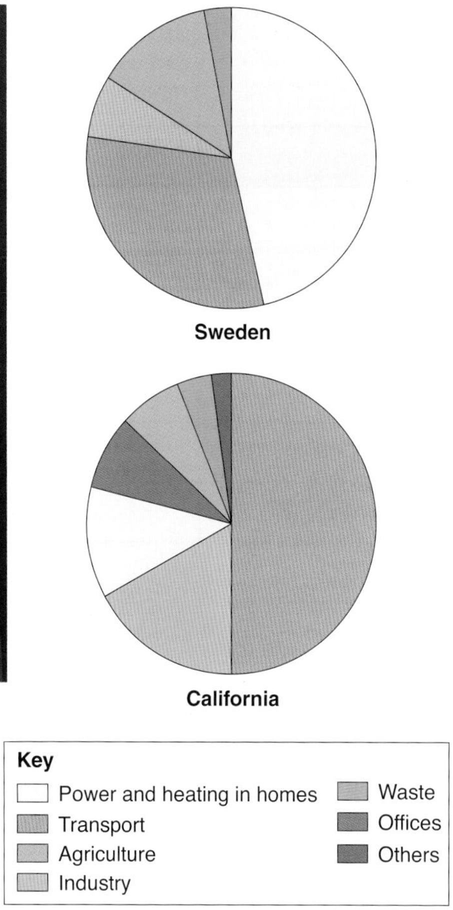

Sweden

California

Key
- Power and heating in homes
- Transport
- Agriculture
- Industry
- Waste
- Offices
- Others

**Figure 13** The source of greenhouse gases in Sweden and California, USA

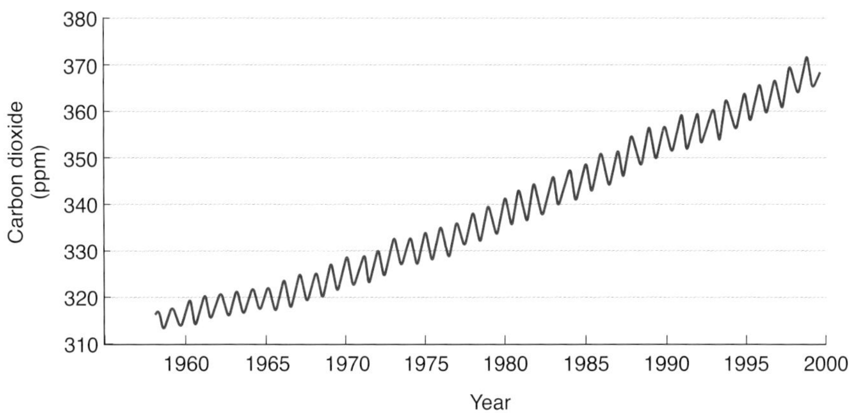


**Figure 12** The rise of carbon dioxide in the atmosphere since monitoring of the atmosphere began in the 1950s (ppm = parts per million)

## Activity

**16** Use Figure 11.

**a)** Describe the source of the energy that is trapped by the greenhouse gases.

**b)** Explain why the greenhouse effect is a good thing for human life.

**c)** Explain what is enhancing the natural greenhouse effect.

**17** Describe the trend of the line on Figure 12.

**18** Use Figure 13.

**a)** Compare the source of emissions in Sweden and California.

**b)** Suggest reasons for the differences you have noticed.

**c)** Suggest how this graph might be different if it were drawn for a **Less Economically Developed Country** such as Mali or Niger in Africa.

| Country | Total carbon emissions (in millions of tons) | Emissions per person (tons) |
|---|---|---|
| USA | 1,446 | 5.37 |
| China | 917 | 0.76 |
| Russian Federation | 431 | 2.91 |
| Japan | 318 | 2.54 |
| India | 272 | 0.29 |
| Germany | 235 | 2.87 |
| United Kingdom | 152 | 2.59 |
| Canada | 111 | 3.76 |
| South Korea | 111 | 2.46 |
| Italy | 110 | 1.92 |

**Figure 14** Carbon emissions from the world's top ten carbon polluters (Source: Union of Concerned Scientists)

## Different points of view on climate change

Many companies and countries are contributing to climate change by burning fossil fuels and releasing carbon dioxide and other greenhouse gases into the atmosphere. It is estimated that **More Economically Developed Countries (MEDCs)** have 20 per cent of the world's population, but consume 80 per cent of the world's resources. They are also the world's biggest polluters and produce more carbon emissions than anyone else. Africa, on the other hand, is the world's poorest continent producing the least carbon emissions. However, as droughts become more common in different parts of Africa, climate change is likely to have bigger impacts here than almost anywhere else. People all over the world are beginning to ask: What should we do about carbon emissions?

### The Kyoto Protocol

Many nations agreed to reduce carbon emissions when they signed up to the **Kyoto Protocol** in 2005. Under this agreement each country will seek to reduce their emission of greenhouse gases by five per cent below the levels they were emitting in 1990. But not every country is happy about Kyoto. Australia and the United States signed the protocol, but do not intend to keep the agreement, mainly because they believe that to meet their emissions targets would damage their economy. This decision has angered many environmentalists.

**Figure 15** Opinions vary about how we should deal with reducing carbon emissions

### Activity

**19 a)** Choose a suitable technique to graph the data in Figure 14.

**b)** Explain why the emissions per person column is so different from the total emissions column.

**c)** Explain what is likely to happen to the total emissions in China and India as these two countries become wealthier.

**20** Study Figure 15. Write a paragraph for a radio script that discusses the point that the cartoonist is trying to make.

**21** Explain why climate change is an issue of international concern.

## Going Further

### Using the internet to research geographical issues: weblogs

The internet has given people the ability to have their own say on any subject. A weblog or blog is an internet site in which the creator expresses an opinion and encourages people to respond. Weblogs can focus on all sorts of issues from television, fashion, music, food or politics, right through to topical issues in science such as global warming. The views expressed by newspapers or television programmes can be controlled by editors, but the internet is not controlled or regulated in this way. For this reason, weblogs are interesting to geographers because they provide an unedited source of conflicting opinions on geographical or environmental issues.

A Google™ web search for *global warming weblog* in December 2006 found 576,000 entries. Extracts from three weblogs in the top ten Google™ hits for this topic are reproduced in Figure 16.

**Web extract 1. Double Blind**
Anybody pushing extreme arguments (such as claiming that the only solution to Climate Change is to cut greenhouse gas emissions to 10 per cent less than 1990 emission levels) has to be viewed with a suspect eye, especially since their science that they're pushing is mostly junk.

**Web extract 2. University of British Columbia**
The signs of global warming are gradually appearing in the North-west of North America. Measurements taken by University of Washington scientists, since the 1950s, show that glaciers are shrinking in the region, some by as much as a third of their water volume. Mild winters and hotter, drier summers have promoted a massive infestation of British Columbia's forests by the mountain pine beetle.

**Web extract 3. *An Artsy Fartsy blog* by Scott Thingpen**
**Ten myths about global warming**

1. Agriculture will benefit – may make some crops grow faster, but also will accelerate weeds, pests and droughts; crops may not grow well where they once did as climate zones shift.

2. It's being handled by our government – The current US Administration advocates studying, not dealing with, global warming; its energy policy completely based on burning more coal and oil. Most state and local governments are unprepared for major changes.

3. It's not a big deal compared to national security – Global warming is actually the most serious threat to the widest range of human concerns. Our national and world security is directly threatened by negative climate effects on weather, water supply, disease, agriculture, marine resources, and health.

**Figure 16** Extracts from three weblogs found using a Google™ search

**22** Read the weblog extracts in Figure 16. Remember that Google™ had them all ranked in the top ten weblogs for this topic, meaning that there are more links to these weblogs than any of the other 576,000.
- **a)** List the facts.
- **b)** List the opinions.
- **c)** How reliable or accurate do you think is the information that each contains? Rank the sites in order of their reliability. How did you make your decision? What else do you need to know about these bloggers?

**23** Explain why geography students:
- **a)** should use weblogs when they are researching topics
- **b)** should be cautious of what they read on the internet.

**24** Approximately 80 per cent of the world's population does not have regular access to a phone line. Suggest the likely global distribution of weblogs. Why does it matter if weblogs are clustered in certain geographical locations and not present in others?

# Chapter 8
# Problem-solving exercise

**Your enquiry ...**

Why did these fires break out? Were they caused by extreme weather?

How were people affected by the fires?

Why do people live so close to the forest? Do they know it's dangerous?

How can this forest ecosystem be managed?

## Managing weather hazards in Australia

When a weather event becomes extreme it can put people and property at risk. In this chapter you will investigate the extreme weather events of 2002–03 that led to forest fires in the southeast region of Australia. At the end of this exercise you will produce a plan that could reduce the risk of further forest fires.

**Your decision ...**

How can this suburb be made a safer place to live?

**EXAMTECHNIQUE**

Parts A and B of the problem-solving exercise will test your geographical skills. Questions will commonly ask you to:

- describe a climate graph (page 11)
- describe the location (pages 120 and 154)
- describe the distribution of a feature (e.g. an ecosystem) (page 143)

So a good way to prepare for Paper 3 or 4 is to practise these skills. Use the cross-references above to re-read the Exam Techniques before you try the activities on these problem-solving pages.

**Figure 1** The forest fires of January 2003

## Part A: the links between climate and ecosystems in Australia

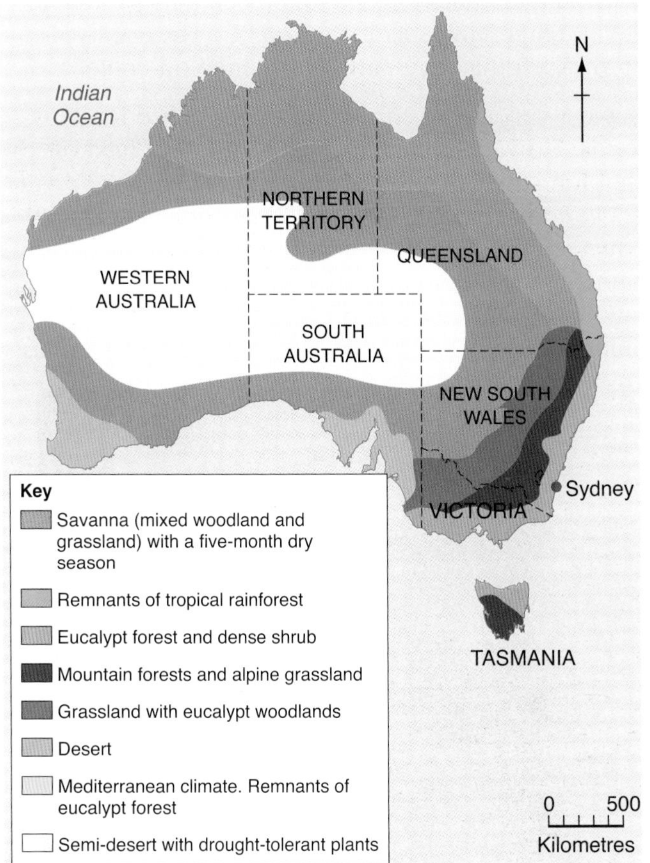


**Figure 2** Ecosystems in Australia

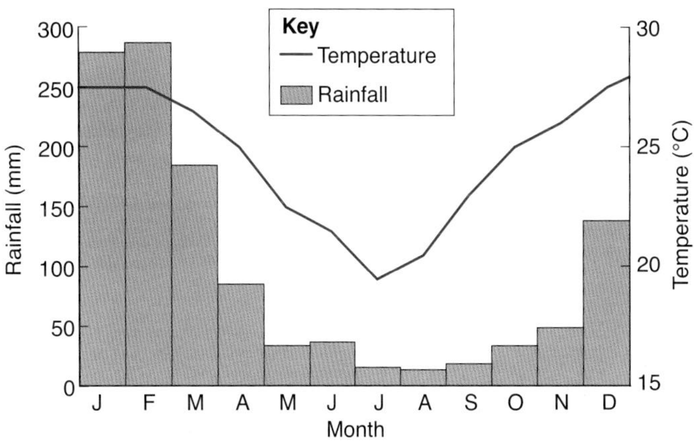


**Figure 3** Climate graph for Queensland

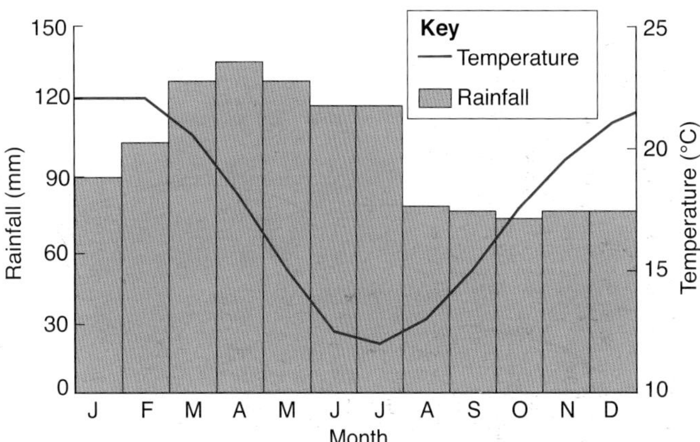


**Figure 4** Climate graph for Sydney

### Activity

**1** Use Figure 2 and an atlas. Copy and complete the following sentences.

**The savanna ecosystem is in the ....................... part of Australia and occurs in parts of the states of western Australia, .................... and .................... The eucalypt forest ecosystem is in the states of .......... and .......... .**

**2** Describe the location of Sydney.

**3** Look at the climate charts, Figure 3 and Figure 4.

**a)** Copy and complete the table on the right.

**b)** Give four differences between the climate of Sydney and that of Queensland.

| | Queensland | Sydney |
|---|---|---|
| Highest temp. (°C) | | |
| Lowest temp. (°C) | | |
| Temp. range (°C) | | |
| Total annual precipitation (mm) | | |

**4** Describe the climate of the eucalypt forest ecosystem.

**5 a)** Compare the climate pattern of Sydney to that of Queensland.

**b)** Suggest why the rainforest in Queensland grows well all year. Use evidence from the graph.

## Forest fires in the eucalypt forests

Many species of trees and shrubs that are native to Australia contain flammable oil and resins. These oils ignite at temperatures as low as 60 °C. The eucalypt forests that grow in south-eastern Australia have particularly high oil content.

Unmanaged eucalypt forests have a very dense shrub layer. This dense forest is good for insects, birds and lizards. However, kangaroos and wallabies feed on grasslands, so need a more open forest with plenty of grass. In the past, aboriginal people lit small fires to control the growth of shrubs in the eucalypt forests. This management, known as 'firestick' farming, cleared away the dense undergrowth and helped to maintain a healthy population of kangaroo for hunting. Over the last 100 years there has been less fire management of the eucalypt forests. So, the amount of shrubby vegetation has increased, and so has the risk of a big fire breaking out and spreading uncontrollably through the forest.

**Figure 5** Wet tropical rainforests of North-east Queensland

**Figure 6** Eucalypt forests grow on the hills surrounding Sydney and Canberra

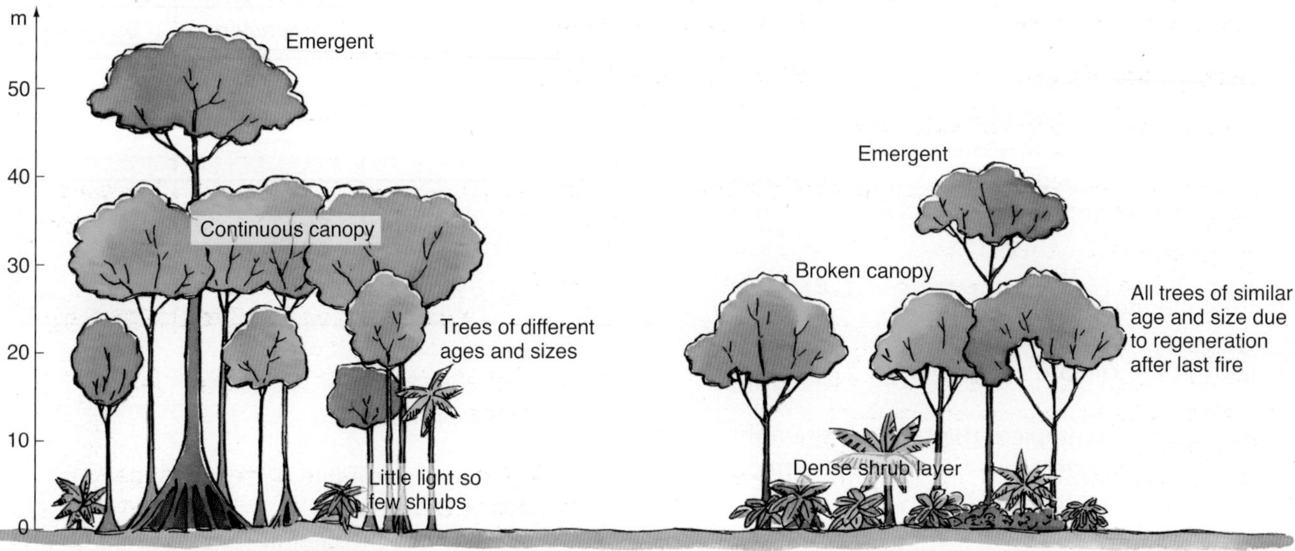


**Figure 7** Comparing the structure of the rainforest and eucalypt forests

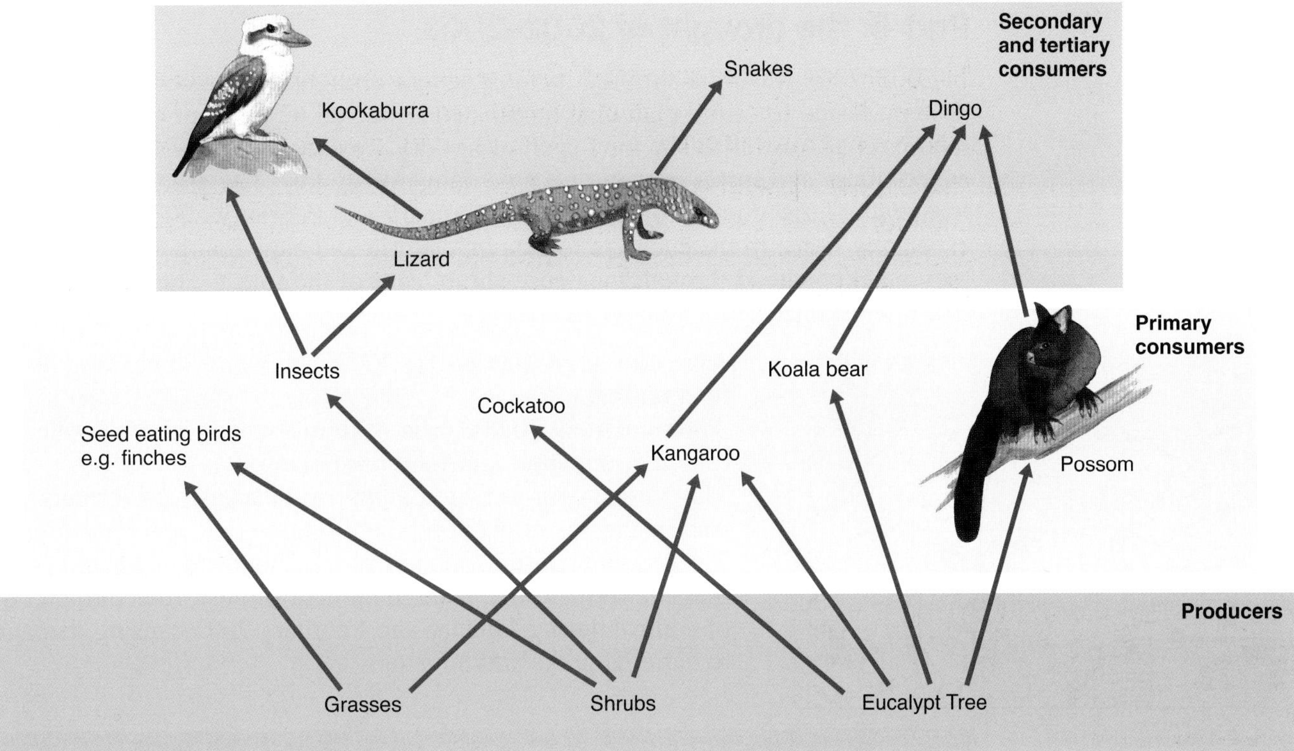


**Figure 8** A food web in the eucalypt forest

## Activity

**6** Study Figures 5, 6 and 7. Copy and complete the following table.

| | **Rainforest, Queensland** | **Eucalypt forest, New South Wales** |
|---|---|---|
| Height of canopy | | |
| Density of the canopy | Forms a continuous canopy | |
| Age and size of trees | Variety of ages and sizes | |
| Amount of open space on forest floor | | |

**7** Explain how the structure of the rainforest will help:
**a)** protect the soil from erosion
**b)** maintain a continuous water supply.

**8** Suggest ways in which the following groups of people might see the forest ecosystems in Sydney or Queensland as a resource.
**tourists** **scientists**
**timber companies** **aboriginal people**

**9** Study Figure 8.
**a)** Describe one food chain in the eucalypt forest.
**b)** Explain what would happen to other parts of the food web if there were no kangaroos in the forest.
**c)** Explain what would happen to this ecosystem if there was no 'firestick' farming. Describe the effect on:
i) the structure of the forest
ii) the food web.

**10** Study Figures 5, 6 and 7. Write a paragraph comparing the structure of the rainforest in Queensland with the structure of the eucalypt forest.

## Part B: the drought of 2002–2003

In 2002–2003 Australia suffered its most severe drought since records began. The drought lasted for more than nine months and affected 62 per cent of the huge landmass of Australia. The long spell of hot dry weather caused high rates of evaporation, and stores of water became dangerously low. The drought also triggered a large number of bush fires in January and February 2003. They were especially fierce in the eucalypt forests in Victoria and New South Wales where they quickly spread through the dense shrub layer of the forest. The fires and extreme weather had a number of effects:

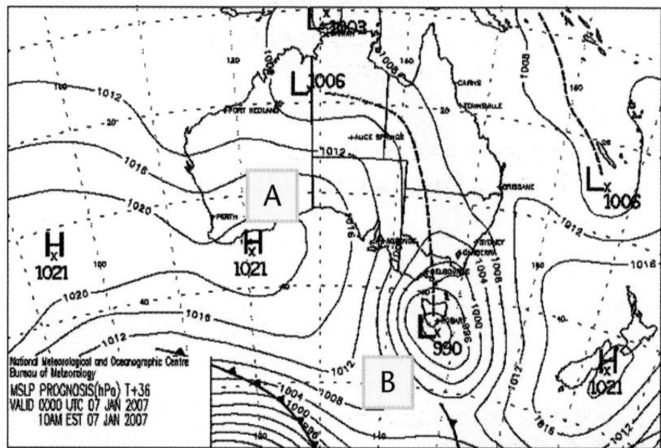


**Figure 9** A weather chart of 4 January 2003: a large number of fires were burning in New South Wales and Victoria on this day

- Agricultural production for 2002–2003 was 30 per cent less than normal.
- Approximately 70,000 jobs were lost mainly in wholesale, retailing, transport and food processing.
- The government provided a huge aid package for farmers and businesses affected by the drought.
- The drought caused soils to dry out. Winds then created massive dust storms. A large number of bush fires burned out of control during January and February 2003 causing damage to national parks and housing.

**Figure 10** A satellite image of south-eastern Australia, January 2003. The red dots show forest fires

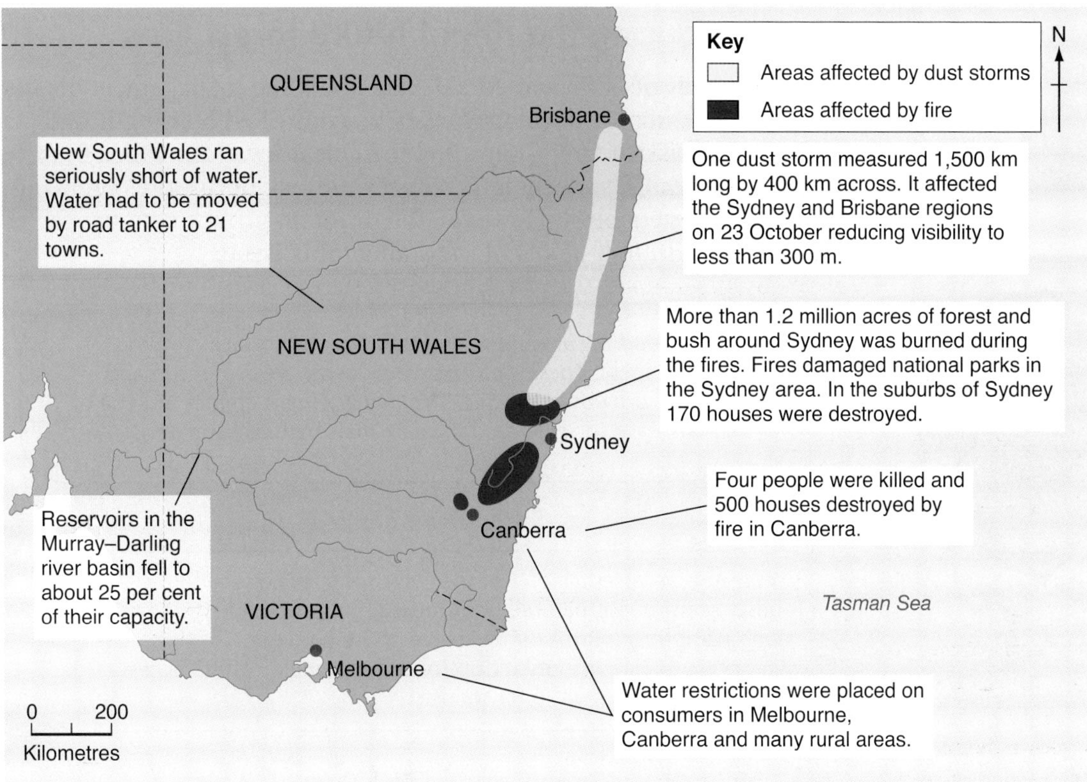


**Figure 11** The effects of the drought in Victoria and New South Wales

## Activity

**11** Look at Figure 9.

**a)** What is the name of the weather system shown at A?

**b)** Describe the kind of weather associated with this weather system in the summer months.

**c)** Explain how this weather system can cause a weather hazard.

**d)** What is the name of the weather system shown at B?

**e)** Describe and explain how this weather system is likely to bring changeable weather to South Island, New Zealand.

| Group affected | Impacts of the drought |
|---|---|
| Home owners | 1<br>2 |
| Farmers | 1<br>2 |
| Other businesses | 1 |
| Government | 1 |

**12 a)** Use the text and Figure 11 to complete a table showing the main impacts of the drought.

**b)** Suggest how the water shortages would have affected businesses, fire fighters and home owners in the region.

**13** Use Figure 10. Describe the distribution of the forest fires.

**14 a)** Use Figure 9. Describe and explain the wind direction over Sydney on 4 January 2003.

**b)** Study Figure 10. Could this satellite image have been taken on 4 January 2003? Explain your decision.

**c)** Suggest how the emergency services might use images such as Figures 9 and 10 to plan their reaction to the forest fires.

## Part C: reducing the risk of future forest fires

The forest fires of 2003 started a debate about the management of Australia's forests. Managing the eucalypt forests by controlled burning is one possible way to reduce the risk of fire. Controlled fires clear away the fallen branches and scrub vegetation. This technique reduces the risk of big fires breaking out and spreading out of control. However, the different groups who use the eucalypt forests have different points of view about this issue.

Aboriginal representative

Hotel owner

National Park ranger

Home owner in suburbs of Sydney

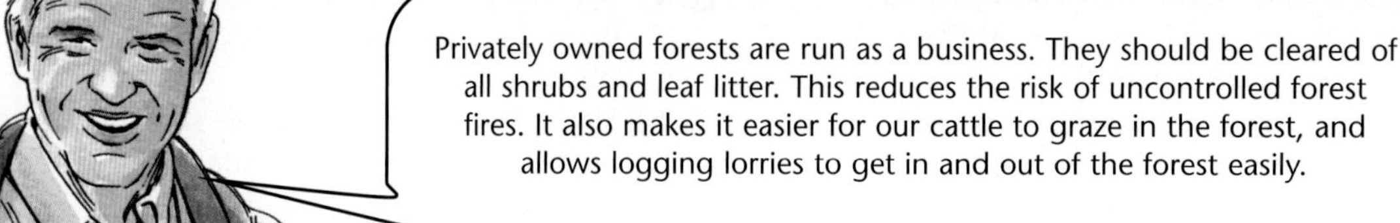


Private landowner of a forest

**Figure 12** Opinions about managing the eucalypt forests

| Alternative strategies | Explanation |
|---|---|
| **1 Urban planners could control the growth of suburban Sydney** | Sydney has grown rapidly and sprawled into the forests. Wealthy residents enjoy living in the suburbs close to the forests but their homes are at risk from fire. Planners could restrict new suburban development in forest areas. |
| **2 The Australian government could sign up to the Kyoto Protocol and agree to reduce carbon dioxide emissions** | The 2002–2003 drought may have been made hotter and drier by climate change. If Australia reduced its greenhouse emissions, the chances of another severe drought and fires would be reduced. Australian home owners might have to reduce their energy use by, for example, reducing the amount of air-conditioning used. |

**Figure 13** Alternative strategies to reduce the risk of fire

## Your decision

**15** Use the opinions in Figure 12. Copy and complete the following table.

| | Arguments for controlled burning | Arguments against controlled burning |
|---|---|---|
| Economic | | Burning is hazardous and expensive |
| Environmental | | |
| Social (how different groups might be affected) | | Smoke pollution will cause health problems for residents in the suburbs |

**16** Study Figure 13. Discuss these alternative strategies. Suggest how you think each of the following groups of people might respond to these ideas:

- house builders
- members of Sydney's fire brigade
- energy suppliers
- estate agents
- Australia's government.

**17** Describe and justify your own plan for reducing the risk of future forest fires in the Sydney area (some advice is given in the exam technique on page 68).

EXAMTECHNIQUE

## Getting the best mark for part C of this problem-solving exercise

Part C is your opportunity to suggest how the eucalypt forests should be managed to reduce the risks of forest fires in south-eastern Australia.

**Step 1**

The first thing to do is to decide which of the three options has most advantages and least disadvantages. Are you going to recommend:

- using controlled fires to clear the national parks
- controlling the sprawl of suburban housing into the forests
- signing up to Kyoto and reducing carbon emissions?

You could even suggest a combination of these three approaches.

**Step 2**

In order to get a good mark, you will need to justify your plan. This means explaining why you think your plan will be successful.

| Key questions to ask yourself | Comment |
|---|---|
| Is my plan realistic, affordable and achievable? | Cutting carbon emissions would create the biggest long-term benefits but controlled fires would be cheaper and very effective in the short term. |
| Which groups of people will benefit from my plan? | Tourists dislike controlled burning, but this plan would benefit home owners. What do the National Park Rangers and forest owners think? Whose views are more important? |
| How will the environment be affected? | Aboriginal people claim that controlled burning is good for the environment. Can you think of a better plan? |
| Why is this plan better than the alternatives? | Are the other options too expensive? Would they upset too many people? |

**Tip**

Suggest how different groups of people might benefit from your plan:

- Aboriginal people would approve of my plan because …
- Firefighters would be better off because … and this is important because …
- Local tourist businesses would benefit by … and this would be good for jobs because …

# Unit 2 Water, Landforms and People

## Chapter 1 The Big Picture

## Water: a vital resource

Water is essential for all life. We all need to drink 2.5 litres of water a day to stay healthy. On top of that we need water for cooking, washing, cleaning and flushing the lavatory (the safe disposal of sewage is known as **sanitation** and uses a lot of the UK's water).

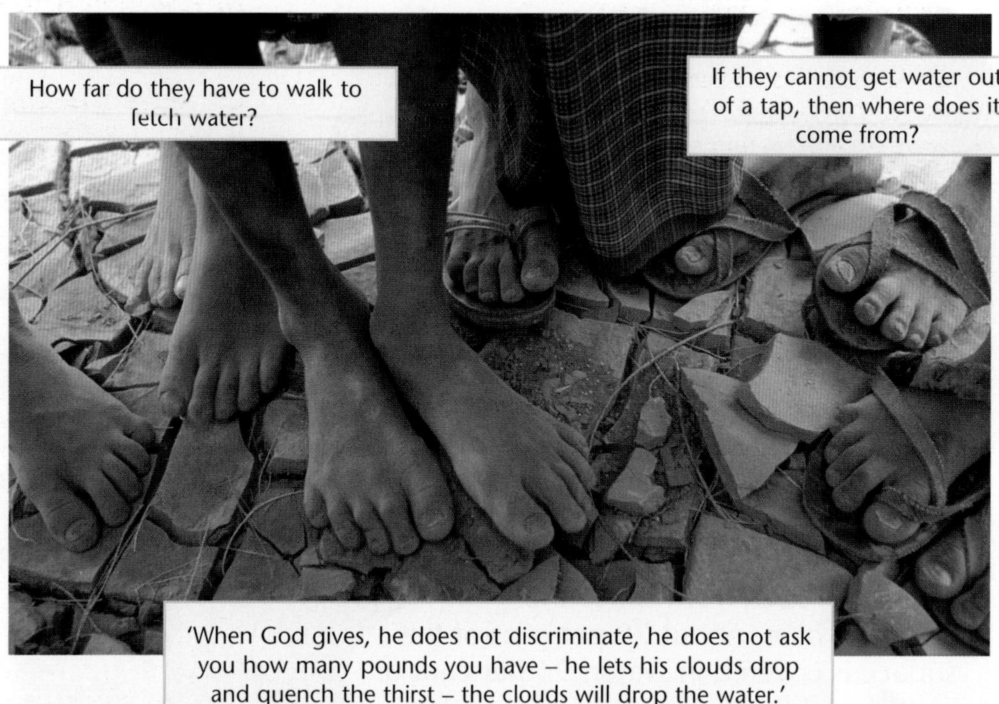


**Figure 1** Currently there are about one billion people who do not have access to clean water. That is roughly one-sixth of the world's population

**Figure 2** A US golf course. The average American uses 600 litres of water a day

## Improving quality of life: Millennium Development Goals

The United Nations has set the target of halving the number of people that do not have access to clean water and sanitation (the safe disposal of sewage) by 2015. To meet this target we could:

- waste less water by fixing leaks
- use water more efficiently, for example, by using grey water (waste water from washing) to water the garden
- increase the amount of fresh water supplies.

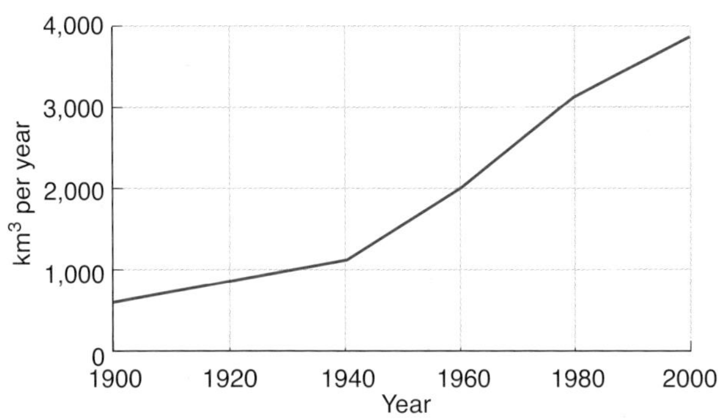


**Figure 3** Estimated annual world water use, 1900–2000 (km³)

### Activity

**1 a)** Working with a partner, make a list of all the ways that you use water every day.
**b)** How many of these uses are essential and how many could you live without?

**2** Use Figure 3. Describe what is happening to the amount of water the world uses.

**3 a)** Study Figure 4. Which regions are:
i) likely to reach their target
ii) unlikely to reach their target?
**b)** Discuss why we need to set these targets.

**4** Produce a 400-word newspaper article explaining:
**a)** why we need to achieve the Millennium Development Goal for water and sanitation
**b)** how we could achieve it.

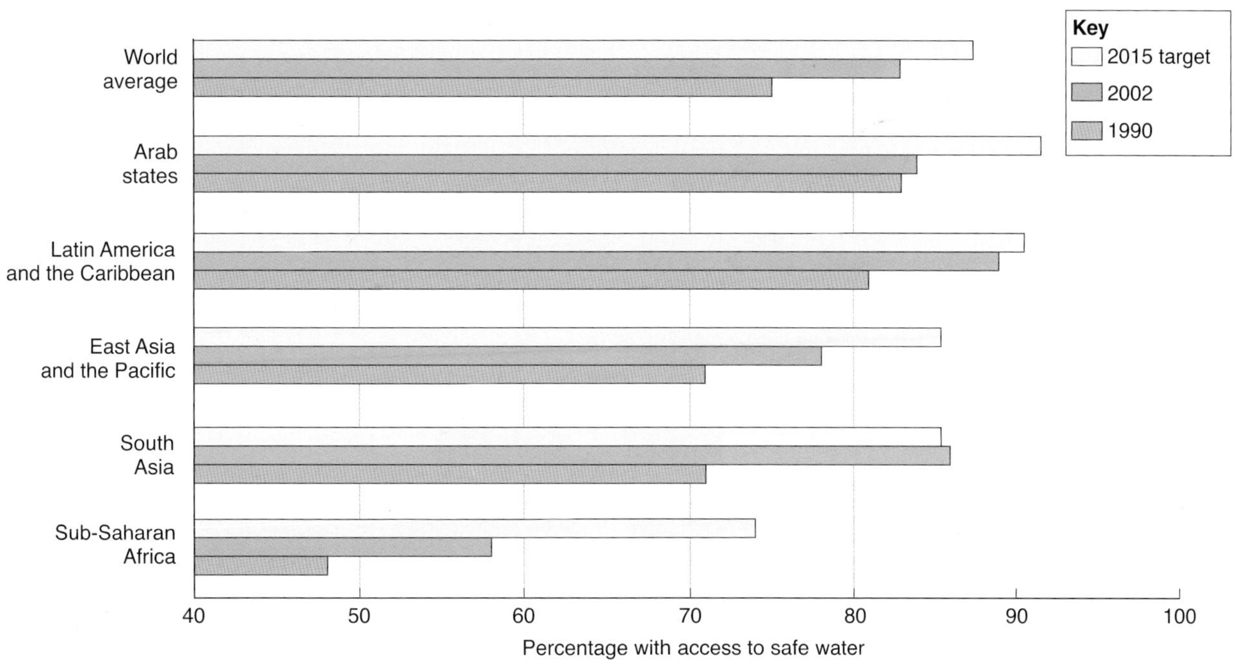


**Figure 4** Will each region achieve its Millennium Development Goal for safe water?

# Chapter 2
# The drainage basin

**KEY QUESTIONS**

- What is the water cycle?
- How does the water cycle work?
- What factors control the flows of the water cycle?

## The water cycle

Less than three per cent of all the world's water is fresh water – the kind of water needed for life. It is, however, continually recycled in a system called the **water cycle**. The water cycle is driven by the sun's heat, which evaporates water into the **atmosphere**, and by gravity, which continually makes it flow downwards.

As with all systems, the water cycle has a set of **stores** with **flows** connecting them:

- A store is a place where water is found and will collect, for example there are seven stores in the water cycle diagram below. Another store that could be included is water found as ice, either in ice sheets or 'glaciers'.
- A flow is the way in which water moves from one store to another.

**Figure 1** How the water cycle works

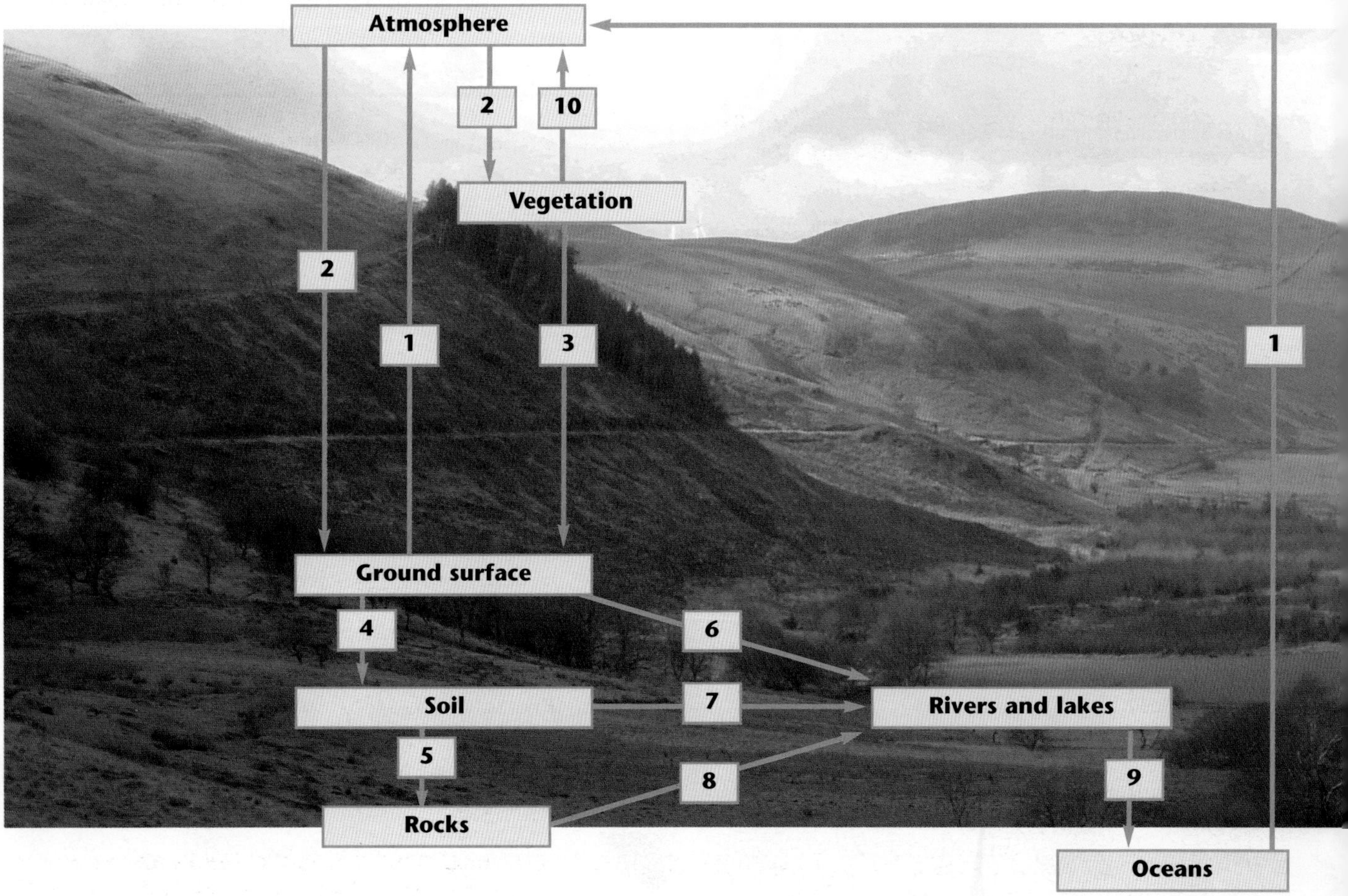

Atmosphere
2
10
Vegetation
2
1
3
1
Ground surface
4
6
Soil
7
Rivers and lakes
5
8
9
Rocks
Oceans

**Key** **Stores**

**Flows**

1 Evaporation 2 Precipitation 3 Stemflow 4 Infiltration
5 Percolation 6 Overland flow 7 Throughflow
8 Groundwater flow 9 River flow 10 Transpiration

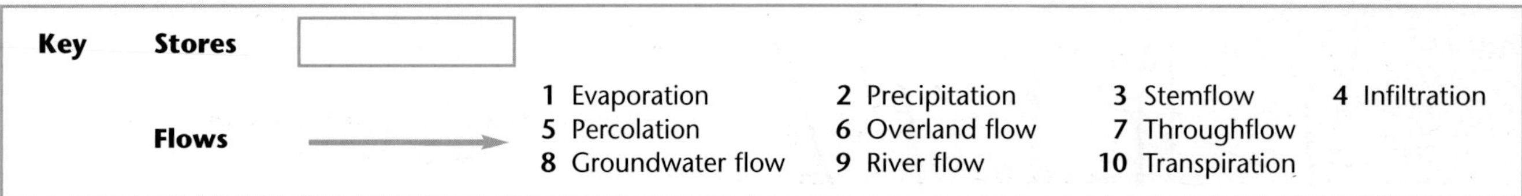

### In the air

The atmosphere contains less than 0.0001 per cent of the world's water. Water moves quickly through this store. It moves 'upwards' by **evaporation** from the ground surface, rivers, lakes and oceans, and by **transpiration** from plants. The energy for this upwards movement comes from the sun.

As air rises, it cools. All air contains moisture and if this air cools it will eventually condense to form tiny droplets of liquid water. **Condensation** is the change of water from a gas to a liquid. These tiny water droplets may not be heavy enough to fall to the ground but may coalesce to make bigger droplets that will eventually fall as rain. If the air temperature is below freezing, **precipitation** will occur in the form of snow or hail. Precipitation is therefore the flow from the atmosphere to the ground or **vegetation store**. The Met Office classifies 36 different types of precipitation!

### On the ground

On hitting the ground surface, water will flow as **infiltration** into the soil and as **overland flow** across the surface. Once in the **soil store** it will flow more slowly downhill as **throughflow**. **Percolation** will eventually let water flow through the bedrock where it continues to travel as **groundwater flow**.

Rates of infiltration, throughflow and groundwater flow will depend on the type of soil and rock:

- Clay soils or soils with the smallest particles do not let water pass through easily and become waterlogged. Such soils are said to be **impermeable**. Rocks such as granite that do not allow water to pass through them are also considered to be impermeable.
- Sandy soils are more free draining because soil particles are larger. Such soils will have faster throughflow rates. Chalk and sandstone are sedimentary rocks that contain many pore spaces; water moves easily through these **porous** rocks.
- Limestone, another sedimentary rock, has many **joints** and **bedding planes** through which water can flow. Limestone also dissolves in rainwater forming underground rivers and caverns. Water can flow along these joints and bedding planes, making limestone **permeable** but not porous.

Eventually water will flow into rivers and lakes, which will flow into the seas and oceans. The average time taken for a raindrop to travel around the water cycle in the UK is ten days! Most water droplets will have evaporated back into the atmosphere before ever reaching the sea.

a)

b)

c)

Worms help water flow through the soil!

d)

**Figure 2** Water cycle flows

### Activity

1. Study the four illustrations in Figure 2.
   **a)** Name the flow shown in each picture.
   **b)** State how the water is moving in that part of the water cycle.
2. Describe the water cycle in your own words using the terms **stores** and **flows**. This is a common exam question. When you have finished, check your descriptions with a partner.
3. This section contains many new terms. Make a list of twenty unfamiliar words and write your own definitions for each one. You may like to classify them into different categories.
4. How would the different flows through the water cycle change due to climate and vegetation in Antarctica compared with the Amazon rainforest?
5. How will the water cycle change in the UK between summer and winter?

## Factors controlling river flow in the drainage basin

A **drainage basin** is the area from which a river collects its water. There are four ways in which water can enter a river, which are shown in Figure 3. The first is by **channel precipitation**, which is where rain falls directly into the river. The main flows of water to the river are:

- Overland flow – water flowing quickly across the ground surface.
- Throughflow – water flowing through the soil.
- Groundwater flow – water moving very slowly through rocks.

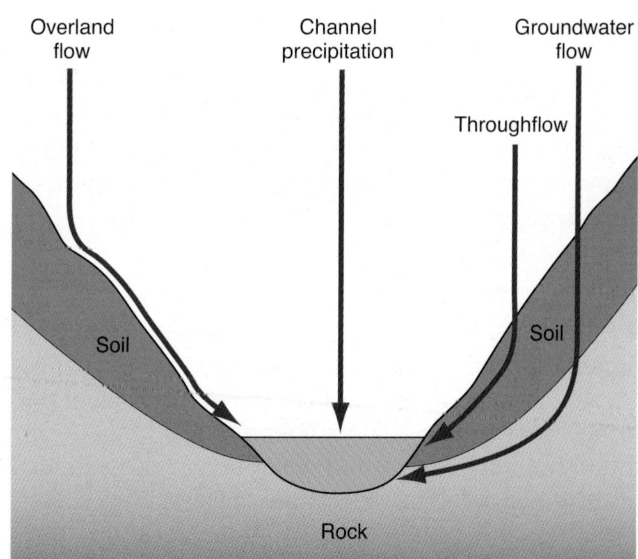


**Figure 3** The four ways in which water enters a river

A river **hydrograph** may be drawn to show how the river is affected by its flow. Hydrographs can show how the river changes throughout the year or following a storm.

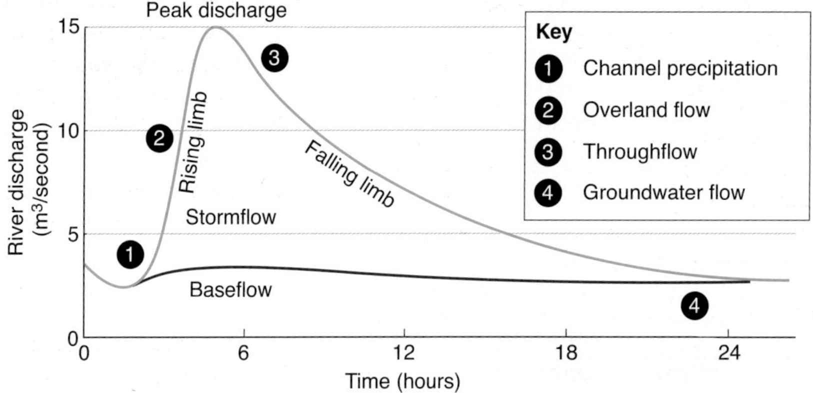


**Figure 4** A flood hydrograph showing the flow of the river following a single rain event

The flood hydrograph in Figure 4 shows that after two hours of rain, the river **discharge** starts to increase rapidly. Raindrops that fall into the river will increase the discharge very slightly. Water flowing over the ground will flow quickly into the river causing the river flow to rise. On the graph this is called the rising limb. Flooding occurs when conditions cause water to flow more quickly across the ground surface rather than infiltrating into the soil. Flooding conditions occur when:

- the ground is already saturated with water
- the ground is frozen
- the surface is impermeable like tarmac
- the rainfall is so intense it cannot all soak into the ground.

The river will reach its highest flow when water reaches it through the soil as throughflow. Throughflow will occur for many hours or even days after the storm and causes the river flow to fall much more gently than it rises. Groundwater flow is slower at reaching the river and is the reason why rivers in the UK don't tend to dry up even after very little rain. Once the rain has stopped, water will stop reaching the river as overland flow and the flow of the river will gradually fall. Water is continually reaching the river by seeping through the rocks in its bed. This normal river flow is called **baseflow** and is the contribution made by groundwater flow.

**Figure 5** Some springs flow all year as they are fed by groundwater flow

### Activity

**6** Explain why UK rivers continue to flow even in times of low rainfall.

**7** Describe the changes in river flow in the hydrograph in Figure 4 on page 74. Use figures and times from the graph in your answer and refer to the labels on the graph.

## Going Further

### How do drainage basin characteristics affect the shape of a flood hydrograph?

There are many factors which affect the shape of a flood hydrograph and geographers have to know how factors in the drainage basin will affect the flow of a river. Below is a list of ten factors that will change the flow of a river and therefore its flood hydrograph. The tasks should make you think how each factor changes the flow of a river.

| | |
|---|---|
| 1 Drainage basin size | Large or small |
| 2 Season | Winter or summer |
| 3 Type of vegetation | Forest or moorland |
| 4 Rainfall duration | Three days of rain or two hours |
| 5 Rainfall intensity | Four hours of drizzle or a four-hour downpour |
| 6 Soil type | Clay or sandy soil |
| 7 Rock type | Impermeable clay or porous chalk |
| 8 Previous rainfall | After a dry spell or during a wet period |
| 9 Human influence | City area or countryside drainage basin |
| 10 Drainage basin shape | Long and thin or oval shape |

**8 a)** Study the factors that affect the flow of a river listed in the table (1–10). For each factor sketch a pair of flood hydrographs showing how the factor might cause the graph to be a different shape.

**b)** Describe the shape of the flood hydrographs for each factor.

**c)** Explain why the graphs have a different shape. Factor 1 is done for you below.

a) Effect of drainage basin on river flow.

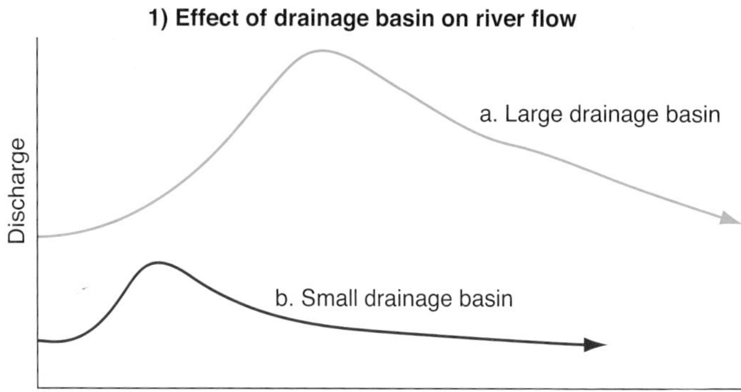


b) The large drainage basin has a higher discharge and a later peak flow, whereas the smaller drainage basin has a peak discharge only one-quarter of the larger basin and a much earlier peak flow.

c) The larger drainage basin will collect more water and this means that it will have a higher discharge. The water will take longer to flow down the river in the larger basin and so the peak flow time will be later.

## An upland drainage basin, Plynlimon

In this section you will study the main factors controlling the water cycle and, therefore, the flow of the river. Two small drainage basins are considered: one forested and one open moorland.

The imaginary boundary between two drainage basins is called the **watershed**; it is always the highest point between two rivers. On Figure 6 the rivers in the north-

**Figure 6** An Ordnance Survey map of the area. Scale 1:50,000 Sheet 136

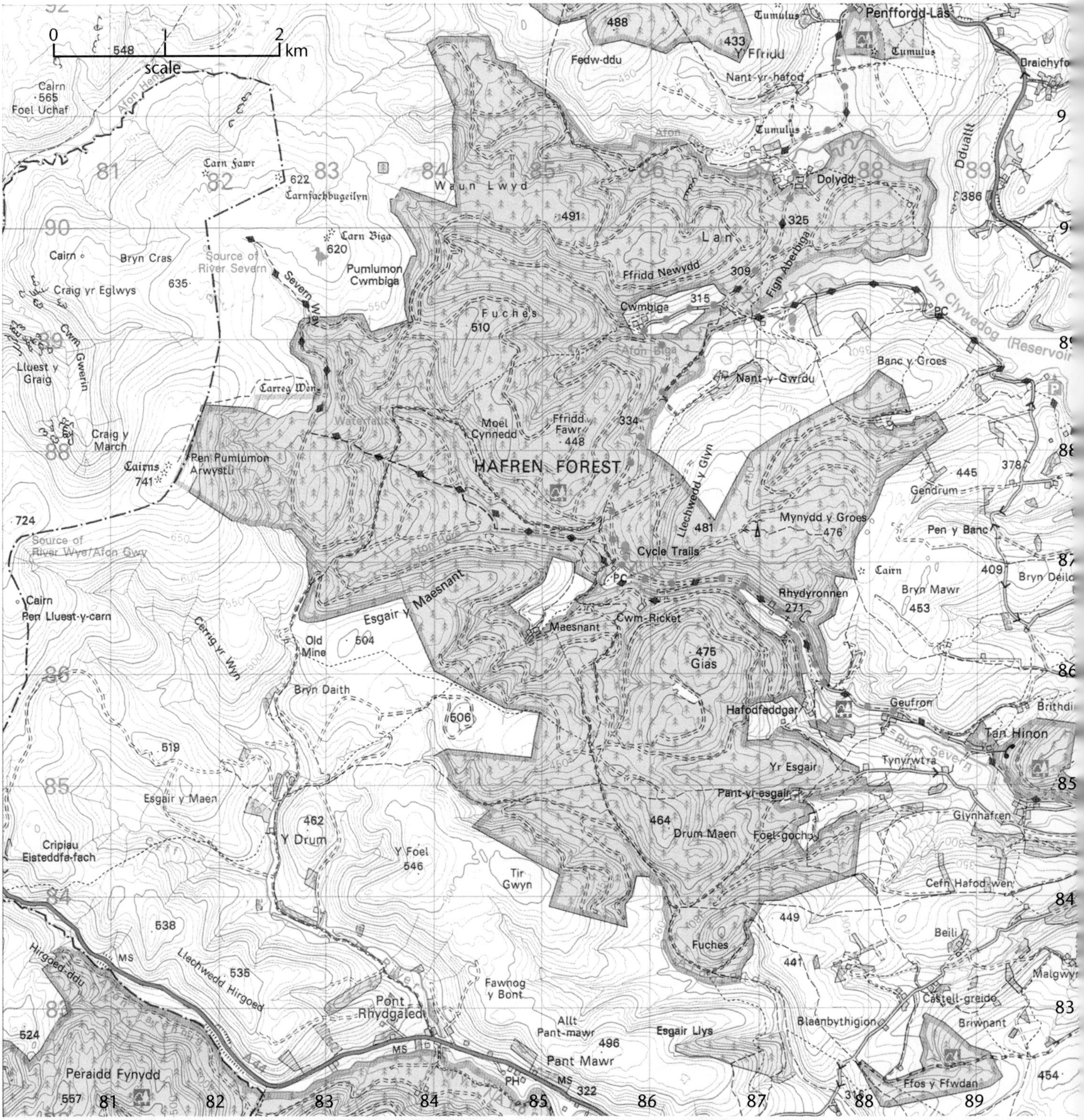

**Figure 7** A gauging station on the River Severn, Hafren Forest flume

west corner, such as the Afon Hengwm, flow westwards towards the Welsh coast and into Cardigan Bay. The rivers on the rest of the map, such as the River Wye and River Severn, flow south-east into the Bristol Channel.

Although the source of the Severn is only 40 km from the Welsh coast, the rain falling on the upper parts of Plynlimon will flow for 350 km to eventually reach the ocean. The county boundary, the dashed and dotted line running through square 8187, follows the watershed between the west and south-east flowing rivers.

The Plynlimon drainage basin is one of the most studied in the world. Figure 7 shows one of the gauging stations built so that the river flow can be accurately measured. Walk across the open moorland and you will find rain gauges. These send information on daily rainfall totals. This allows a comparison to be made between the inputs into the **hydrological cycle** and the outputs to the system, in this case river flow. Comparisons have been made of the moorland and forested drainage basins and the factors controlling river flow have been closely analysed.

## Activity

**9** Starting in the east of square 8984 follow the River Severn upstream until the source is reached in square 8289 (your teacher may let you sketch the main channel and its tributaries onto tracing paper).

**a)** What is the distance the river travels between 900846 and its source at 823898?

**b)** How many tributaries flow into the main channel of the River Severn over this stretch?

**c)** What is the main land use of the upper part of the Severn drainage basin?

**10** Starting at the confluence at 841826 follow the River Wye upstream until the source is reached at 804870.

**a)** What is the distance the river travels between these two points?

**b)** How many tributaries flow into the main channel of the River Wye over this stretch?

**c)** What is the main land use of the upper drainage basin of the River Wye?

**11** At which point would you expect more water to be flowing: at 841826 on the River Wye or at 900846 on the River Severn? Explain your answer.

**12** Describe how the flood hydrographs would be different on the Upper Wye and Severn for a single rain event.

**13** Explain how the differences in the drainage basins of the Wye and Severn cause the hydrographs to be different.

## Natural factors controlling river flow on Plynlimon

The flow of a river changes from hour to hour, day to day and season to season.

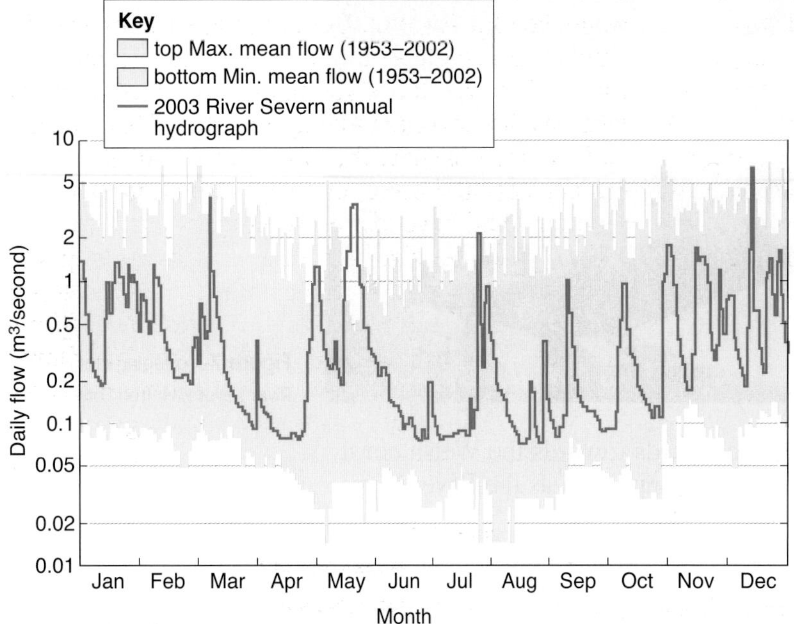


**Figure 8** Annual hydrograph for the River Severn, Plynlimon (Hafren Forest flume). This shows maximum and minimum daily mean flows for the period from 1953 to 2003

### Size of the drainage basin

The larger the drainage basin, the greater the discharge of the river. On the Ordnance Survey map, Figure 6 (on page 76), you can see that the River Severn at 900847 has a drainage basin area of approximately 25 $km^2$. Rivers with a drainage basin of this size typically have flow rates of less than one $m^3$ per second. The River Severn flows through Gloucester 250 km from its source; its drainage basin is now calculated to be 10,400 $km^2$. With such a large area from which to gather its water, the river is now much wider and deeper.

### Climate

Climate is a major factor controlling river discharge. The most important climate feature is rainfall. The source of the River Severn at Plynlimon receives more than 2,500 mm of rain a year. It rains on two out of every three days! The soil in winter is often saturated, causing more overland flow to reach the river quickly. The annual hydrograph in Figure 8 shows a series of peaks in river flow after high rainfall.

Temperature is another feature of the climate that affects river flow. High temperatures increase evaporation rates. Freezing temperatures cause more overland flow as frozen ground is impermeable. Britain's largest floods occur when rain falls on snow covering the ground and melting it. The thawing water runs as overland flow into the river causing rapidly rising rivers with high peak discharge rates.

**Figure 9** Upper Wye drainage basin

### Soil

The soil of the drainage basin will affect river flow. The soil of the Plynlimon area is thin moorland soil that is saturated for most of the year. If water infiltrates easily into the soil, more water will reach the river by throughflow through the soil. Water will take longer to reach the river and flow will be more even throughout the year. Free-draining sandy soils allow high infiltration. Clay soils become impermeable when wet, leading to more overland flow which causes a river to rise more rapidly.

## Rocks

Impermeable rocks, such as granite, do not allow water to drain through them. When the soil above becomes saturated, water flows as overland flow. Porous rocks like sandstone and chalk allow large quantities of water into them, and this slows the flow of water through the drainage basin. Rivers in sandstone and chalk areas flow more evenly and are less likely to flood as more water reaches the river by groundwater flow. In the Plynlimon area the rocks are shale. Water flows through the joints and **faults** in the rock providing the river with essential groundwater.

## Vegetation

The River Wye and River Severn upper catchments are next to one another. They share the same watershed for five km. Both drainage basins are of similar size and have the same climate, soil and rocks. However, the Wye drainage basin is moorland, whereas the Severn is mainly forested. This makes it an ideal area to study the effects of woodland on a drainage basin. Forests intercept more rain than moorland and have higher evaporation rates. The roots of the trees also let more water infiltrate into the soil. Rivers from forested areas often have lower peak discharge rates and more even flow throughout the year. **Deforestation** causes more overland flow and flooding. In some drainage basins thousands of trees have been planted to reduce flooding downstream.

**Figure 10** Concept map showing factors that control river flow

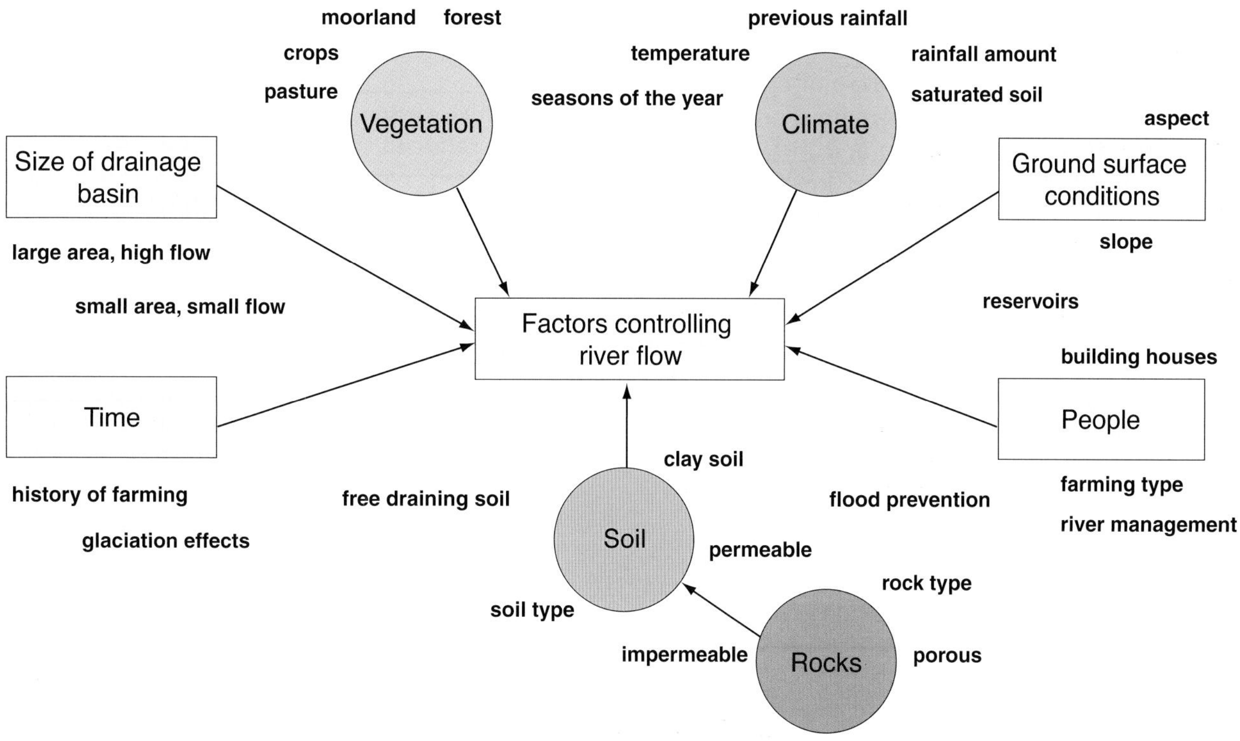


## Activity

**14** Work in pairs. Study Figure 10 for about one minute. Close the book and draw your own concept map of what causes changes in river flow.

**15** List ten factors that would cause a river to flood.

**16** The Plynlimon study found that forested areas had little effect on river discharge. Explain this result.

## Human factors controlling river flow

The main way in which humans affect river flow is from farming activities that involve cutting down natural forest land. This can dramatically change the water cycle locally. It is common in the UK for wide areas to be drained so crops can be planted by cutting small channels or drains across the landscape. Water flows through the soil into these drains and into the rivers more quickly causing them to rise more dramatically following any intense rainfall.

In southern China terraces have been cut by hand into the sloping hillsides (Figure 11). Terraces allow more crops to be grown because the rain soaks into the flat land of the terrace. The greater infiltration of water into the soil on the terraces allows the plants to grow better. The terraces also reduce soil erosion.

Bangladesh is at the **confluence** of three great rivers – the Ganges, the Brahmaputra and the Meghna. The drainage basin covers over 1.5 million km$^2$. Flooding in Bangladesh may be increasing because of changes in the water cycle over 1,000 km upstream. Forested areas are being cleared for agriculture and for firewood as the population increases in China and India.

In Sahastradhara in northern India, deforestation caused by limestone mining has led to severe local effects and devastated the area's tourism. Tree felling causes more water to flow into the tributaries of the Ganges, which has reduced infiltration into the soil and percolation into the limestone rocks below. The water table has dropped by more than 10 m causing local springs to dry up. Water supply to houses has been cut to a few hours a day and river beds fill quickly with rocks eroded from the hillsides.

**Figure 13** Itaipu Dam on the Brazil–Paraguay border

**Figure 11** Land terracing in China. These terraces are 400 years old

| Effects of deforestation: Recycling of water in the ecosystem is reduced to twenty per cent | |
|---|---|
| **Atmosphere** | Less evaporation, total rainfall is reduced<br>High overland flow. Reduced cloud formation |
| **Ground surface** | Bare earth is baked hard by the hot sun |
| **Soil** | Soil erosion washes the topsoil away<br>There is less throughflow in the soil<br>Less organic matter in the soil reduces soil water content<br>Bare earth means less infiltration into the soil |
| **River channel** | Run-off is increased dramatically |

**Figure 12** Effects of deforestation on river flow

Dams may be built to control flooding downstream, provide hydro-electric power or to maintain river flow in times of drought. If the reservoir is large enough it may change the water cycle more dramatically. In China, the Three Gorges Dam will alter the flow of the Yangtse river. More than a million people will have to be rehoused and the world's biggest artificial lake, 650 km$^2$, will be formed. The effects of a lake this big are unknown, but evaporation will be higher over the lake surface and local rainfall patterns could change.

## The water cycle of an urban area

Flash floods hitting cities are making headlines. The building of more extensive areas of housing is radically changing local water cycles. Large areas of concrete and tarmac are impermeable and cause increased overland flow. Water travels quickly through large storm drains below the city. If rainfall intensity is very high, mainly in summer thunderstorms, the storm drains cannot cope with the large quantity of fast-flowing water, causing localised flooding and flash floods.

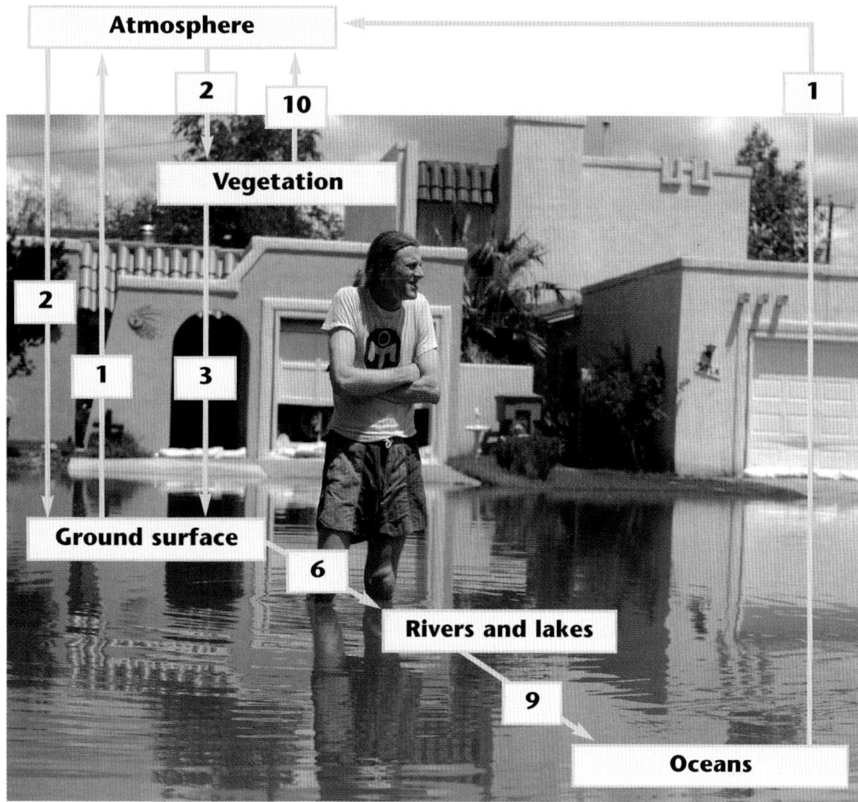


Figure 14 The water cycle in an urban area

**Key**

**Stores**

**Flows**

1 Evaporation
2 Precipitation
3 Stemflow
6 Overland flow
9 River flow
10 Transpiration

| Month | Average monthly flow ($m^3$/second) Ganges, Dhaka 2000–2005 | Average monthly rainfall (mm) Dhaka 2000–2005 |
|---|---|---|
| Jan | 1,910 | 17 |
| Feb | 1,451 | 51 |
| Mar | 1,165 | 92 |
| Apr | 1,017 | 223 |
| May | 1,228 | 245 |
| Jun | 4,144 | 360 |
| Jul | 18,797 | 317 |
| Aug | 38,403 | 207 |
| Sep | 37,325 | 223 |
| Oct | 17,349 | 91 |
| Nov | 5,916 | 15 |
| Dec | 3,060 | 15 |

Figure 15 Monthly river flow on the Ganges and rainfall data for Dhaka

### Activity

**17** The author has written the section on human factors controlling river flow as a series of examples. Write a set of bullet points which best classify the human factors that control river flow.

**18** Study Figure 15.

**a)** Draw an appropriate graph for the two sets of data in the table.

**b)** What is the connection between the flow of the River Ganges and the average monthly rainfall at Dhaka?

**c)** Does the rainfall data at Dhaka give a total explanation for the river flow data? Explain your answer.

**19** Compare the water cycle of a forested area with that of an urban area.

**20** What causes flash floods?

**21** Study Figure 13 showing the Itaipu Dam. Explain how the creation of a large reservoir may change the local climate of the area and the river flow downstream.

# Chapter 3
# Water resources

**KEY QUESTIONS**
- What are the main sources for our supply of fresh water?
- How does water supply vary from one region of the world to another?
- How have people attempted to manage water supply in different countries and are these water management strategies sustainable?

## What are the main sources of fresh water?

More than 69 per cent of the surface of planet Earth is covered in water. But only about four per cent is fresh water. There are five main types of fresh-water store as you can see in Figure 1.

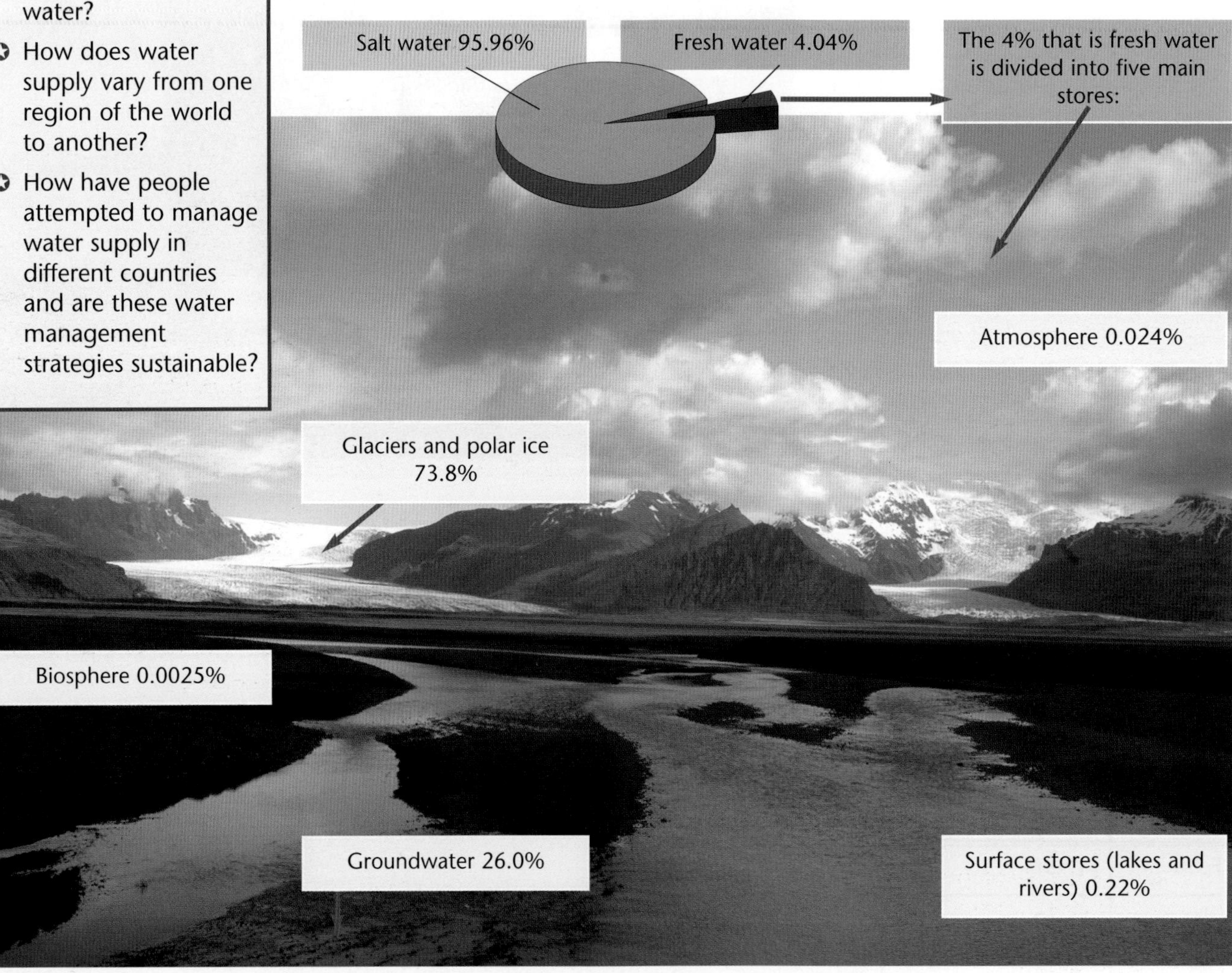


**Figure 1** The sources of fresh water

### Surface and groundwater stores

**Surface stores** include lakes and rivers. Rivers can be dammed to control flooding and create reservoirs for water supply. There are more than 47,000 large dams in the world and nearly half of these are in China. However, surface stores can also be very small. Take **rain-water harvesting**, for example. If you have a water-butt in your garden that collects rain water from the gutters, you are creating a small surface store of fresh water.

**Groundwater stores** occur when water infiltrates into the ground and gets trapped in the fractures and the pore spaces of rocks and sediments. A large store of underground water is called an **aquifer**. Water that enters an aquifer is called **recharge**; water that leaves an aquifer is discharge. When water is taken from either a surface or groundwater store by human action we say the water is **abstracted**. Abstraction is often the main form of discharge from aquifers.

In south-east England a lot of water is abstracted in the summer months when there is little precipitation. Winter rainfall, however, is normally enough to recharge the aquifers. As long as the total annual recharge is equal to the total discharge then the aquifer stays the same size from year to year. However, if winter recharge is low, or demand for water increases, then the level of groundwater falls. This is **over-abstraction**. Low winter rainfall in 2005 and 2006 caused the drought in the South East in 2006. As the population of the region rises, and demand for water increases, experts warn that water shortages will become a more common problem.

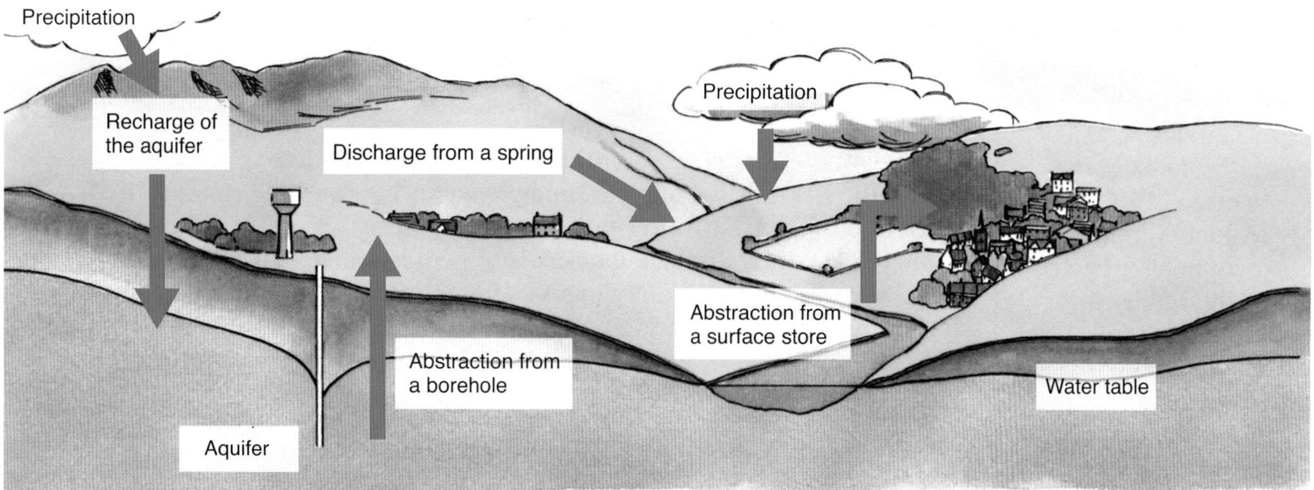


**Figure 2** A cross-section of the main stores of water that we can use are surface stores and groundwater supplies

## Activity

1. Using Figure 1, make a list of the five fresh-water stores. Do this in rank order starting with the largest.
2. Define the following terms when applied to an aquifer:
   - **discharge**
   - **abstraction**
   - **over-abstraction.**
3. Explain how rainfall recharges an aquifer.
4. Study Figure 3. Describe the distribution of aquifers that had:
   **a)** significantly lower levels (below –5 m)
   **b)** slightly lower levels (0 to –5 m).
   **c)** Suggest how these low groundwater levels might have affected people.

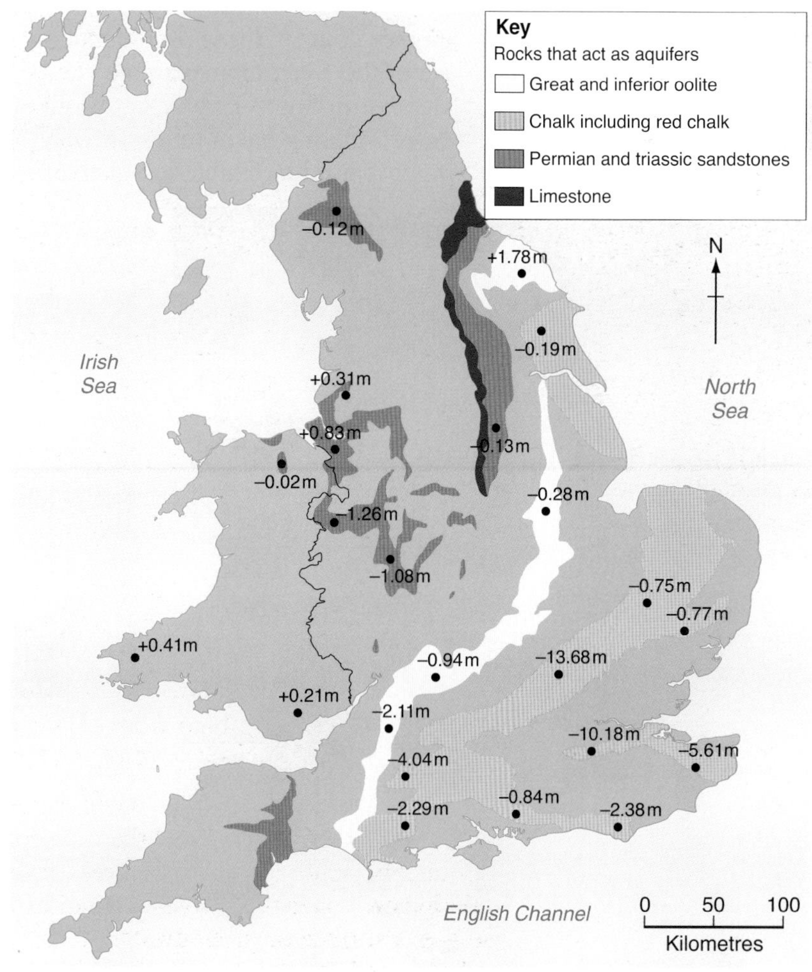


**Figure 3** Water table levels in UK aquifers, May 2006, compared with normal height

## How much water do we need?

The amount of water that the world uses has increased dramatically over the last hundred years. As the population has grown, the amount of water used by industry and agriculture has increased. However, not everyone has access to a clean and safe water supply. Approximately one billion people have to walk for at least fifteen minutes to collect water. The United Nations (UN) estimates that unless immediate action is taken there will be five billion people without clean water in less than 25 years' time. One way this could be avoided is by building more dams. Would this be a good idea?

- There are 47,000 large dams in the world.
- About 60 million people have been displaced by the reservoirs created behind these dams.
- An area larger than Zimbabwe has been flooded by the creation of the world's dams.

**Figure 4** Facts about the world's dams

### Are more dams the answer?

Large dam projects create conflict. Dams control the flow of rivers so can reduce the risk of flooding and supply water. They can also generate **hydro-electric power (HEP)**. However, dams have many disadvantages. For example, dam projects often displace thousands of people when their homes are flooded. When a new dam is built, not everyone will get a clean, safe water supply. **Irrigation** projects often use up to 80 per cent of the water supplied by a dam, leaving very little for ordinary people to use, especially in rural areas.

Building a dam alters the flow of water in the river and this can cause problems for people who live further downstream. For example, the river may carry less water and sediment, so farmers who rely on seasonal floods may no longer get the water and silt they need. If a river that has been dammed then flows into another country these problems may create a **trans-boundary conflict** over the use of the river. One example can be seen in the use of water in the River Mekong in South East Asia. About 80 per cent of the rice production in the lower Mekong basin relies on water and silt from river floods. But as more water is used in China, less arrives in Cambodia, in the lower basin of the river.

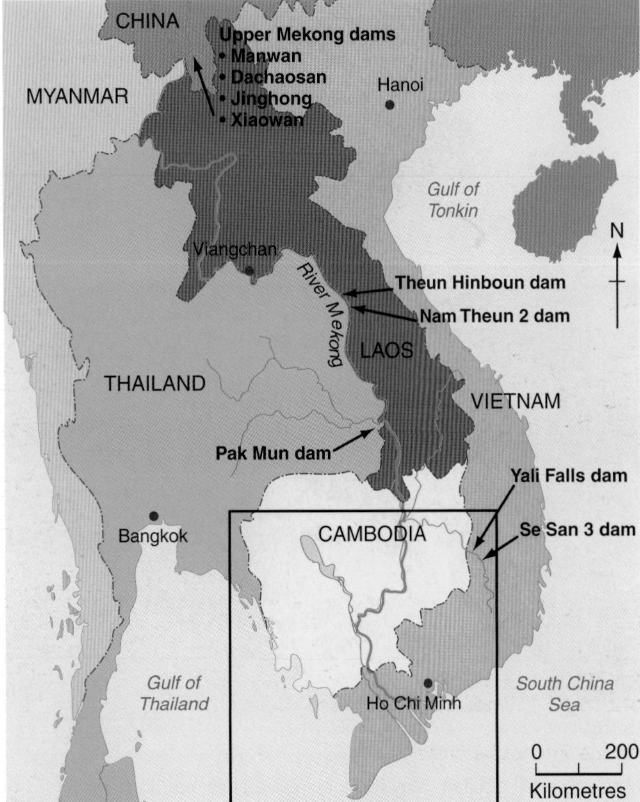


**Figure 5** Major dam projects built or under construction on the River Mekong (the area of Figure 6 is shown by the box)

**Figure 6** Flooding in Cambodia and Vietnam on the Mekong in 2004. 30,000 people had to leave their homes during the floods that lasted for 59 days

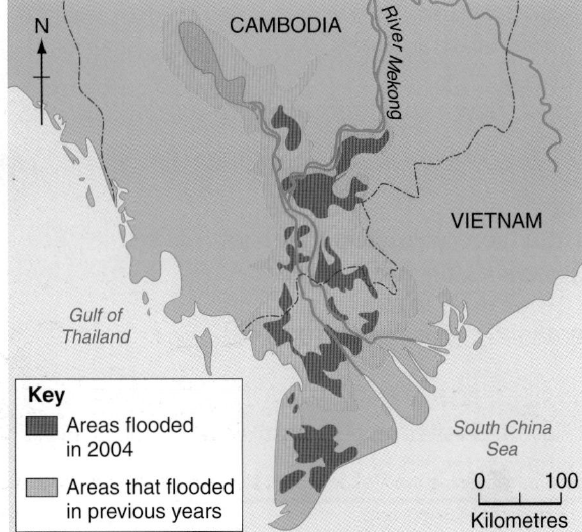

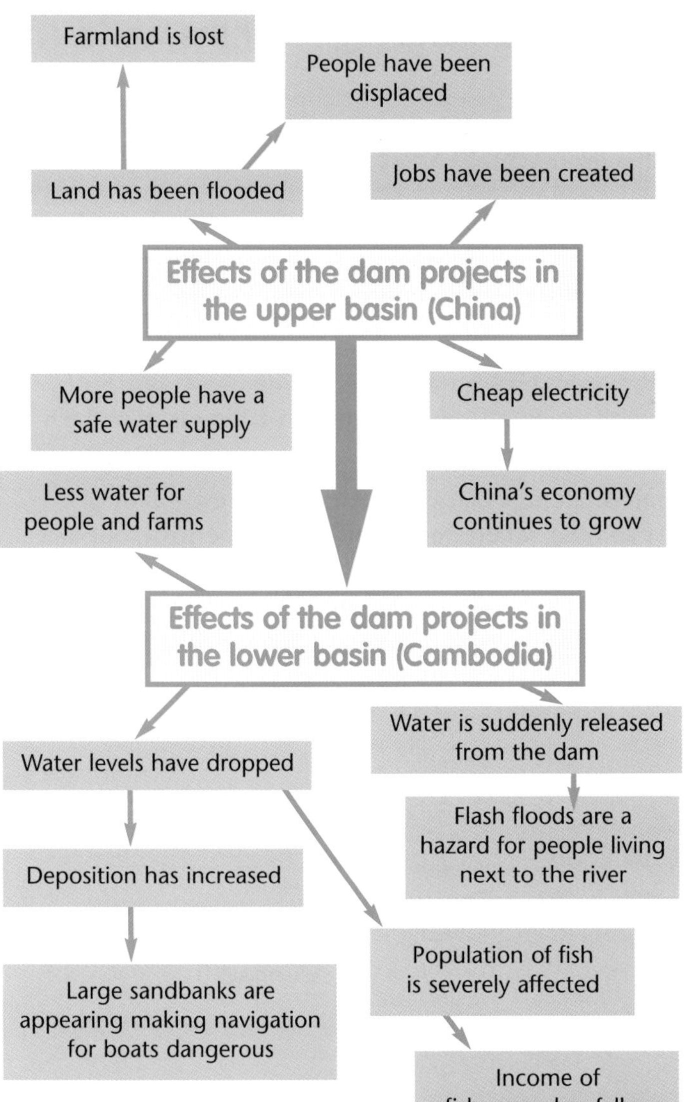


◀ **Figure 7** Advantages and disadvantages of dam projects on the River Mekong

## Activity

**5** Use Figures 5 and 6 to describe the location (see page 155) of the:
- **a)** Pak Mun dam
- **b)** mouth of the Mekong.

**6** Describe the distribution (see page 143) of the dams on the Mekong river and its tributaries.

**7**
- **a)** Describe the location of the floods in 2004.
- **b)** Suggest how building more dams in the future might reduce the risk of flooding.

**8** Study Figures 5 and 7.
- **a)** What are the advantages of building more dams on the Mekong?
- **b)** Explain why some countries benefit from these dams more than others.
- **c)** Do you think Thailand should complete the Pak Mun dam? Explain the advantages and disadvantages that this dam is likely to create.

**9** Water can be described as a **renewable resource**, but it is not always used **sustainably**. Use your understanding of this case study to explain why water use is not always sustainable.

**Figure 8** A ferry crossing the Mekong. As water levels in the river have dropped, the river has become more dangerous for boats like this one

## How does water supply vary from one region of the world to another?

The supply of fresh water is not even. There are three factors that control the amount of fresh water in a particular region.

### Activity

**10** Use Figure 9 to describe the distribution (see page 143) of rainfall in South Africa.

**11** Explain why Lesotho is able to sell water to South Africa and why South Africa wants to buy it.

### 1 Spatial variations in the distribution of precipitation

Patterns of rainfall vary at continental, regional and local scales (see Unit 1 Chapter 2, page 10). So, for example, on average South Africa has about half as much rainfall as the UK. But rainfall is not distributed evenly over South Africa. The east coast receives a lot more rain than the west (see Figure 9). This is because moist air comes in from the Indian Ocean forming rain clouds over the highlands of eastern South Africa.

Geographical patterns of rainfall don't necessarily match the distribution of population. The UK is a good example, where most rain falls in the west, but the greatest population densities are in the south-east. Some countries take advantage of their plentiful rainfall by selling it to neighbouring countries. For example, parts of Lesotho receive 1,200 mm of rain a year (similar to mid-Wales) but Lesotho has only a low population. This is good for Lesotho because it can sell its excess water to parts of South Africa where the population is higher but rainfall is lower.

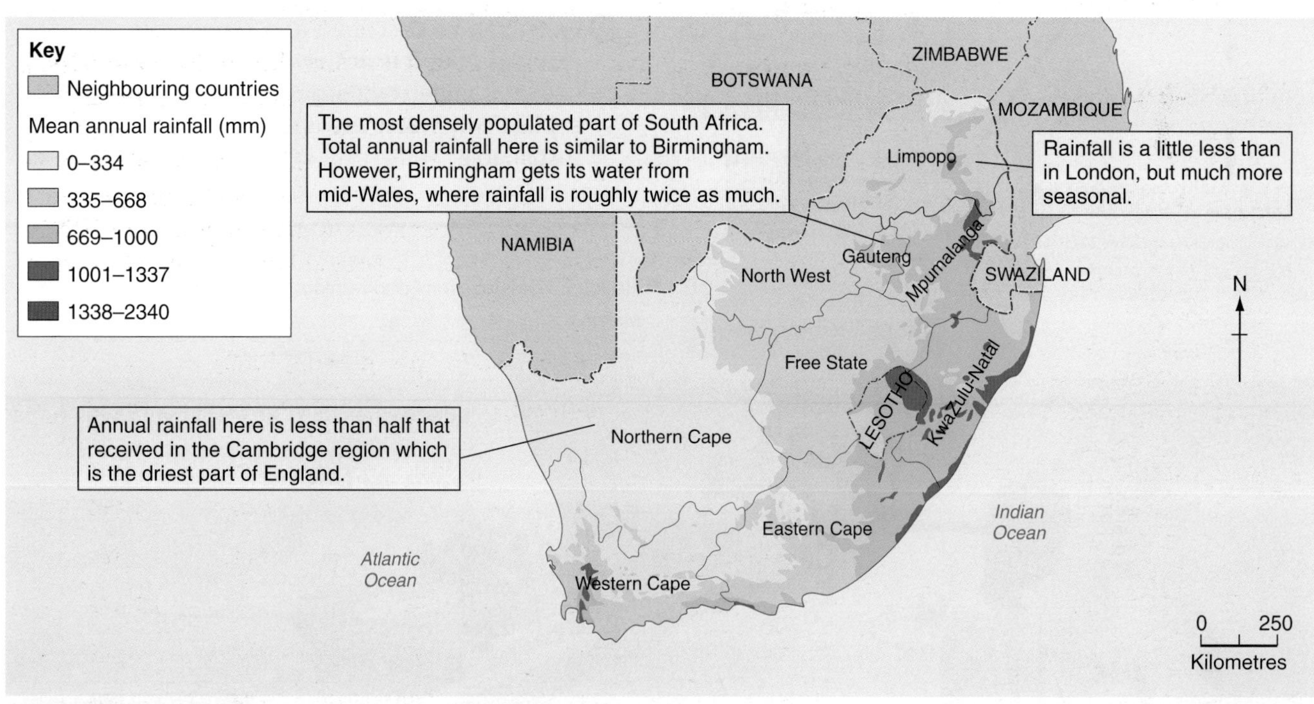


**Figure 9** Average annual rainfall in South Africa

www.weathersa.co.za is the meteorological office for South Africa.

### 2 Seasonal patterns of precipitation

The amount of precipitation also varies through the year. Although some rainforest and desert regions have precipitation which is roughly even throughout the year, most places experience some variation. For some regions this difference can be quite extreme, resulting in a dry season and a wet season. In parts of South Africa, for example, there are several months when there is almost no rain (see Figure 10 on page 87).

| | Jan | Feb | Mar | Apr | May | Jun | Jul | Aug | Sep | Oct | Nov | Dec | Total |
|---|---|---|---|---|---|---|---|---|---|---|---|---|---|
| **Johannesburg, Gauteng** | 125 | 90 | 91 | 54 | 13 | 9 | 4 | 6 | 27 | 72 | 117 | 105 | 713 |
| **Calvina, Northern Cape** | 14 | 12 | 26 | 27 | 22 | 34 | 23 | 24 | 13 | 11 | 13 | 9 | 228 |
| **Polokwane, Limpopo** | 82 | 60 | 52 | 33 | 11 | 5 | 3 | 6 | 17 | 43 | 85 | 81 | 478 |

**Figure 10** Rainfall (mm) for selected cities, South Africa

## 3 Variation in demand

Population size can affect the demand for water. As the population of a region grows, the demand for water increases and this can lead to problems of over-abstraction.

There is also a link between demand and wealth with people in **More Economically Developed Countries (MEDCs)** generally using more water than people in **Less Economically Developed Countries (LEDCs)**. The average American family uses 1,304 litres of water a day whereas the average African family uses 22 litres of water a day. This may be because:

- water abstraction is expensive
- people in MEDCs are wealthier so they use more water in non-essential ways such as using dishwashers and swimming pools.

Some groups of people have very poor access to water. In sub-Saharan Africa, people living in urban areas are twice as likely to have access to water as people living in rural areas. In the **informal settlements** of Africa's cities people do not have access to piped water and cannot afford to drill a borehole (see Unit 3 Chapter 4, page 150). They are forced to buy water from private sellers from the back of carts. As a result, people who live in cities in LEDCs can pay up to 50 times the amount for water as people who live in cities from MEDCs.

### Activity

**12** Use Figure 10.
- **a)** Draw three rainfall graphs.
- **b)** Which graphs show a distinct seasonal pattern?
- **c)** In which months is water supply an issue?

**13** Suggest five reasons why families in MEDCs use more water than families in LEDCs.

**14** Use Figure 11 to investigate the following questions. You should present your findings with a series of graphs.
- **a)** Do MEDCs use more water for domestic purposes than LEDCs?
- **b)** Do MEDCs use more water for industrial purposes than LEDCs?

**15**
- **a)** Compare the water use in Iceland, Japan and South Africa.
- **b)** Suggest reasons for the differences you have noticed.

| | | Water use ($m^2$ per person, 2000) | | | |
|---|---|---|---|---|---|
| | | **Domestic** | **Agricultural** | **Industrial** | **Total** |
| **MEDCs** | Australia | 184 | 941 | 125 | 1,250 |
| | Canada | 292 | 176 | 1,026 | 1,494 |
| | United Kingdom | 35 | 5 | 121 | 161 |
| | United States | 215 | 698 | 779 | 1,692 |
| | Iceland | 187 | 1 | 361 | 549 |
| | Japan | 137 | 435 | 124 | 696 |
| **LEDCs** | Lesotho | 11 | 5 | 11 | 27 |
| | Somalia | 2 | 374 | 0 | 376 |
| | South Africa | 59 | 257 | 37 | 353 |
| | Turkmenistan | 88 | 5,075 | 40 | 5,203 |
| | Congo, Dem. Rep. | 4 | 2 | 1 | 7 |
| | Mali | 4 | 605 | 1 | 610 |

**Figure 11** Water use in selected countries

## Investigating a major water management and transfer scheme

The Lesotho Highlands Water Project (LHWP) is an example of a large-scale water management scheme. There are four phases to the project, which involves the construction of six major dams in Lesotho and 200 km of tunnel systems to transfer water to areas with low water supply in the neighbouring country of South Africa. It is the largest water-transfer scheme in Africa, diverting 40 per cent of the water in the Senqu river basin in Lesotho to the Vaal river system in the Orange Free State of South Africa (see Figure 12). The River Vaal then carries the water into Gauteng Province. This is a very industrial and highly populated region of South Africa which has a high demand for fresh water.

The project was agreed between South Africa and Lesotho in 1986. So far only one of the four phases has been completed. The third major dam of the project, the Mohale dam, was finished in 2002.

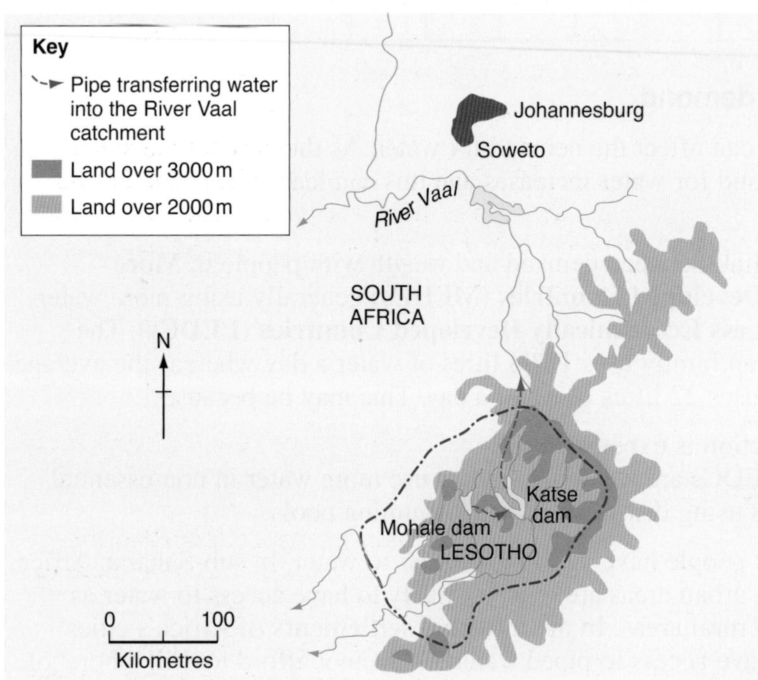


**Figure 12** A map of the LHWP water management and transfer scheme

### What are the advantages and disadvantages of the LHWP?

Lesotho is one of the world's poorest countries. Its **Gross National Income** per person is US$590, it has an unemployment rate of around 50 per cent and no natural resources to sell except water. The Lesotho government is hoping that the LHWP will help to develop the country. The income received from selling water through the LHWP is providing 75 per cent of the country's income.

The project is predicted to cost US$8 billion, which is being given on loan from the World Bank. The South African government will eventually have to pay this money back. The Lesotho government will receive income for the sale of its water. In the long term this could help Lesotho develop its own water management schemes.

In the short term Lesotho is still struggling with water shortages and poor sanitation. Local people have not had access to any of the water supplied by the dams as all of the water is being piped to South Africa. But the percentage of people with a safe water supply in South Africa has increased from 83 per cent to 87 per cent between 1990 and 2002. In 2002 only 76 per cent of people in Lesotho had a safe water supply and only 37 per cent had sanitation.

Most of the LHWP water is being transferred to Johannesburg in the Gauteng province of South Africa. But many residents of Johannesburg are angry because their water bills increased before receiving the improved water service. Some of these people did not even have access to basic water resources. Bills went up to fund the dam and to pay for repairs to leaking pipes.

Local people launched a campaign to halt the construction of the Mohale dam until the water pipes in Johannesburg improved. In 2000 up to 50 per cent of water was simply being wasted through leaking pipes. Despite this, construction of the Mohale dam continued ahead of schedule.

The dams will provide hydro-electric power (HEP) as well as water. The Muela dam is connected to a 72 megawatt hydro-electric power station which is providing a renewable source of cheap electricity for Lesotho. Lesotho is also benefiting from improved roads which were constructed to gain access to the dam sites.

However, many people have been displaced by the construction of the dams and the flooding of the reservoirs. The Katse dam, the first major dam of the project, completed in 1998, affected more than 20,000 people. Many of these people were relocated and given compensation but they claim the money they received was too late. They were also given training so that they could find new jobs, but the training has been criticised and most of the displaced people are still in low-income jobs.

New job opportunities have been created working on the construction of the project. About 20,000 people have moved into informal settlements to work on the dams. However, this has led to a massive increase in AIDS, prostitution and alcoholism.

The project has also destroyed thousands of hectares of grazing and arable land. Since only nine per cent of Lesotho is considered arable, this could lead to huge problems in the nation's food supply.

The project will affect the flow of water downstream of the dams. As well as a decrease in the amount of water it is thought that the dams will reduce the amount of sediment, oxygen levels, nutrients and even the temperature of the water. This will have negative impacts on people, wetland habitats and wildlife, including many endangered species.

▲ **Figure 13** The Mohale dam. You can see this dam on Google Earth: reference location: 29 27'29.97"S, 28 5'56.17"E

| | |
|---|---|
| **River** | Senqunyane |
| **Capacity** | 958 million m$^3$ |
| **Height** | 145 m |
| **Material** | A concrete-faced embankment filled with 7.8 million m$^3$ of rock |
| **Interconnecting tunnel** | To Katse (32 km long) |
| **Water transfer capacity** | 10.1 m$^3$ per second |
| **Initial loan** | US$45 million (funded to Lesotho and to be repaid to the World Bank by South Africa) |
| **Number of affected people** | 7,400, many of whom lost their homes |

◀**Figure 14** Factfile on the Mohale dam (completed 2002)

## Activity

**16** Summarise the aims of the Lesotho Highlands Water Project.

**17** Use the text on these pages to complete a copy of the following table. You should find more to write in some boxes than in others.

| | **Short-term advantages (+) and disadvantages (–) of LHWP** | **Long-term advantages (+) and disadvantages (–) of LHWP** |
|---|---|---|
| Lesotho | +<br>– | +<br>– |
| South Africa | +<br>– | +<br>– |

**18** Summarise what each of the following groups of people might think about the LHWP:
**a)** a farmer in the Lesotho Highlands
**b)** a government minister in Lesotho
**c)** residents in Johannesburg.

**19** Do you think the LHWP is an example of a good, sustainable water management project? Explain your reasons.

# Are there alternative ways to manage South Africa's water?

South Africa has 539 large dams, which is almost half of all the dams in Africa. But despite this, there are still a large number of South Africans without access to clean drinking water. Many of these people live in rural, remote parts of South Africa; they are too isolated to become part of the big projects such as the LHWP and they are too poor to drill boreholes to tap into groundwater supplies. Instead they have to rely on cheap small-scale methods of **rainwater harvesting**.

## A case study of sustainable water management on a small farm

Ma Tshepo Khumbane is a South African farmer who teaches rainwater harvesting techniques. Her management strategies are affordable and practical for families, no matter how small the farm is or how little money they have.

Rainwater harvesting can be carried out by individual households or involve whole communities. These methods of water management are not usually big enough to have negative impacts on the surrounding drainage basin so they are sustainable. They use ways that are cheap, practical and easy to maintain using appropriate technology. A number of these techniques are shown in Figure 15; they are designed to:

- collect and use rainwater, for example, by collecting water from the roof of the farm
- maintain soil moisture by encouraging as much infiltration as possible; in this way groundwater stores are recharged.

### Activity

**20** Choose five techniques shown in Figure 15. For each technique explain how it either collects rain water or recharges groundwater.

**21** Explain why this type of management is sustainable.

**Figure 15** Rainwater harvesting techniques used by Ma Tshepo Khumbane

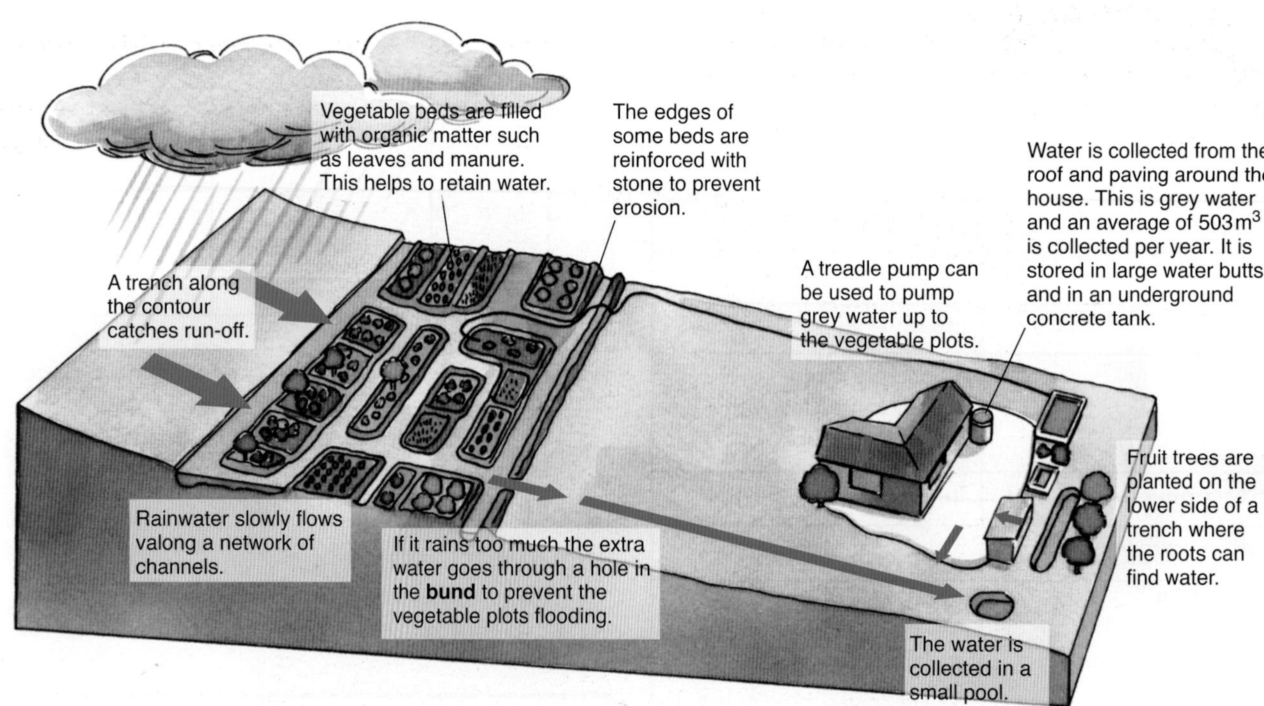

The village of Athol in Limpopo province is one community to have benefited from the teachings of Ma Tshepo Khumbane. In 1982 the community was struggling with drought and malnutrition. Despite having no regular access to water, the villagers of Athol have learned to manage their water sustainably by collecting rainwater and maintaining soil moisture. The villagers' next aim is to build a small stone dam to collect and store rainwater; this will provide a more secure water supply. They are appealing to the government to provide tractors to speed up the process.

**Figure 16** Ma Tshepo Khumbane inspects vegetable-growing in an earth basin. The good soil in the middle of each basin collects rainwater

## Going Further

### Appropriate technology

In South Africa most water is drawn from wells using hand pumps. This can be hard work for women and children. In the 1970s and 1980s money was invested in diesel pumps. These pumps abstract water much more quickly, but they are expensive to install and maintain. An engineer has to service the pump regularly and parts can be expensive.

Now there is an alternative to hand pumps and diesel pumps that is more appropriate to the level of technology and wealth in poorer South African communities. A company has invented a children's roundabout that pumps water out of a borehole. The children play on the roundabout and save their mothers a lot of work! There are now 52 roundabouts located in informal settlements in South Africa.

The roundabouts cost about US$5,000. Advertising companies pay a monthly fee to display adverts on bill-boards next to the pump. This earns enough to cover the cost of buying the roundabout. Roundabouts such as the one at the Thabong nursery school in Davieton (Figure 17) are sustainable because they improve quality of life and should have no long-term negative effects on the environment.

**22** Compare the effects of diesel pumps with the effects of hand pumps.

**23** Explain the advantages of the new roundabout pumps.

**24** Explain why this water management technique is more appropriate for poor communities than a diesel pump.

**Figure 17** Roundabout waterpump at the Thabong nursery school in Davieton

# Chapter 4
# Flood hazards

**KEY QUESTIONS**

- What are the causes of floods?
- What effects do flood hazards have on human activity?
- How can flooding be managed?

## What caused Carlisle to flood in 2005?

NEWS RELEASE

7 January 2005

Major storm set to batter the UK tonight

The Met Office has issued an emergency flash warning of exceptionally severe weather for Scotland, north and east England overnight, with winds gusting up to 90 m.p.h. Gusts of 70 m.p.h. are expected across much of the country, but gusts across southern Scotland, northern and eastern England may reach 90 m.p.h. in places. Considerable damage to trees, some structural damage to buildings and disruption to transport is expected. In addition, further heavy rain is expected over much of Scotland, Northern Ireland, north and west England and Wales with flooding expected in places. Heavy snow is also possible in Scotland affecting high ground for a time. The Met Office is issuing warnings well in advance, advising the public to take extra care during this period of severe weather and more details on the forecast can be found on our website.

**Figure 1** A Met Office press release

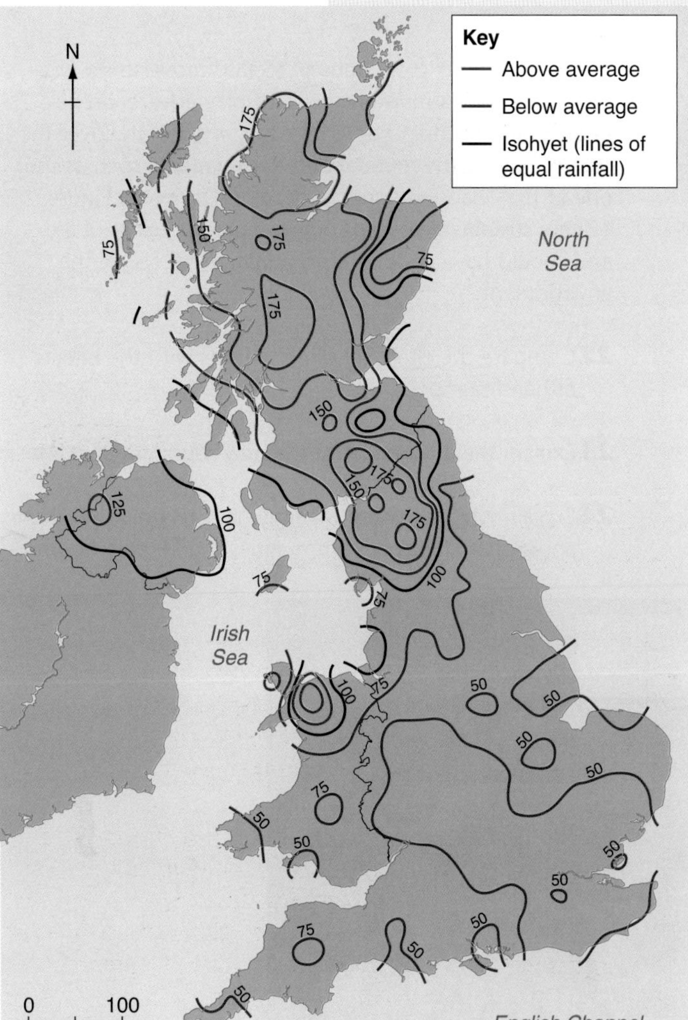


**Figure 2** Rainfall map for January 2005. This map shows the large differences in rainfall across the UK for January caused mainly by the storms

In this case study you should be able to:

- explain the causes of the flood event
- describe which areas were affected by the flood
- describe how different groups of people reacted to the event
- comment on the solutions to help reduce flooding in the future.

The predictions from the Meteorological Centre in Figure 1 were correct, but the storm arrived earlier than expected on Saturday 8 January and the weather was going to be even more extreme. A severe weather event was about to hit the northern UK.

The low pressure centre stopped moving, causing very high rainfall totals over north Wales, north-west England and western Scotland, with Cumbria being the worst affected. South-east England was having an exceptionally warm January day.

Figure 2 shows the large differences in rainfall across the UK for January caused mainly by the storms early in the month.

## The causes of the Carlisle floods

1 An intense area of low pressure moved across western Britain. The intensity of the storm caused high rainfall.
2 The conditions on the cold front stopped the storm from moving away to the south. Because of this, the low pressure stopped moving and remained over the same areas, causing record-breaking river flow in the North-West, while flow levels were below average in the South-West.
3 Carlisle is at the **confluence** of three main watercourses, the rivers Eden, Petteril and Caldew. The rain falling across the region flowed down these rivers and came together in the town.
4 Records from *Carlisle News* and *Star* show that five full flood warnings were given out on 15 December. This means that the ground was already saturated, and any water from the January storm would have flowed as **overland flow**, causing rivers to rise quickly and increase the flood risk.
5 The town of Carlisle had developed across the **flood plain** of the River Eden causing more overland flow. This would have contributed to increased flooding.

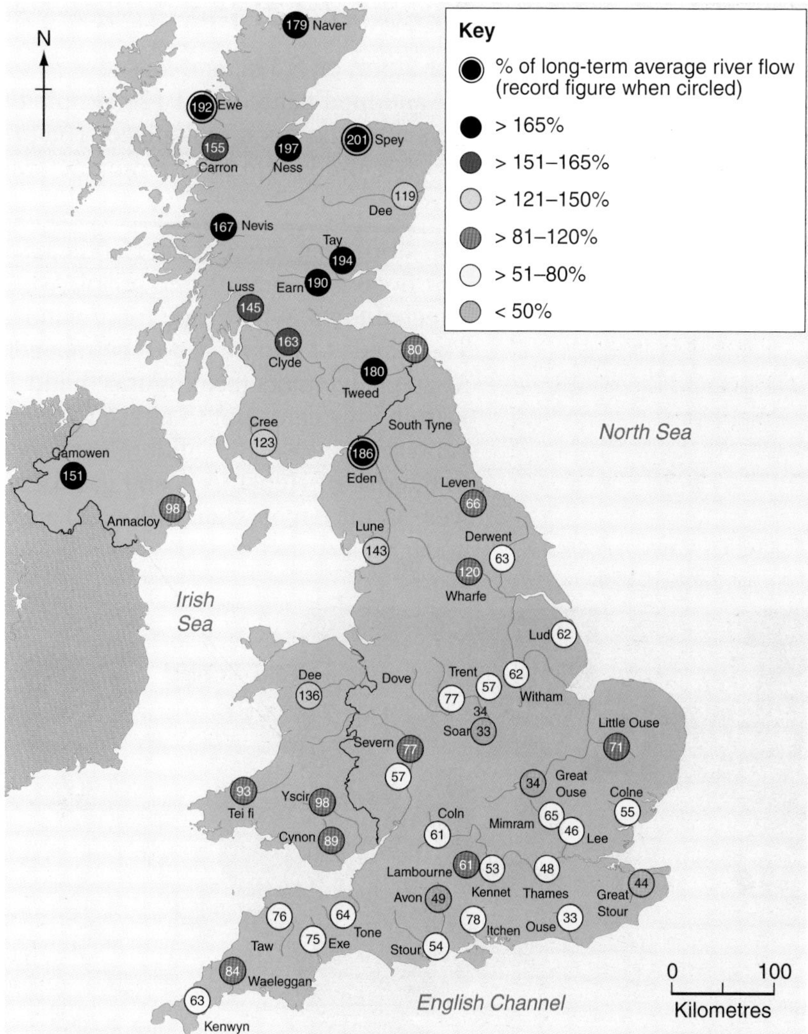


**Figure 3** River flow map for January 2005, Centre for Ecology and Hydrology. This map shows how the area of the storm produced record river flows in many rivers in northern England and Scotland while flow levels were below average in the South

### Activity

**1** Study Figure 2. Describe the distribution of the areas with rainfall totals above the average for January of 100 isolines.

**2** Study Figure 3. Describe the distribution of rivers with exceptionally high flow.

**3** What were the causes of the high river flow on the River Eden?

**4** What other factors caused Carlisle to flood on the morning of Saturday 8 January 2005?

**5** The storm which caused the Carlisle floods was described as an extreme weather event.
**a)** Explain why this was the case.
**b)** Comment on whether you think these events will be more common in future.

## The effects of the Carlisle floods

The storm on 8 January caused 1,700 homes to be flooded. The flood water left silt and mud behind, and 120 people had still not returned to their homes 500 days after the flood took place. The premises of local businesses were flooded, which caused them to lose money. Transport was disrupted and schools were closed.

The storm that brought the flood caused the Environment Agency to issue over 100 flood warnings. Three people were killed in Carlisle, Cumbria, the worst affected town, where gale force winds of up to 100 mph were measured. Thousands of people had to be moved to emergency accommodation by boat and rescue helicopters (see Figures 4 and 5). The police helped with the evacuation, warning residents not to return to their homes in order to avoid contact with the contaminated water. Children were warned not to play in the receding waters due to the risk of Hepatitis A and gastroenteritis infections. All of Carlisle's 65 buses were in the depot when it flooded and the police and fire stations were both under water.

**Figure 4** A woman is rescued from her home in Carlisle

**Figure 5** Lifeboats are used as the flood worsens

## How can flooding be managed in the future?

The early warning system worked well. The Meteorological Centre had forecast severe weather conditions for 7 and 8 January, and an emergency severe weather warning was released. The Environmental Agency issued twenty flood warnings and two severe flood warnings for the rivers in the area. The warnings were given by text, phone calls and even through loudspeakers. The weather forecast had allowed accurate predictions of the storm, but many people did not evacuate the area. The storm remained stationary over the region, and so flooding was even worse than expected. Sandbags were distributed and residents were air-lifted from their flooded homes. The flooding had made any movement out of town by road impossible. The emergency services had also been flooded.

A flood defence scheme to improve the standard of protection was already in the planning stages at the time of the January 2005 storm. Options included flood walls, pumping stations, concreting the river banks and dredging. The River Eden and Petteril Flood Alleviation Scheme was started in May 2006 and is expected to be completed by 2010. Temporary flood defences have been installed which involve movable scaffolded flat walls. Sheeting is added and kept down by the weight of the rising water.

### Activity

**6** What were the effects of the January 2005 storm on Carlisle? Make two lists under the headings: short-term effects and long-term effects.

**7** Compile a list of people affected by the storm and another list of those responsible for helping with flood prediction and alleviation.

**8** How can the impact of floods be reduced? Write lists under these three headings:
- monitoring and preparation
- flood event options
- flood management.

**9** Using your knowledge of river processes and drainage basins, explain how flooding and flood risk can be reduced in the future in Carlisle.

**www.metoffice.co.uk**
The national weather centre site for all your weather and climate needs.

**www.wiseweather.co.uk**
An alternative weather site to the meteological centre.

**www.environment-agency.gov.uk**
This site includes an overview of areas that flood in the UK as well as the active flood warnings.

## Going Further

### Controlling the mighty Mississippi

Floods on the River Mississippi are naturally occurring events. Major floods have happened in these years: 1849, 1850, 1882, 1912, 1913, 1927, 1937, 1993 and 2005. The 2005 flood was caused by Hurricane Katrina; the earlier floods were caused by high rainfall events.

The Mississippi flows across a wide flood plain on most of its journey to the sea, over which it naturally floods. Sandbanks are constantly shifting in its channel as sediment is deposited at times of low flow and eroded during floods. The river erodes sideways across its flood plain. Meanders increase in size before cut-offs at the neck of the meander cause the channel to change position.

#### River facts

- The River Mississippi, with its tributary the Missouri, is the fourth-longest river in the world. It is approximately 3,780 km long, its length changing from time to time by cut-offs and river engineering (see page 109).
- Its **drainage basin** covers an area of 3,225,000 km$^2$.
- It collects water from 31 American and two Canadian States. Its major tributaries include the Missouri and the Ohio. The river reaches the sea near New Orleans.
- It is estimated that more than 400 million tonnes of mud is carried out of the river's **mouth** every year. These deposits of silt form a **delta**.

#### Why do we need to control the River Mississippi?

The task of controlling the Mississippi is the responsibility of the United States Army Corps of Engineers. Control of the river will:

- reduce the risk of flooding and the damage this would cause
- improve navigation on the river to increase trade to inland ports
- stabilise the land surface. This will allow settlement and industry to use the land of the flood plain and water from the river without the risk of the river suddenly changing its course.

River engineering or river management techniques that have been used to control the flow of the river include:

- Levees – natural banks which are increased in height artificially. These hold the flow in but may cause larger flood events to be worse.

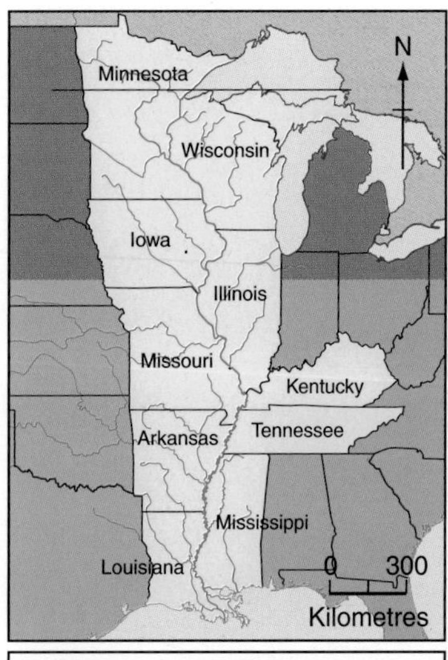

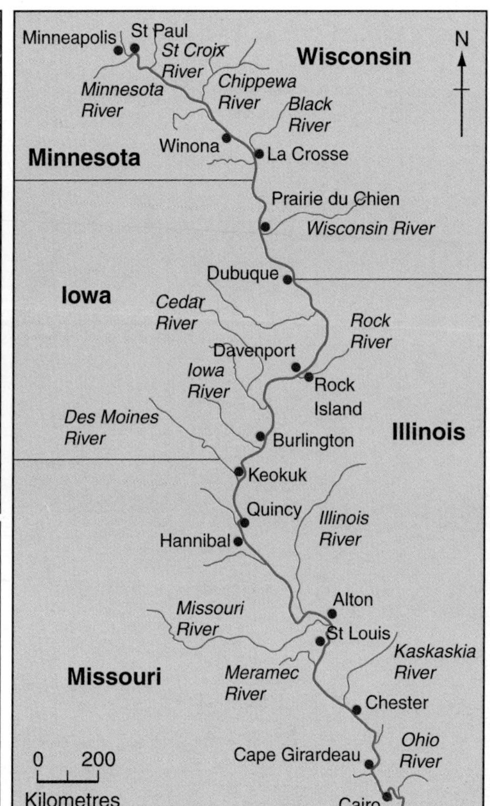


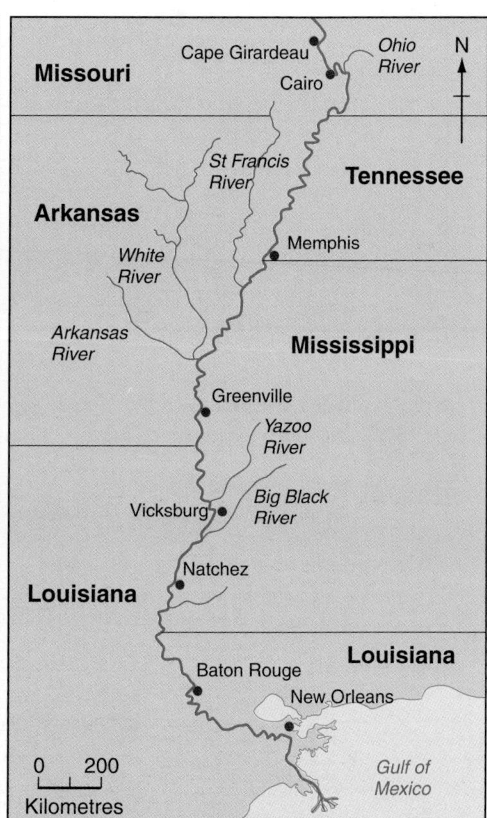


**Figure 6** The Mississippi drainage basin

- **Floodways** – alternative channels built to carry water at times of flood.
- Channel improvement – river straightening
  – **revetments** (concreting the banks)
  – dredging
  – **wing dikes** (walls built into the river channel).
- **Reservoir construction** – to store flood waters.
- **Soft engineering** – planting of trees
  – creation of wetlands to slow flood water flow.

## The great debate

Yet flood control is difficult and expensive, and floods continue to occur on the Mississippi. Some scientists believe that although flood prevention measures stop smaller floods, they can make larger floods worse. There is evidence that soft engineering is a better way to control river flow. By recreating wetlands the environment is returned to nature, species diversity increases and areas are becoming tourist hotspots.

**Figure 7** Levee collapse and flood

**10** Use the information in this section and the internet to explain why the Mississippi should be controlled.

**11** Explain how successful the United States Corps of Engineers has been at controlling the Mississippi.

**12** Construct a flood hydrograph for Figure 8 to show the highest ever flow in 1993 in the Mississippi and then answer the following questions:

**a)** What date was the highest ever flow on the Mississippi at St Louis?
**b)** Describe how the water levels changed from 1 June to 31 August.
**c)** How long did the people of St Louis have to prepare for the flood?
**d)** What would you have done if you lived in St Louis at the time?

| Date | June | July | August |
|---|---|---|---|
| 1 | 25.30 | 32.00 | 49.50 |
| 2 | 24.80 | 32.50 | 48.50 |
| 3 | 24.50 | 34.50 | 48.00 |
| 4 | 24.20 | 36.30 | 47.20 |
| 5 | 24.20 | 37.10 | 46.60 |
| 6 | 24.30 | 37.90 | 46.60 |
| 7 | 25.70 | 38.60 | 45.70 |
| 8 | 28.50 | 40.30 | 44.50 |
| 9 | 29.40 | 41.40 | 43.40 |
| 10 | 29.60 | 42.30 | 42.30 |
| 11 | 29.40 | 42.80 | 41.20 |
| 12 | 29.30 | 43.00 | 40.60 |
| 13 | 29.10 | 42.80 | 39.90 |
| 14 | 28.80 | 42.80 | 39.90 |
| 15 | 28.30 | 43.30 | 39.70 |
| 16 | 28.00 | 44.20 | 39.10 |
| 17 | 27.80 | 45.40 | 38.60 |
| 18 | 27.80 | 46.50 | 37.50 |
| 19 | 27.90 | 46.80 | 36.90 |
| 20 | 27.50 | 46.90 | 36.00 |
| 21 | 27.80 | 47.00 | 35.10 |
| 22 | 27.70 | 46.90 | 34.80 |
| 23 | 27.60 | 46.60 | 33.80 |
| 24 | 28.20 | 46.50 | 33.50 |
| 25 | 28.50 | 46.50 | 33.30 |
| 26 | 30.00 | 46.40 | 32.90 |
| 27 | 31.20 | 46.00 | 32.50 |
| 28 | 31.00 | 45.90 | 32.50 |
| 29 | 31.80 | 46.00 | 32.00 |
| 30 | 32.00 | 46.90 | 31.70 |
| 31 | | 48.40 | 31.10 |

**Figure 8** Table of flow heights for the Mississippi River at St Louis, summer 1993

Unit 2

# Chapter 5 Drought hazards

**KEY QUESTIONS**

- What are the causes of drought and desertification?
- What effect do these hazards have on human activity?
- How can drought and desertification be managed?

## Investigating the 2006 UK drought

In the summer of 2006 parts of England were suffering their worst water shortage for 30 years. This **drought** was caused by low rainfall over a period of many months.

The water shortage was worst in south-east England. By February 2006 this region had experienced fourteen consecutive months of below-average rainfall. This period included the winter months of 2004–2005 and 2005–2006. The lack of rainfall during the winter was the main cause of the water shortage. Winter rainfall is needed to recharge the groundwater stores that have been used over the previous summer when demand for water, especially from farmers, is much higher. The media, however, pointed out that leaking pipes were another cause of the water shortage.

The long spell of dry weather was broken in spring 2006, when many parts of the UK had exceptionally wet weather for two months. But this was not enough to recharge the reservoirs or groundwater in the south-east. In fact, scientists warned the public that rainfall would need to be above average for at least another six months to end the water shortage. Then June and July were unusually hot. Crops and garden plants dried out as what little moisture that was left in the soil was lost by evaporation.

The drought did not affect all areas of the UK. Rainfall in Scotland, Wales and western and northern regions of England over the same period was close to average. Birmingham, which gets its water from the Elan Valley in Wales, was not affected by the drought.

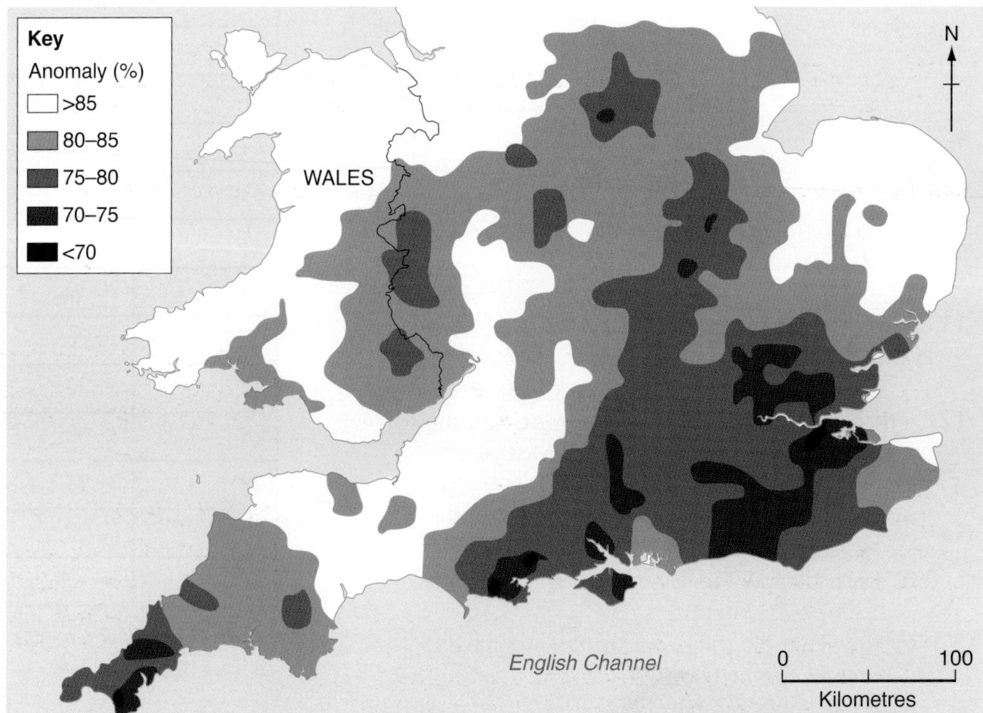


**Figure 1** Distribution of rainfall anomaly (percentage of average rainfall totals) in Wales and southern England

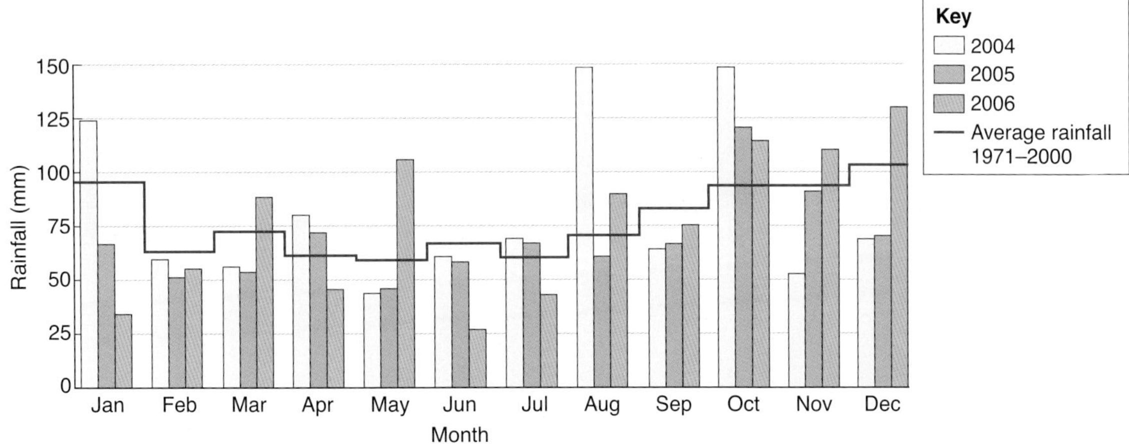


▲
**Figure 2** Rainfall in England and Wales 2004–2006

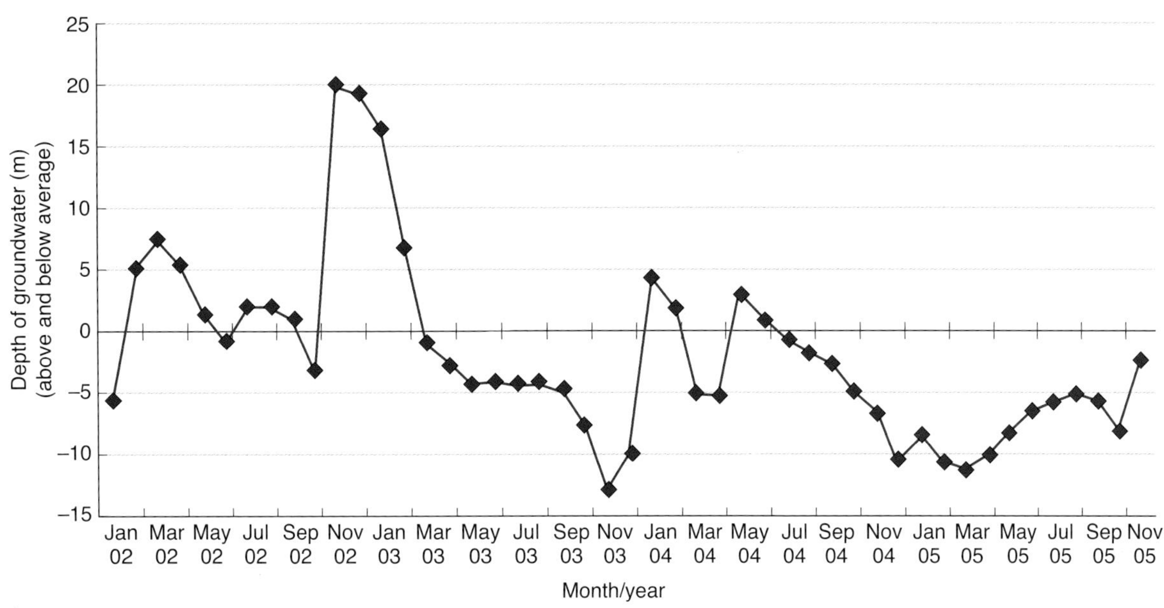


▲
**Figure 3** Depth of groundwater in the chalk rocks of southern England compared with average levels (m)

## Activity

**1 a)** What was the main cause of the drought?
**b)** Explain how high temperatures in June and July 2006 made the problem worse.

**2** Use Figure 1. Describe the distribution (see page 143) of places that had:
**a)** less than 70 per cent of normal rainfall
**b)** more than 85 per cent of normal rainfall.

**3** Study Figure 2.
**a)** In which month of 2004 did the period of low rainfall begin?
**b)** Compare rainfall in January 2004, 2005 and 2006 to the average for that month.
**c)** In which month did the period of low rainfall end?

**4** Use Figure 3.
**a)** Describe the groundwater level in January 2002, 2003, 2004 and 2005.
**b)** Explain why the lack of winter rainfall can cause water shortages in summer months.

## How was this water shortage managed?

Water companies in the south-east of England introduced water restrictions in February 2006. In most areas this meant that customers were unable to use a hosepipe to water their gardens or wash the car. Customers supplied by Sutton and East Surrey faced the tougher restrictions of a drought order. Mid Kent and Southern Water were given permission to impose a drought order, but decided that they didn't need to impose it.

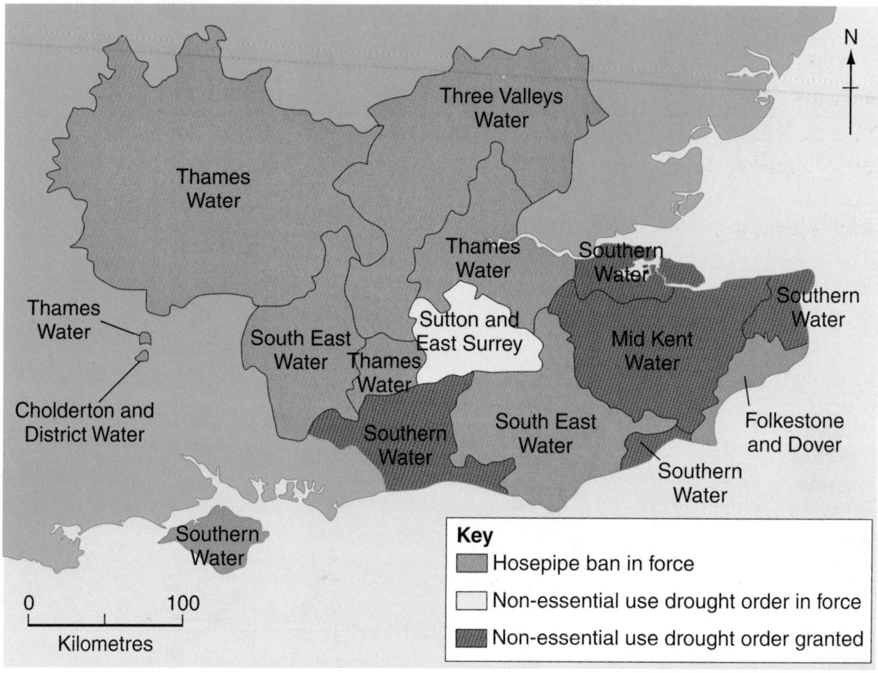


**Figure 4** The area affected by water restrictions

**Level One: hosepipe ban**
Householders cannot use hosepipes to water the garden or wash the car. Lawn sprinklers are also banned. Businesses such as car washes and garden centres can continue to use hosepipes.

**Level Two: drought orders**
Water companies may choose to restrict:
- use of hosepipes or sprinklers
- owners of private swimming pools from filling them
- filling ornamental ponds (unless they contain fish)
- the operation of mechanical car washes
- washing boats, trains or aircraft
- cleaning the outsides of buildings, although you can continue to clean windows with water from a bucket
- the operation of ornamental fountains.

Water companies may apply to the Environment Agency to abstract extra water supplies either from rivers or groundwater.

**Level Three: emergency drought orders**
In the most severe conditions, water companies might need to restrict water supply by:
- shutting off supply to houses and providing water to a standpipe in the street
- cutting off water supplies to homes and businesses for parts of each day.

**Figure 5** How water companies can manage a drought

- Water the garden in the evening.
- Use a watering can to water plants instead of a hosepipe.
- Leave the lawn to grow a little longer than usual.
- Wash-up by hand and then throw the dirty water on the garden.
- Fit a water-butt to your downspout.
- Only use the washing machine and dishwasher when they are full.
- Fit a water displacement device (known as a hippo, see Figure 8) in the cistern of your toilet.
- Fix any dripping taps.

**Figure 6** Tips for water saving

**Figure 8** This water hippo contains granules that soak up one litre of water. When placed inside the cistern of a toilet it reduces the amount of water used by one litre each flush

| Name of water company | Percentage of supply from groundwater | Daily supply to customers (millions of litres) | Leakage (millions of litres a day) | Percentage of supply that is lost by leakage (leakage/supply) x 100 | Leakage (litres per property per day) |
|---|---|---|---|---|---|
| Thames Water | 17 | 2,822 | 895 | (895 / 2822) x 100 = 31.7% | 253 |
| Dwr Cymru Welsh Water | 4 | 876 | 225 | | 167 |
| Severn Trent | 35 | 1,966 | 540 | | 163 |
| United Utilities | 8 | 1,970 | 475 | | 152 |
| Yorkshire Water | 22 | 1,291 | 295 | | 138 |

**Figure 7** Water supplied and leaking from the five water companies with most leaks.
Average amount of water used per household per day (litres) = 1,062

## Activity

**5** Use Figure 4 to describe the distribution (see page 143) of water companies which restricted water use during the drought.

**6** Suggest how each of the following businesses would be inconvenienced by a drought order:
- **a)** landscape gardener
- **b)** plant nursery
- **c)** car wash.

**7** Explain the difference for a normal household between a level one and level three restriction.

**8** Discuss the list of water-saving tips in Figure 6.
- **a)** Explain how each one of these would save water.
- **b)** Put the tips into rank order, starting with the one you expect would save most water. Justify your choice.
- **c)** Suggest two more ways to save water in the home.

**9** The water companies encouraged people to use less water. Some consumers criticised the water companies for not fixing leaking pipes quickly enough. Explain each of these points of view.

**10**
- **a)** Make a copy of Figure 7. Using the first row as a guide, calculate the percentage of water lost by leakage from each water company.
- **b)** Compare the amount of water lost through leakage to the amount used per household per day. Using this as evidence, argue the point (for or against) that water leakage was a significant factor in the drought.

## Investigating drought and desertification in Mali and Niger

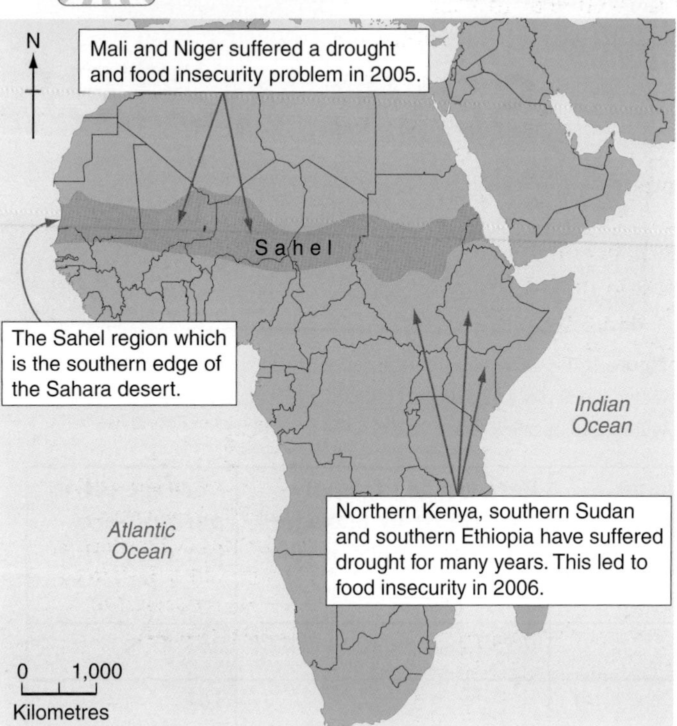


▲ **Figure 9** The location of recent droughts in Africa

In 2004 the **subsistence** farmers of Mali and Niger were hit by a double problem: a particularly severe drought and a plague of locusts virtually destroyed their crops. By July 2005 the crisis came to the attention of the world's media. By then it was estimated that 3.3 million people (including 800,000 children) were at risk from a serious food shortage. UNICEF, already working in Niger because it has a programme of long-term aid in the country, was struggling to cope with the scale of the problem and asked for extra help to enable it to give emergency aid.

### Activity

**11 a)** Give two reasons for the food crisis of 2005.
**b)** Describe the effect of the drought on people.

**12** Use Figure 9 to describe:
**a)** the distribution of Sahel countries
**b)** the location of recent droughts in Africa.

**13 a)** Compare the two images in Figure 10.
**b)** Suggest how images like this could be used to provide an early warning of developing famine.

**Figure 10** False colour satellite images. Regions where vegetation is less dense than usual (because of drought) are brown. Regions where vegetation is healthy are shown in darker green ▼

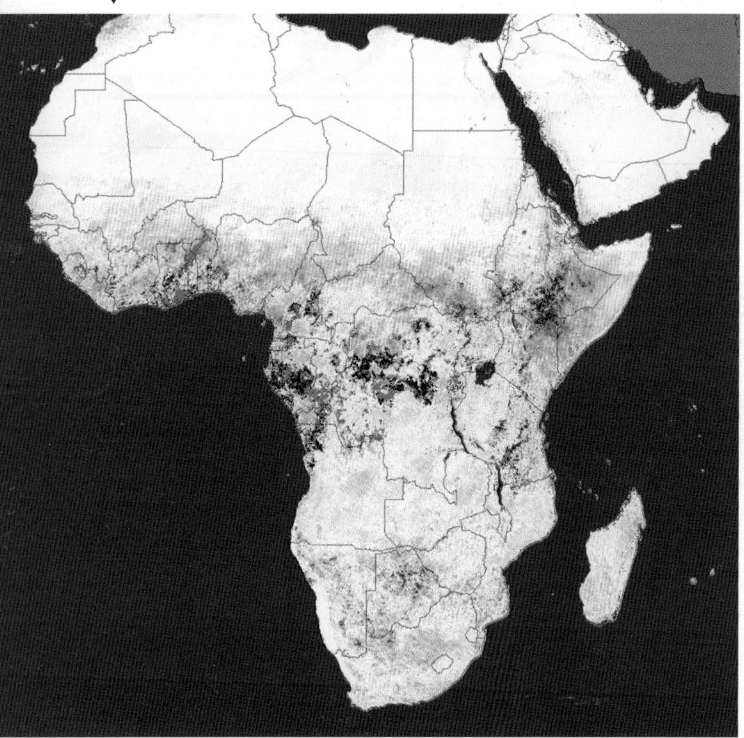

July 2004 – the drought damaged natural vegetation and crops. A famine developed over the next 9–12 months

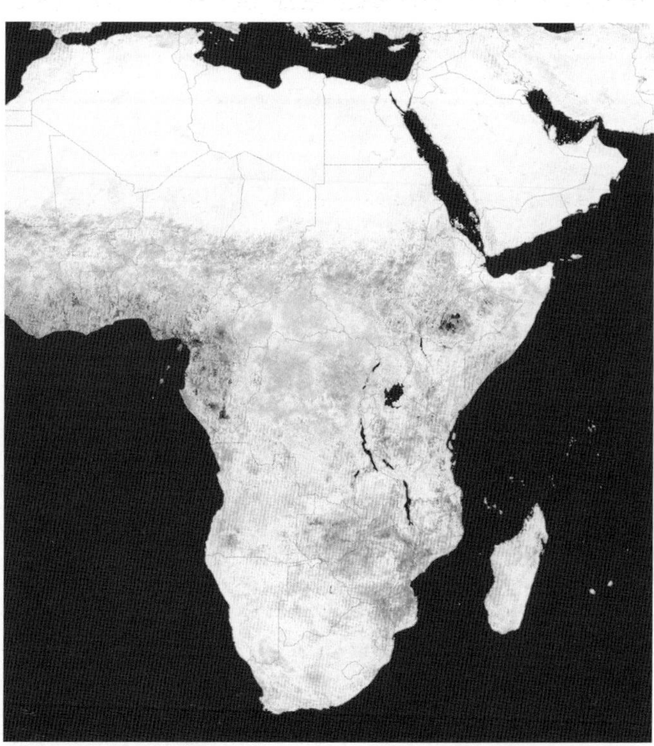

July 2005 – in this month rainfall was better than average, helping to produce a better crop

## What is desertification and how is it caused?

Rainfall in the Sahel region of Africa is extremely variable from year to year. Rainfall is lowest in the north of the region. Cattle and goat herding are possible here. Rainfall of around 600 mm per year is usual in the southern **Sahel**. This is sufficient for some crops to be grown.

The drought in Niger and Mali during 2004–2005 is just one of several recent water shortages in the Sahel region of Africa. This region is experiencing climate change: annual rainfall totals in most years since 1968 have been lower than in earlier years of the twentieth century. As a result, the area is becoming more arid and the crops are less reliable. There is less natural vegetation than 40 years ago so when it is windy the dry soil is easily blown away. It is as though the Sahara desert is expanding; a situation that is described as **desertification**.

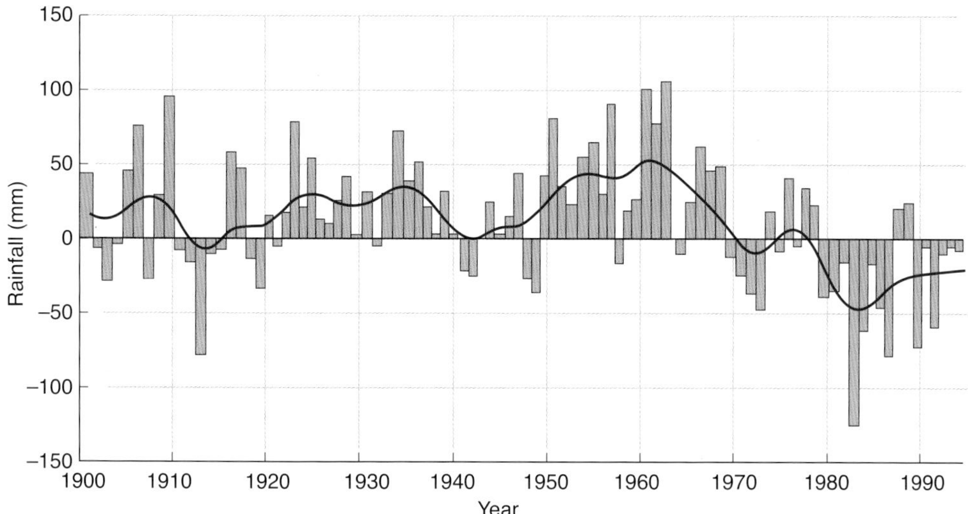


**Figure 11** Annual rainfall anomalies in Sahel countries 1900–1995. Each bar represents whether the total rainfall in each year was above or below average. The line shows the trend

**www.wateraid.org.uk**
A number of Non-Governmental Organisations (NGOs), such as WaterAid, work in Mali to try to improve the amount of fresh water available.

### Activity

**14** Use Figure 11.

**a)** How many years between 1900 and 1965 had:
- i) above-average rainfall of 50 mm or more?
- ii) below-average rainfall of –50 mm or less?

**b)** How many years between 1965 and 1995 had:
- i) above-average rainfall of 50 mm or more?
- ii) below-average rainfall of –50 mm or less?

**c)** Using evidence from Figure 11 compare rainfall patterns in the Sahel before 1965 with the period from 1965 to 1995.

**15** Use the internet link to WaterAid, above, to research how this charity is helping to solve problems of water shortages in Africa. From the home page click on the drop-down menu under the heading 'Where we work'. Select Mali and then Ethiopia.

**a)** Prepare a short report that focuses on:
- a comparison of the water problems facing the two countries
- how WaterAid and other NGOs are tackling problems in urban or rural areas in the two countries.

**b)** Use the website to:
- suggest how water and sanitation are linked to disease and poverty
- explain why WaterAid thinks it is essential to involve women in their projects.

## Managing the problems of desertification in Mali and Niger

The twin problems of lack of water and soil erosion can be managed and the future of Sahel countries can be sustainable. What is needed is a combination of low-technology rainwater harvesting and soil conservation strategies, similar to those used in the drier regions of South Africa (see pages 90–91). These include:

- tree-planting schemes
- building small rock dams
- collecting rainwater from the roofs of buildings
- building terraces on steeper slopes
- building stone lines on gentle slopes
- planting grass strips along the contours of gentle slopes.

### How do bunds help?

One strategy that has been used successfully in crop-growing regions of Burkina Faso and Mali is the construction of low stone lines known as bunds. Stones are placed along the contours on gentle slopes. Sometimes the bunds are reinforced by planting tough grasses along the lines. The stones and grass encourage rainwater to infiltrate the soil and reduce the amount of rainwater that is lost by run-off. They also prevent soil **erosion**.

### Activity

**16** Explain how stone lines are able to:

**a)** reduce soil erosion
**b)** increase soil moisture
**c)** increase the amount of grain grown.

**Figure 12** How bunds work

Farmers report that this technique increases their yields of grain crops (sorghum and millet). Fields that have stone lines produce 30 per cent more grain than an ordinary field in a year that has poor rainfall, and twenty per cent more in a year that has average rainfall.

## Going Further

### Why is the Sahel becoming drier?

The reasons for desertification are complex. Some scientists believe that the region naturally experiences a cyclical climate: wetter periods are separated by drier periods that last for decades. Other scientists believe that the climate is changing as a result of human actions. Desertification could be a symptom of global warming. Alternatively, the Sahel climate may have become drier because of smoke and pollution produced in the industrial countries of Europe. Another common theory is that local people are to blame for climate change in the Sahel: population growth and overgrazing could have made the local climate drier. This theory is examined in Figure 13.

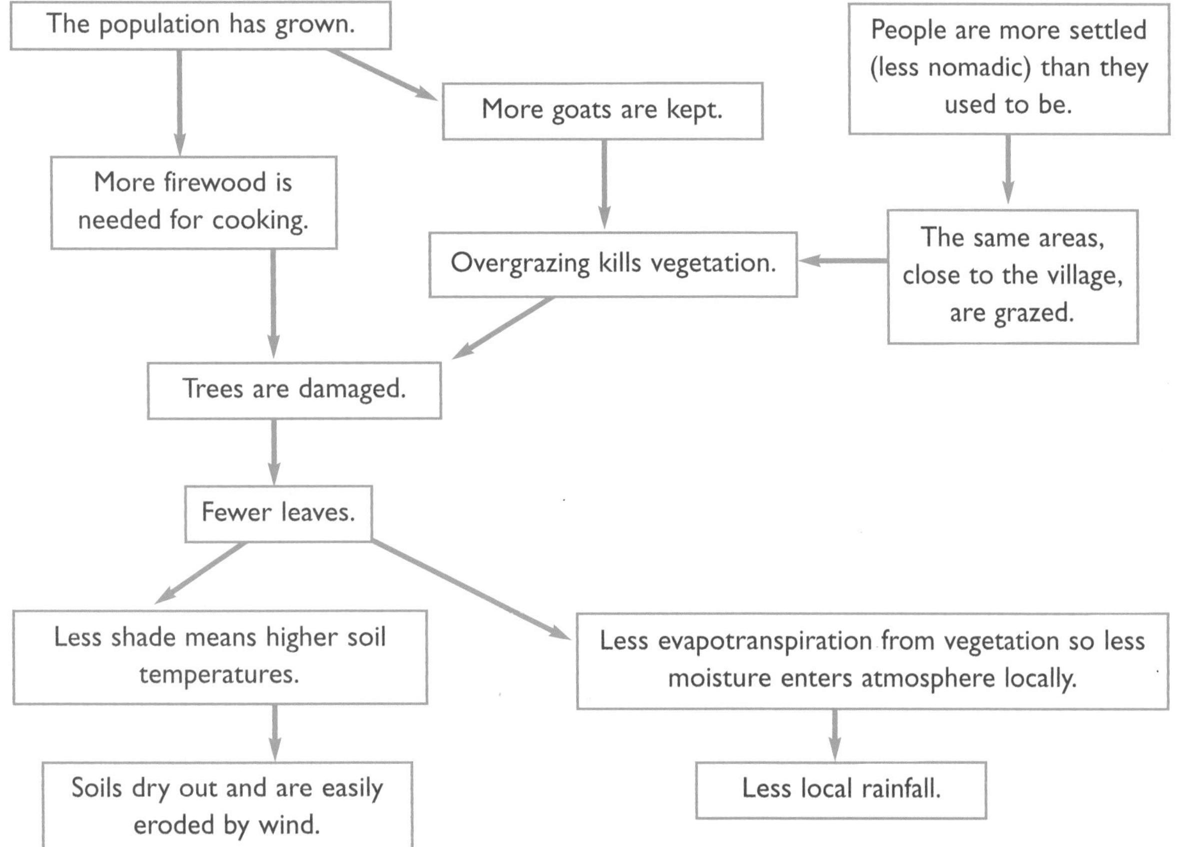


**Figure 13** How population growth may have caused desertification

**17 a)** Explain how larger, more settled populations of people may have led to lower rainfall totals in the Sahel.

**b)** If Figure 13 describes the main cause of desertification, suggest how the problem could be tackled.

# Chapter 6
# River processes and landforms

**KEY QUESTIONS**

- How do river processes shape the land?
- How do landforms affect people's lives?
- How does human activity affect the way a river shapes the land?

## River processes

From the moment water begins to flow over the surface of the land in a channel, gravity gives it the power to erode the landscape. The shape of the land changes as the river flows from its upland **source** to its **mouth**. The gravitational energy also enables the river to transport material or **load** downstream. In this chapter you will learn about the processes that enable the river to change its landscape, the way in which it carries material and how these processes can affect people's lives.

The photo in Figure 1 was taken five km from the source of the stream. The photo has been annotated to show the main features of an upland river valley. There are two main processes that produce these features: **weathering**, the breaking up of rock, and **erosion**, the wearing away of the landscape as soil and rock are loosened and move downhill.

**Figure 1** Ashes Valley, Little Stretton, Shropshire. This stream is one of the most studied in Britain, with more than 40,000 students visiting it every year

Near the source of the river, the steep gradient gives the river energy to erode and transport a large quantity of material as its load. As the river erodes downwards, it wears away its channel and produces a narrow valley with steep V-shaped sides. The **sediment** in the stream is large and angular compared with further down the river's course.

The load of the stream is carried in four ways:

1. **Solution** – minerals from the rocks are dissolved in the water.
2. **Suspension** – the smallest clay-sized particles are easily carried by the stream.
3. **Saltation** – larger particles that bounce along the bottom of the riverbed.
4. **Traction** – the largest material is dragged along the bed of the river.

One litre of water weighs a kilogram and so you can imagine how much power even a small stream has when it is flowing fast. When the small stream at Boscastle flooded the town it was able to empty the car park in the village and sweep the cars out to sea. It had a huge amount of erosive power.

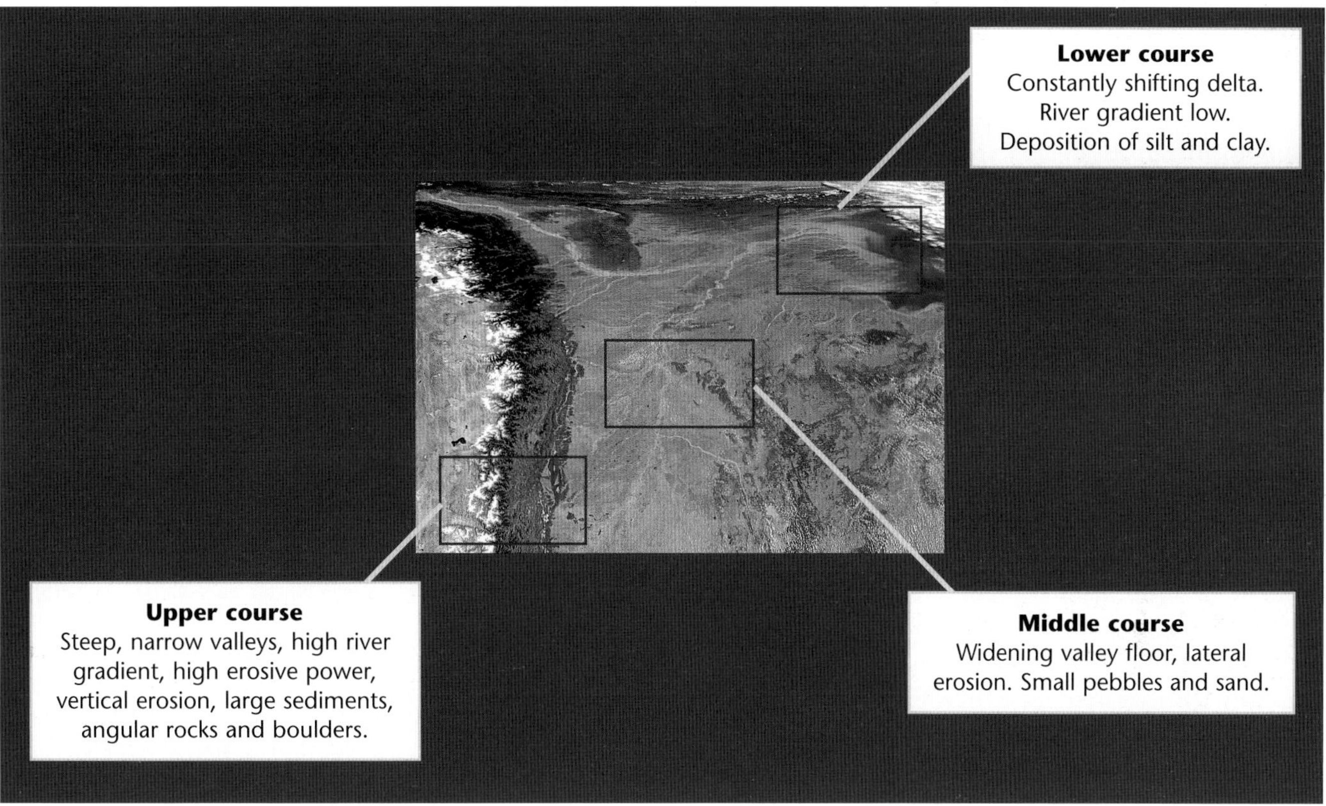


**Figure 2** The Ganges–Brahmaputra river basin

## Activity

1. Draw four sketches to illustrate the ways that a river transports material.
2. Study Figure 1. Explain how two of the features annotated in the photo were formed.
3. A student has collected sediment data from two sites in Ashes Valley and put it into a table (Figure 3).
   **a)** Use the information in Figure 3 to draw a graph to compare the sediment size for the two sites.
   **b)** Describe how the size of sediment changes downstream in Ashes Valley.
   **c)** Explain the process that causes sediment size to change.
4. Why is Ashes Valley such a good place for geography students to visit?
5. Look closely at Figure 2. Describe how the river changes from its source to the mouth and explain what causes the changes.

| **Site 12 Upstream** | | | | |
|---|---|---|---|---|
| | 16.1 | 22.0 | 2.7 | 10.1 |
| **Sediment size length (cm)** | 10.4 | 10.5 | 1.9 | 10.4 |
| | 22.0 | 9.0 | 7.8 | 3.0 |
| | 6.5 | 3.6 | 4.6 | 1.5 |
| **Measurements taken at four even distances across the stream.** | 12.0 | 7.9 | 2.2 | 6.4 |
| | 7.4 | 2.1 | 2.0 | 6.0 |
| | 7.4 | 3.5 | 4.1 | 1.6 |
| | 6.5 | 8.9 | 3.9 | 3.8 |
| | 11.0 | 8.4 | 3.7 | 5.4 |

| **Site 1 Downstream** | | | | |
|---|---|---|---|---|
| | 7.8 | 11.1 | 2.7 | 2.4 |
| **Sediment size length (cm)** | 7.6 | 2.1 | 1.9 | 6.1 |
| | 3.6 | 7.0 | 7.8 | 1.8 |
| | 1.5 | 1.3 | 4.6 | 10.6 |
| **Measurements taken at four even distances across the stream.** | 1.4 | 2.7 | 2.2 | 6.0 |
| | 2.2 | 5.1 | 2.0 | 2.0 |
| | 9.0 | 1.1 | 4.1 | 6.7 |
| | 0.9 | 1.3 | 3.9 | 2.1 |
| | 4.3 | .0 | 3.7 | 4.7 |

**Figure 3** Sediment size from two sites in Ashes Valley, Little Stretton

## How do meanders form?

**Figure 4** Features of river meanders on the River Severn at Ironbridge

A **meander** is a bend in the river. Meanders occur along the length of a river, increasing in size as the river flows towards its mouth. At a river meander both the forces of erosion and **deposition** are at work. As the river flows towards lower, less steep land, it slows down and begins to bend. The river flows faster on the outside of a bend so has more power to erode the banks. On the inside of the bend water flow is slower. The river loses the power to transport the sediment it is carrying so material is quickly dropped. In this way the river deposits its load on the inside of the bend. The material is sorted with the larger stones falling first, then the sand-sized particles and finally the finest silt and clays, called **alluvium**. Study any river meander closely and this pattern of rock size is always seen on the beach on the inside of the bed.

Meanders are not static features of the landscape; they move and change across the river's valley floor. As a river erodes its outer bank the meander gets larger. Eventually erosion on the outside of the bend will cause a **cut-off** at the neck of the meander, shortening the course of the river. The river channel is straighter and steeper. This causes erosion to begin again and new meanders are formed.

The erosive power of the river depends on four processes at work:

1 **Hydraulic action** – water crashes into gaps in the soil and rock, compressing the air and forcing particles apart.
2 **Abrasion** – the flow picks up rocks from the bed that smash against the outside bank.
3 **Corrosion** – the water dissolves minerals in the rocks.
4 **Attrition** – where eroded rocks smash against one another, wearing them down into more rounded particles.

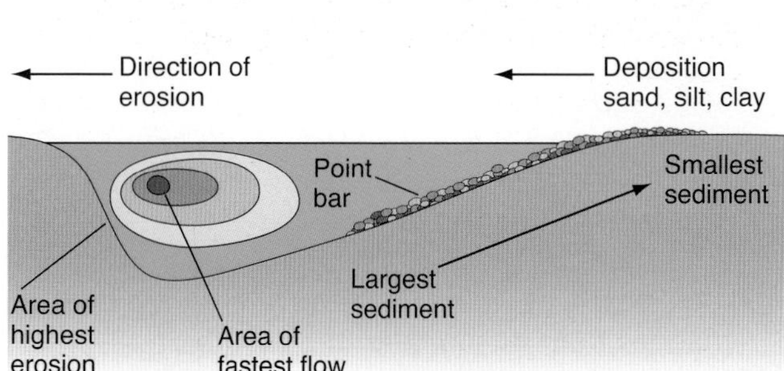


**Figure 5** Processes at work on a river meander

## The impact of human activity on river processes

The Mississippi is an example of a meandering river where river engineering in managing the river's course in one location has caused changes further downstream. The US Army Corps of Engineers has straightened the Mississippi by more than 250 km. This helps to reduce flooding and allows ships to travel quickly upstream to inland ports. However, the **revetments** (concrete riverbanks) that have been used to straighten the river have led to a reduction in river erosion and so less sediment is carried in the river. As a result, less deposition now happens at the mouth of the river, causing coastal retreat and the loss of local wildlife habitats on the river **delta**.

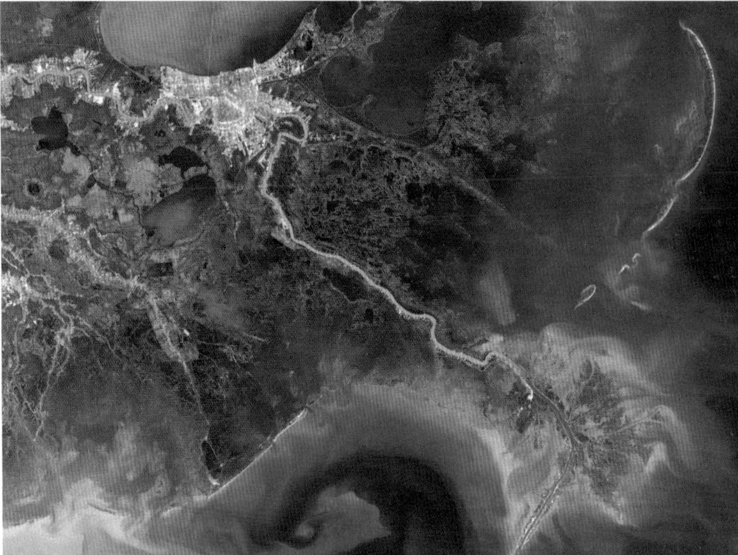

**Figure 6** Meanders on the River Mississippi, near New Orleans

**Figure 7** River straightening and concrete banking (revetments) by the United States Army Corps of Engineers

### Activity

**6** Create a set of diagrams to explain the processes causing river erosion.

**7** Match the description with the correct erosion process:
- hydraulic action
- corrosion
- attrition
- abrasion.

**a)** A gradual process that occurs at roughly the same rate at all levels of river flow.
**b)** This process needs high flow rates and large eddy currents or waves to erode the bank.
**c)** Occurs at high flow rates where the river has the power to pick up large stones from its bed. The competence of the river causes saltation of large bedload sizes causing high levels or erosion at high flow rates.
**d)** This process doesn't erode the bank of the river but it is the process by which sediment size decreases downstream.

**8** All geographers are expected to know what an ox-bow lake is. Research what happens at a river cut-off to cause an ox-bow lake. Describe the processes that lead to the formation of an ox-bow lake. Use diagrams to help with your explanation.

**9** Study Figures 4 and 6, photographs of river meanders. Explain how a river landform like a meander can affect human activity and how river processes can affect people's lives.

## How does a river landform affect people's lives in Bangladesh?

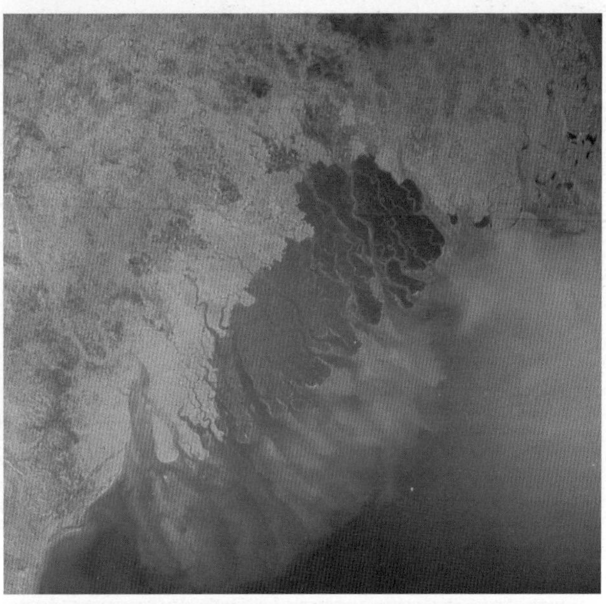

**Figure 8** Satellite image of the Ganges delta. Deltas form at the mouth of the river where silt and clay-sized sediment are deposited to create new islands in the sea

Bangladesh has a population of 139 million people. It is one of the most densely populated areas of the world, 780 people live in each km$^2$. Bangladesh is situated on the delta of the Ganges and Brahmaputra rivers. Eighty per cent of the country is less than 5 m above sea level. Figure 8 shows how the river splits into smaller streams called **distributaries** as the land flattens and the river loses erosive power.

Annual **monsoons** bring high rainfall across the vast **drainage basin** of the rivers, flooding up to a third of Bangladesh each year. As the floods recede from the eroded channels, sand banks stretch further out to sea and deposition begins again.

The constantly changing landscape of the river delta means that people live on shifting islands called 'chars'. It is usual for a family to have to move their home every year, so why is this area so heavily populated?

### Living in the region

Advantages of living in Bangladesh include the following:

- The clay and silt deposited by the river are highly fertile. Three crops a year can be grown without artificial fertilisers.
- The coastal waters are excellent for fishing.
- The land can be dredged to form lagoons, ideal for cultivating prawns for export.
- New land has no ownership so can be claimed.
- There are many natural harbours for the small fishing boats.

However, economic development is slow because:

- It is difficult to build roads and railways on land that is constantly changing.
- No settlement can be permanent.
- Industry has no raw materials as all the land is composed of alluvium.
- Land is flooded every year.
- Investment is very risky because of cyclone and flood damage.

**Figure 9** Life on the delta in Bangladesh

## What is the future for the people of the Ganges delta?

The Ganges and Brahmaputra rivers fall steeply through the mountains in their upper courses, generating high erosive power. Here the river splits, creating islands in its course, it is called **channel braiding**. This is a sign that the river is transporting large quantities of sediment. This sediment, composed of sand, silt and clay, is eventually deposited on the delta.

Dams are being constructed upstream to provide hydro-electric power and to reduce flooding. In the rapidly growing urban areas the river is also being straightened and the banks concreted. This is causing a reduction of sediment deposited downstream. With the population continuing to grow, this means land will be lost on the river delta, some of which is rich agricultural land.

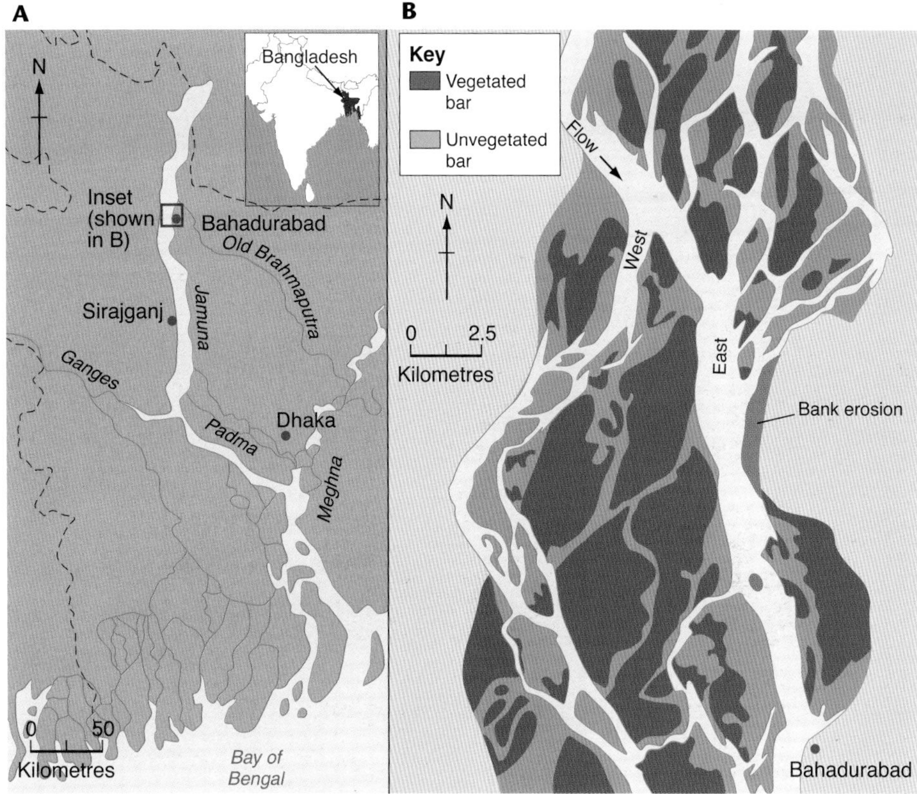


**Figure 10** A: Ganges delta; B: The high level of channel braiding on the delta

### Predictions for the future

- The population of the area will grow.
- Land will be lost on the river delta.
- Annual floods will increase in size.
- Global warming will cause sea levels to rise and the delta will be submerged as the sea advances.
- Rich agricultural land will be lost.
- Millions of people will be made homeless and migrate inland.
- Annual floods will increase in size.
- **Global warming** will cause sea levels to rise, submerging the delta as the sea advances.

### Activity

**10** Make a sketch of Figure 8. Label areas of deposition, chars and distributaries.

**11** Draw two spider diagrams, one for advantages and one for disadvantages of living in Bangladesh.

**12** How are river processes changing the lives of people on the Ganges delta?

**13** Describe the landscape of Bangladesh.

**14** Explain how the delta is formed. An annotated diagram could be used.

**15** Write an article for WaterAid (see page 103) through the eyes of a ten-year-old living on the Ganges delta. You should include why people live on the delta, the dangers of life in this constantly changing landscape and what the future could hold.

## Gullfoss Waterfall, Iceland – how landforms affect people

Gullfoss Waterfall is located in central southern Iceland, 100 km east of the capital Reykjavik. It is where the River Hvítá drops a total of 31 m in two steps. The River Hvítá is formed from **meltwater** from spectacular glaciers flowing from the country's ice sheets. This large quantity of water cascades over the falls and has great erosive power. All waterfalls have similar features as they are formed by the same processes of erosion.

**Figure 11** Gullfoss Waterfall. Both steps of the falls can clearly be seen from this viewpoint

Rapidly flowing meltwater with high erosive power

First step 11 m

Hard volcanic rock resists erosion

Second step 20 m

Soft sedimentary rock erodes easily

Undercutting of harder rock will eventually cause it to fall

Water behind the plunge pool erodes the back wall of the waterfall

Plunge pool

Gorge downstream of falls

The waterfall retreats upstream creating a gorge

**Figure 12** Features, causes and processes producing the waterfall at Gullfoss

A waterfall is caused when a band of harder rock resists the power of a river flowing over it. At Gullfoss this harder rock is a highly resistant volcanic lava. The water flowing over this step gives the river much greater erosive power to erode the rock below, in this case a soft sedimentary sandstone. The water at the bottom of the falls hits rocks that have been eroded from above and they scour the bottom of the falls to create a **plunge pool**. **Undercutting** occurs where the base of the waterfall is worn away, causing the top of the falls to become unstable. Eventually it will fracture and the rocks will fall into the plunge pool. The waterfall at Gullfoss retreats upstream on average 30 cm a year. Below the waterfall is a **gorge**. This is three km long with a depth of between 40 m and 70 m. All the rock from this gorge has been transported downstream by the River Hvítá!

## How does Gullfoss Waterfall affect people?

### Advantages

The waterfall at Gullfoss is one of Iceland's major tourist attractions with more than 300,000 visitors a year. It became famous when Sigridur Tomasson, the daughter of the landowner, threatened to kill herself by jumping over the falls to protest against the plan to destroy them as part of a hydro-electric scheme in the area. Her protest caused the government to buy the falls and turn them into a national monument.

**Figure 13** Sigridur Tomasson

Gullfoss and nearby Geyser are just 90 minutes from Reykjavik and form part of the 'Golden Tour'. Visitors to the waterfall contribute to the local economy by:

- visiting the large café and gift shop on site
- paying £45 for a day excursion from Reykjavik
- staying overnight in one of many local hotels and guesthouses.

This creates employment for the local people of the area, who in turn spend their wages on local services. Each Krona spent by tourists creates up to five Krona in the economy. This is called the multiplier effect.

The site is promoted by the Icelandic Government across the world to encourage tourism.

### Disadvantages

The peak of the tourist season is in July and August; this means that employment is only seasonal. Jobs in tourism are often poorly paid. The waterfall at Gullfoss is over-used compared with other sites in Iceland and this 'tourist honeypot' creates problems of parking, litter and footpath erosion around the site.

### Activity

**16** Use the data on visitor numbers in Figure 14 (below) to draw a graph.

**17** Describe how the numbers of tourists are changing.

**18** Describe the advantages and disadvantages of the effects of these tourists on the local area and across all of Iceland.

**19** It is always best to use a diagram in the exam to describe and explain how the waterfall was formed. Study Figure 12 on page 112 for one minute only, and then attempt to draw your own diagram of how the Gullfoss Waterfall was formed.

**20** Are all waterfalls found in the upper course of the river near to its source? Research these well-known examples of waterfalls in an atlas or on the internet:

- Niagara Falls (USA/Canada 49 m high)
- Victoria Falls (Zambia/Zimbabwe 108 m high)
- Angel Falls (Venezuela 979 m high)
- Yosemite Falls (USA 739 m high)
- Sutherland Falls (New Zealand 580 m high)

| Year | Number of tourist arrivals |
|---|---|
| 1990 | 142,000 |
| 1995 | 190,000 |
| 2000 | 303,000 |
| 2002 | 278,000 |

**Figure 14** Numbers of visitors to Gullfoss Waterfall

# Chapter 7
# Coastal processes and landforms

**KEY QUESTIONS**

- What are the processes that shape the coast?
- How are coastal landforms created?
- How can we manage conflicts between different groups of people using the coast?

## The coastal battleground

The British Isles coastline is constantly changing as the processes of coastal erosion, **transport** and deposition take place. Land is disappearing into the sea on the Yorkshire Coast at Holderness at nearly 2 m a year. In other places land is being created. When Harlech Castle on the Welsh coast was built in the thirteenth century, ships could deliver supplies if it was under siege; today it is 800 m inland.

### Wave attack

Some coasts suffer from high wave attack, while others are safer. The erosive power of the wave is controlled by **fetch**, the distance a wave travels as it builds its strength. The south-west coast of Britain is battered by strong wave attack, as the waves travel over 4,000 km across the Atlantic Ocean, slowly building up their energy. Ask any surfer where the best waves are to be found – the larger the fetch, the bigger the waves. The strength of the wind also controls the wave's energy. A sailor will tell you that the stronger the wind the higher the wave. The **prevailing wind** in Britain is from the south-west, which is the same direction as the longest fetch.

A storm attacking the Dorset coast will produce waves 10 m high, with massive erosive power. It is no surprise that the Jurassic coast of Dorset is a World Heritage Coast with some of the best coastal scenery in the world.

### Weakness of the rocks

The harder the rock the more it resists erosion. The hard chalk cliffs of the south coast resist attack, while the soft boulder clay cliffs of Yorkshire crumble away. Waves will attack any line of weakness in a rock such as:

- **joints** – small cracks found in sedimentary rocks as they contract when formed
- **bedding planes** – lines separating the layers of sedimentary rock
- **faults** – major cracks in the rock caused by earthquakes or plate movement.

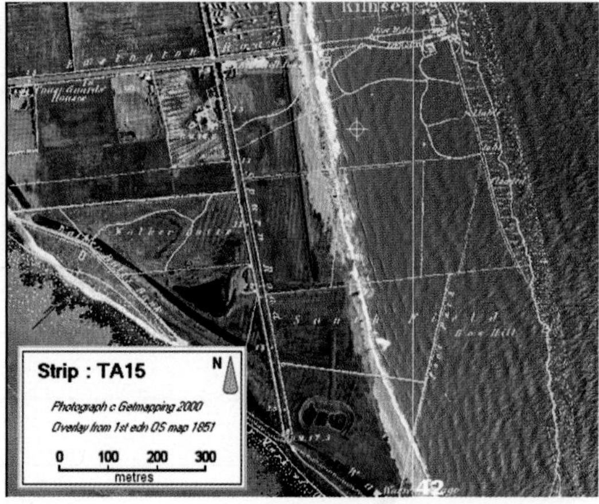


**Figure 1** Aerial photograph of Holderness coast overlaid with the 1851 Ordnance Survey map

**Figure 2** Coastal erosion in Denmark

## Coastal protection

A wide beach or wave-cut platform in front of a cliff will cause a wave to lose energy as it slows towards the shore. The wave will hit the shingle in front of the cliff and its energy will be lost. The cliff may only be attacked at the highest tides. Many coasts are protected by coastal protection schemes which involve putting barriers in front of the coast to absorb the power of the wave attack. There are many different types of barrier. They are all expensive, and stopping erosion on one stretch of coast will increase erosion in another.

**Figure 3** Dorset chalkland coast, south-west coast

**Figure 4** Holderness coast boulder clay, east coast

### Activity

**1** Copy and complete columns 2 and 3 in the table below.

| Factor controlling erosion | Cause of high erosion | Cause of low erosion |
|---|---|---|
| Fetch | Long distance | Short distance |
| Prevailing wind | | |
| Wind speed | | |
| Rock hardness | | |
| Weaknesses in rock | | |
| Level of natural protection | | |
| Level of beach engineering | | |

**2** Study Figures 3 and 4. Answer these questions in full sentences.
- **a)** Which coast has the greatest fetch?
- **b)** Which coast suffers most wave attacks?
- **c)** Which of the two rocks is harder?
- **d)** Which rock has most lines of weakness?
- **e)** On which coast is erosion greater?

**3** Rank the seven factors controlling erosion from the table on the left. Start with the most important factor first as rank 1.

**4** Explain why the chalk cliffs in Figure 3 are much higher than the boulder clay cliffs at Holderness in Figure 4.

## Coastal erosion: processes and landforms

The processes of coastal erosion are the same as those that cause river erosion:

- **Hydraulic action** – water crashes into lines of weakness in the cliff pushing air further into the gap and forcing the rock apart.
- **Abrasion** – waves use rocks and pebbles as ammunition against the cliff to wear it away.
- **Corrosion** – minerals in the rock dissolve in the water.
- **Attrition** – eroded rocks smash against one another and are worn down into smaller, more rounded pieces.

### Eroding hard rock cliffs

On a cliff composed of hard rock such as granite, limestone or chalk, abrasion is a relatively slow process. Hydraulic action is the dominant erosional process. This process relies on any weaknesses in the rock caused by bedding planes, faults and joints. It opens up gaps in the cliff for further erosion to take place. Corrosion also occurs, but more slowly, and is more significant in limestone and chalk cliffs.

Waves will erode the base of the cliff by undercutting it to produce a **wave-cut notch**. The cliff will eventually be undermined causing a rockfall onto the beach. (This is similar to the way in which a waterfall moves upstream to create a gorge.) As the cliff retreats, a gently sloping area is left behind; this is called a **wave-cut platform**.

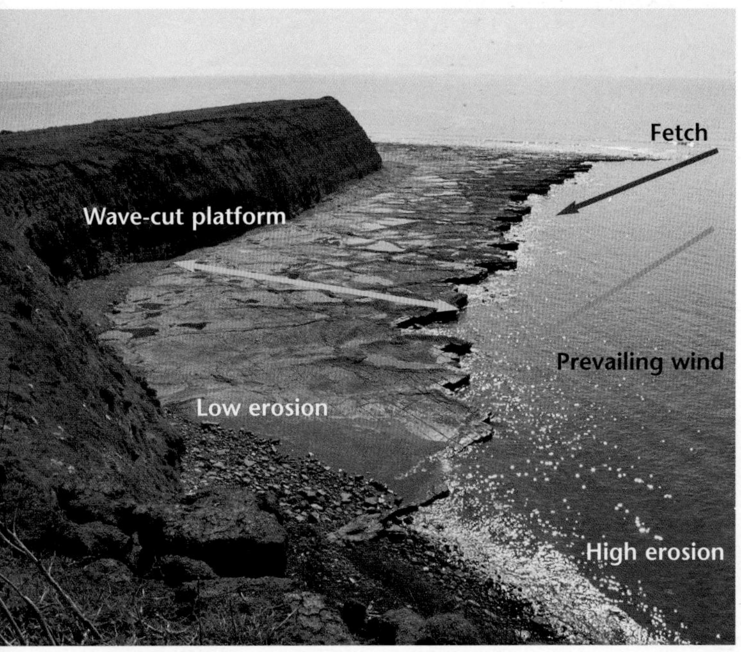


**Figure 5** Wave-cut platform on the Dorset coast

**Figure 6** Old Harry stack, Studland peninsula, Dorset coast

On a coast where the rock is heavily faulted by earth movements or has bedding planes, more spectacular coastal landforms are produced. Erosion starts by punching a hole in the cliff to form a **cave**. This erodes further – many caves have large rocks in them ideal for abrasion. If the cave is in a narrow headland, waves can attack from both sides to form an **arch**. Eventually the top of the arch will become unstable and fall, leaving behind a **stack**. The stack will reduce in height leaving a **stump**, all that is left as the cliff line retreats.

## Eroding clay cliffs with soft rock

On a cliff composed of soft rock such as clay, abrasion is the dominant erosion process. The rock quickly crumbles as it is hit by the power of the waves carrying pebbles from the beach. Hydraulic action adds to the fast erosion rates. Corrosion also occurs but it is not so important as the other processes are so rapid.

Clay cliffs also suffer from **rotational cliff slumping**. Rain seeps through the upper layers in the cliff to the clay below and the cliff becomes unstable as wave attack erodes the base. The cliff slumps towards the beach as the clay layer slumps. These types of cliff are very unstable and are dangerous to walk across.

**Figure 7** Rotational cliff slumping at Naish Farm, near Barton-on-Sea, Dorset

## Activity

**5** Study Figure 6. Explain in detail how Old Harry stack on the far right of the photograph was formed. Include all the following terms in your description:

**fetch wave attack prevailing winds chalk bedding planes joints fault lines abrasion hydraulic action erosion cave arch stack**

**6** Use the internet to search for an image of 'The green bridge of Wales'. Print a copy, describe its location and then annotate the image to show how the bridge was formed.

**7** You could use Old Harry Rocks as a case study of a coastal landform. However, sometimes an exam question will ask you how it affects people as well as to explain how it was formed. Look closely again at Figure 6. Explain how the footpath going out along the headland has been formed and how the landform might affect people.

**8** Compare the erosion of hard cliffs with that of softer clay cliffs.

## Coastal deposition: processes and landforms

Depositional processes create new coasts. As rivers transport their load towards the sea, sediment is constantly being deposited at its mouth. The two satellite images below (see Figures 8 and 9) show Cardigan Bay, Wales. New land is being created across the mouth of the river by sediment moving along the coast to the South and from rivers as they flow into their **estuaries**. Both images are remarkably similar because they are produced by the same coastal depositional processes.

### Transporting beach sediment

Material moves along the beach by a process called **longshore drift**. Waves nearly always hit a beach at an angle, not straight on. Pebbles on the beach are therefore pushed up and across the beach by each wave. When the water from the wave drains back to the sea it does so straight down the beach, pulling pebbles with it. There is, therefore, a movement of pebbles along the beach in the same direction as the waves that hit it. On some days the pebbles will move in one direction. When the wind direction changes the pebbles will move in another. Over the course of a year, the pebbles will travel in the direction of the prevailing wind. On the coast of Wales, the prevailing wind is from the south-west. Longshore drift transports the beach material up the coast from south to north.

**Figure 8** Harlech spit

**Figure 9** Ynyslas spit (near Borth)

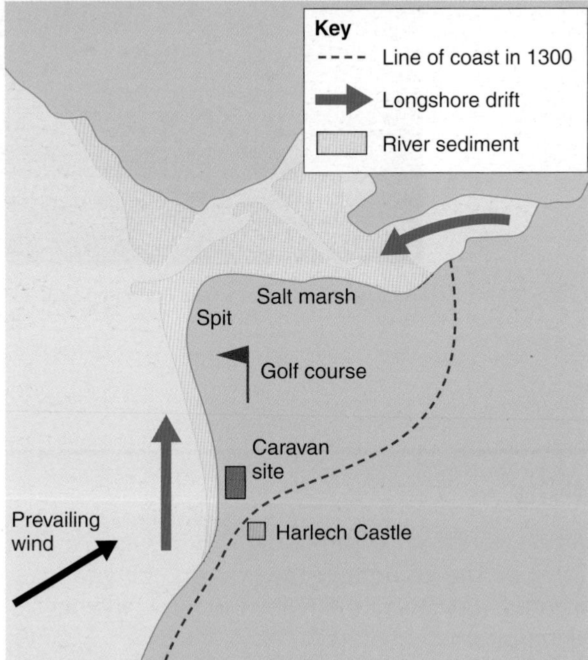


**Figure 10** The formation of Harlech spit

## Coastal depositional landforms

A **spit** is the name given to the narrow stretch of land created when longshore drift carries sediment across the mouth of a river. Salt marshes often develop on the landward side of the spit as the river deposits mud in the calm water found there.

A **tombolo** is where a stretch of land is created by longshore drift connecting the coast to an island. The most famous example in Britain is Chesil Beach, which joins the island of Portland to the Dorset coast. It stretches for more than 15 km in a south-easterly direction. The beach is up to 200 m wide and has a maximum height of 14 m. Trapped behind the beach is a **lagoon**, known as The Fleet. Look closely at the sediment on the beach and you will see it is perfectly sorted by longshore drift.

When longshore drift moves material to stretch right across a river's mouth a **bar** forms. At Slapton Lea in Devon water passes under the bar to reach the sea. The Slapton Lea beach and lagoon is a nature reserve.

**Figure 11** Chesil Beach looking north-west from Fortuneswell, Isle of Portland

### Activity

**9** Study Figures 8 and 10.

**a)** Create your own case study of a coastal landform by using the information on Harlech. It should include:
- a description of the landform
- an explanation of how it was formed (don't forget to mention longshore drift)
- the advantages and disadvantages to the people of the area
- effects on groups of people such as birdwatchers, golfers, holiday makers, local teenagers working in the cafés at Harlech, local business owners, and English Heritage which owns Harlech Castle.

**b)** Compare your case study with that of a river landform, Gullfoss Waterfall (see page 112).

**10** Draw a diagram to explain the process of longshore drift. Include two arrows: one for the swash – the direction a wave travels up the beach; and one for the backwash – the direction that the water takes as it returns to the sea.

**11** Find Spurn Head in an atlas. This is Britain's longest spit and is on the East coast. In which direction do you think longshore drift carries the beach sediment along this stretch of coast? Explain your answer.

**12** Look closely at Figure 11. How would you study the movement of pebbles along Chesil Beach? Write a hypothesis, a description of how you would do the study and what equipment you would need.

**EXAMTECHNIQUE**

## Describing a location

### Borth – a surfer's paradise?

When you are asked to describe the location of a place, try to give details of both direction and distance. The paragraph below is a good model answer.

*Borth is a small tourist resort six miles north of Aberystwyth on the west coast of Wales. It looks out onto Cardigan Bay. The local economy is heavily dependent on tourism. Borth attracts visitors because of its long, unspoilt, clean sandy beach. To the north is the Dyfi estuary. The Ynyslas nature reserve and study centre is situated within the dune systems at the head of the spit at the mouth of the river. The lagoon upstream of the spit is a tidal area where new land is being created by the deposition of silt and clays transported by the river.*

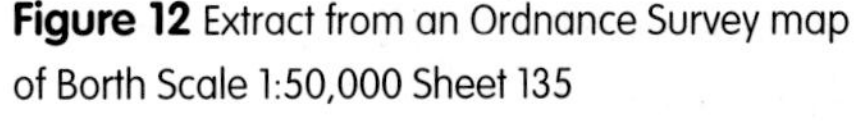

**Figure 12** Extract from an Ordnance Survey map of Borth Scale 1:50,000 Sheet 135

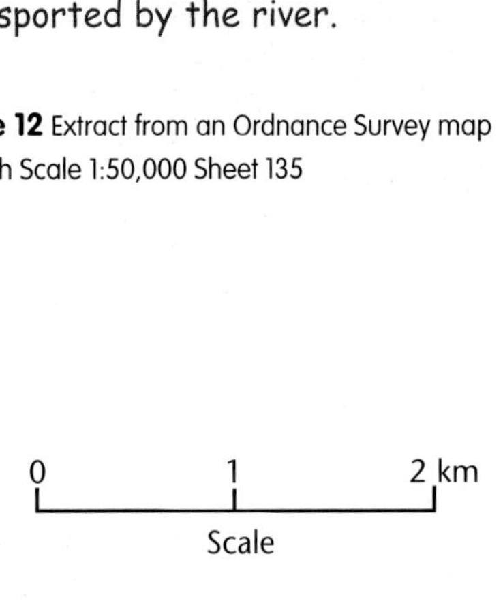


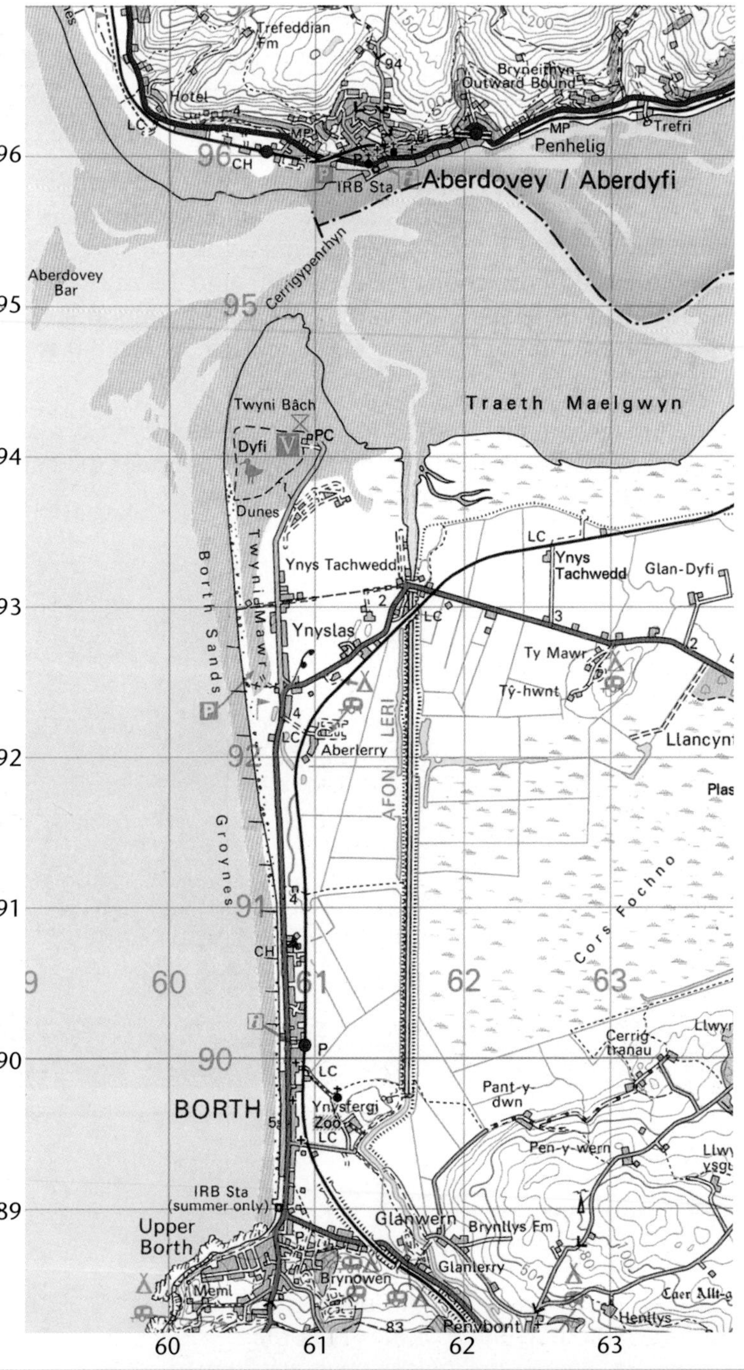


### Should a surfing reef be built?

Ceredigion County Council and the Welsh Assembly Government are currently discussing funding for the construction of a 'surfing reef' to run parallel to Borth beach. This project would be part of Borth's new coastal defence system costing £7 million. The reef would be constructed from 700 tonnes of sandbags positioned 300 m out to sea. It would create higher waves but also deflect waves coming at an angle to the beach so that they hit the shoreline straight on.

**Figure 13** Borth Beach in February. Too cold for surfing? The old groynes which were built to stop longshore drift to the north can clearly be seen

**Ray Quant, Borth councillor** has given the surfing reef his backing, claiming environmental as well as tourism benefits: 'I am convinced that this option should be accepted by the council because it will do so much for the town as well as help with coastal protection.'

**Martyn Sayer, who runs Stormriders surf shop in Aberystwyth** is another big fan of the scheme: 'It is a good natural sea defence and it would improve waves for surfers. You'll have a boomerang-shaped device underwater making the waves stand up. You normally have to go out and go looking for the sandbars but with the reef you could be out there surfing straight away. It would be the first one in England or Wales; I am sure it would attract surfers from all over the world wanting to try it out.'

**Duncan from Machynlleth** says a reef would bring several benefits: 'A curved artificial reef would make the waves stand up and straighten (great for surfers) and stop the drift of pebbles away from Borth where they are currently protecting the town. Also a side benefit would be a great nursery area for juvenile fish, crustaceans and other sea wildlife. So all round a great idea! I look forward to hearing if it is given the go ahead. Also to counter the "safe bathing for others" – the waves would be breaking further out and the shore waters would therefore be calmer. That's the whole idea – protect Borth from the waves! Also as an economic boon – have you seen the ghost town of Borth through the winter? The swell will be there all year, cold weather doesn't put off surfers!'

**Julie from Warwickshire** supports the plans for an artificial reef: 'I have been visiting Borth regularly for the last three years and I love the place. The people are warm and friendly and the beaches at both Borth and Ynyslas are fantastic. I would welcome an artificial reef to the town. The residents rely so much on tourism and give fully of their time to ensure that we have a good holiday. My only concern is the parking and being able to drive down the street in one go ... and not constantly having to pull over.'

**Graham Hesp from Birmingham** has this to say: 'With the Government and the Environment Agency now favouring natural erosion rather than building huge new coastal defences, it is pleasing to hear of people applying some lateral thinking to the obvious problems at Borth.

'However, a great deal of research will need to take place to consider the inevitable environmental impact upon Ynyslas and the Dyfi Estuary. Work undertaken by private land owners further up the coast, between Barmouth and Morfa Dyffryn, has caused a frightening change to the nature of the beach and shoreline. Whilst I applaud the thinking behind the Borth reef, I fear that the impact elsewhere will unfortunately cause it to sink before they can surf.'

**Anne Wells from Warrington** raises several concerns about the proposals for an artificial reef: 'I have just become aware, through the internet, of plans to create an artificial reef at Borth which could attract "thousands of surfers". We have enjoyed peaceful holidays at Borth for a number of years after initially living there for a year in 1974/5 while my husband did an MA at Aberystwyth.

'I would question how Borth could possibly accommodate all these surfers both in terms of car parking, overnight accommodation and the congestion that they could cause to the one narrow street that serves the town. Also how would the new type of waves affect ordinary swimmers of all ages on what is a beautiful safe beach for bathing?'

**Figure 14** Opinions of the scheme taken from a web page discussion group. Viewpoints taken from www.icwales.co.uk

## Activity

**13** Read the viewpoints of the people in Figure 14 and fill in your own copy of the table below.

| | Advantages | Disadvantages |
|---|---|---|
| Environmental effects | | |
| Economic effects | | |

**14** Using your knowledge of coastal processes and landforms, explain how reducing the transport of beach material by longshore drift will affect places such as Ynyslas to the north of Borth beach.

**15** Would you allow the artificial reef at Borth to be constructed? The comments from interested people show that there is conflict between the surfers and the tourism industry who want the scheme, and conservationists who think it is a bad idea. Write a detailed report to the Borth Town Council outlining the reasons for your decision. You must include both sides of the argument and their relative merits. Use the information from Figure 14 to help you.

## Going Further

### Coastal protection in Lyme Regis, Dorset

Lyme Regis is a popular tourist resort on the Jurassic Coast of Dorset. It is a World Heritage Site and the soft cliffs are a magnet for fossil hunters. The sea wall, The Cobb, was built in the thirteenth century to provide shelter for the town and create a safe harbour. It is now one of the town's most famous and popular tourist attractions.

The coast at Lyme is one of the most unstable and actively eroding stretches of coastline in Britain. The soft rocks of the cliffs are particularly prone to rotational cliff slumping. A number of destructive landslides and collapses in the sea wall have happened and action was needed to save homes, businesses and even the lives of local people.

#### Recent coastal management in Lyme Regis

**Phase I** included a new sea wall and promenade in the east of the town at the mouth of the River Lim. It was completed in 1995. Urgent stabilisation work was needed in several locations, including the slopes above the beach, in 2003–2004.

**Phase 2** of the coastal management scheme for Lyme Regis will cost £17 million and include:

- adding extra sand and shingle to the beaches
- extension of The Cobb at Beacon Rocks
- realignment of North Wall Rockery
- building two concrete jetties either end of the main beach
- renewing the sea wall
- cliff stabilisation works
- Cobb Road improvements and general landscape design.

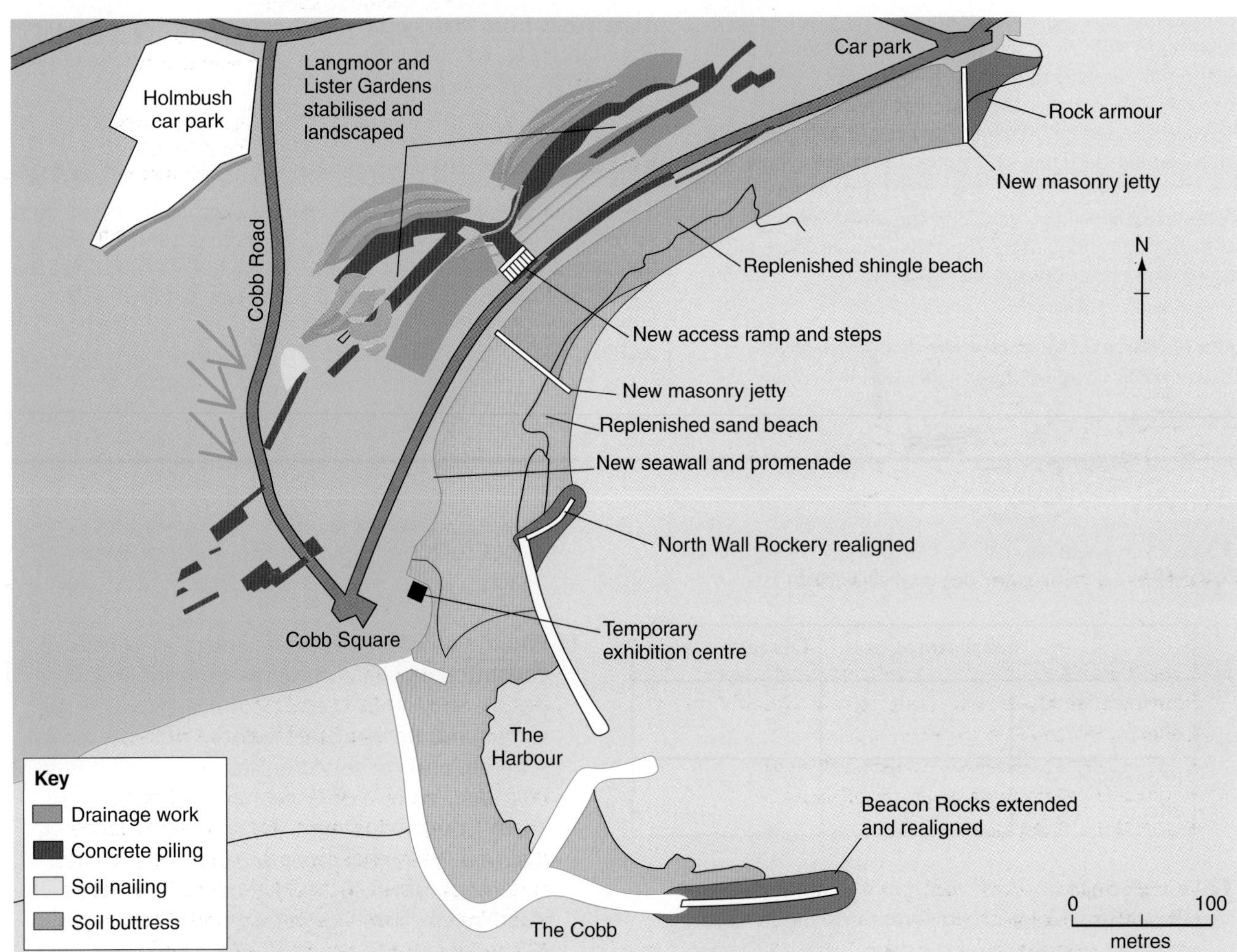


**Figure 15** Phase 2 coastal management at Lyme Regis

Apart from greater cliff stability, the advantages of the Phase 2 scheme will also:

- allow a bigger sand and shingle beach, and access along the beach even at high tide which will protect the sea wall
- increase shelter from rough seas in the harbour and bay
- produce a new promenade along the beach front at Cart Road
- improve access to the town via Cobb Road.

**Figure 16** Starved beach at Lyme Regis

The coastal cliffs that provide spectacular views and abundant fossils are among the most unstable stretches of coastline in the country – and Lyme Regis sits right on top of them.

This diagram shows a simplified cross-section of the land at Lyme Regis and the processes that make it unstable.

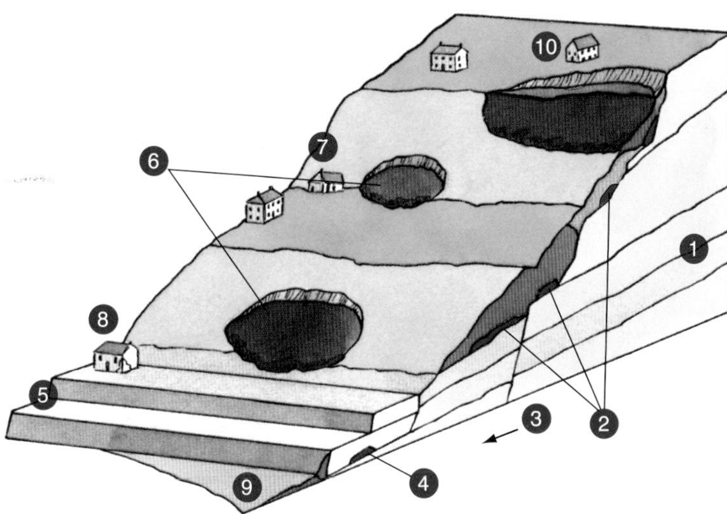


1. The rock deep below the town is made up of strong layers of limestone with shale in between. This bedrock is stable and solid.
2. On top of the bedrock there are unstable slippery clays, green sand, plus other muddy and sandy material. This moves over the strong limestone layers below to form landslides.
3. The layers slope down towards the sea making it easier for the unstable top layer to move during wet weather.
4. The sea eats away at the bottom of landslides and undermines the land. This prevents a toe or plug forming – and means that the unstable material keeps moving.
5. Coastal defences built to protect the town have been undermined by the sea.
6. Localised shallow land slips take place in areas of weakness – usually in arc shapes.
7. Buildings subside as the land moves.
8. Property becomes damaged due to movement of the land behind.
9. The beach is depleted, offering little protection against the sea.
10. Houses under threat as the landslide expands inland.

**Figure 17** The causes of coastal erosion at Lyme Regis

**16** Copy the outline of the coast at Lyme Regis from Figure 15. Try to be as accurate as possible. Add the following information to your map:
- direction of prevailing wind – south-west
- direction of greatest fetch – south-west
- direction of longshore drift.

**17** In what ways has the building of the original Cobb affected the natural coastal processes, the tourist beach and the cliffs of Lyme Regis?

**18** Describe how the new extension of The Cobb at Beacon Rocks and the realignment of the North Wall Rockery affect the coastal landforms of the area.

**19** Write a report to West Dorset District Council commenting on the short- and long-term effects of the scheme for residents, local businesses, tourists and harbour users. It should also include whether you think the plan is sustainable and whether the £17 million investment is value for money.

# Chapter 8
# Problem-solving exercise

## Managing the coastal environment in Essex

The coastline of Essex is one stretch of the UK coastline which is vulnerable to erosion and the risk of flooding due to sea level rise. In this chapter, you will look at the arguments for and against various coastal management strategies. Then you will prepare a plan to manage the Essex coastline near Walton-on-the-Naze.

**Your enquiry ...**

What processes affect this coastline?

Why have these coastal defences been built here?

Is the land valuable?

Are there alternative, cheaper or more effective ways of managing this coastline?

**Your decision ...**

How should this stretch of coastline be managed in the future?

**Figure 1** Sea defences under threat of erosion at Walton-on-the-Naze, Essex

## Part A: what coastal processes affect the Essex coastline?

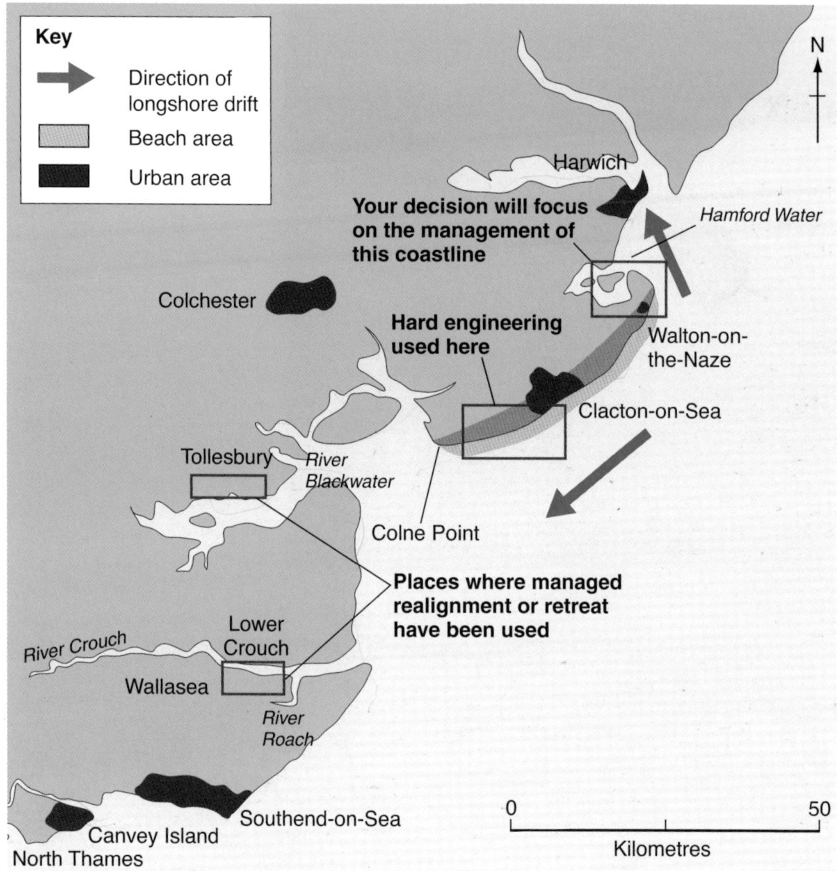


**Figure 2** Location of the enquiry on the Essex coast

The Essex coastline is in serious danger of coastal erosion and flooding. The coastline is sinking and sea levels are rising due to climate change. The combined effect is that the sea along this coastline is rising at between 4 mm and 6 mm per year.

The rivers that flow through Essex deposit mud in their estuaries and on the mud flats and salt marshes of this coast. These mud flats absorb wave energy and provide a natural defence against coastal floods. Over the last 500 years people have built earth embankments to further protect this coastline from erosion and some salt marshes have been drained and converted to farmland. The question is: what should be done in the future? Should the earth embankments be strengthened to keep out the rising sea? Or should farmland be flooded to recreate the natural buffer of salt marshes and mud flats?

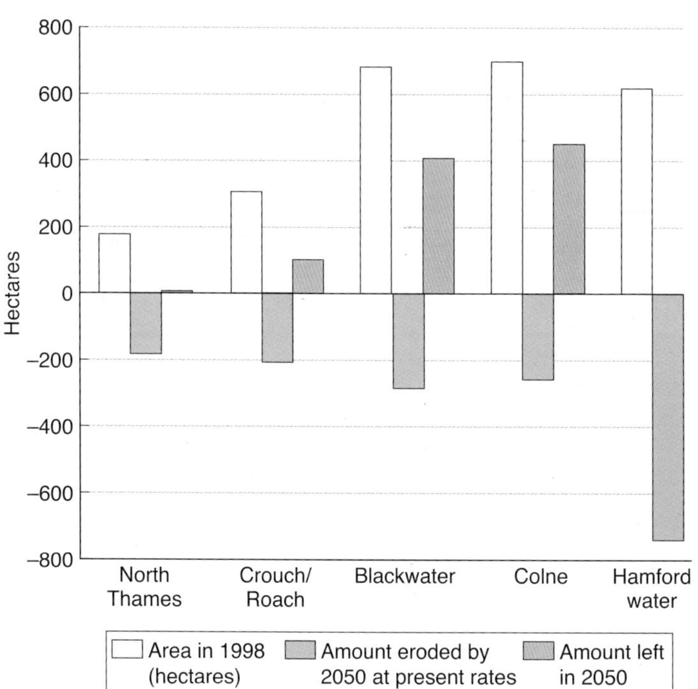


**Figure 3** Future erosion of salt marsh in Essex estuaries

### Activity

**1** Use Figure 2. Describe:

**a)** the location of Hamford Water

**b)** the location of Colne Point

**c)** the direction of longshore drift between Walton-on-the-Naze and Colne Point.

**2** Use Figure 3. Complete the following:

**In 1998 the largest salt marsh was in the .......... estuary. This salt marsh covered an area of ..... hectares. The salt marsh which is likely to lose most land by erosion is ........ By 2050 there will be only two salt marshes larger than 400 hectares each. These are ...... and .......**

**3** Describe three different ways that the sea can erode the coastline.

**Figure 4** Coastal landform at Sandy Point, near Point Clear, Essex

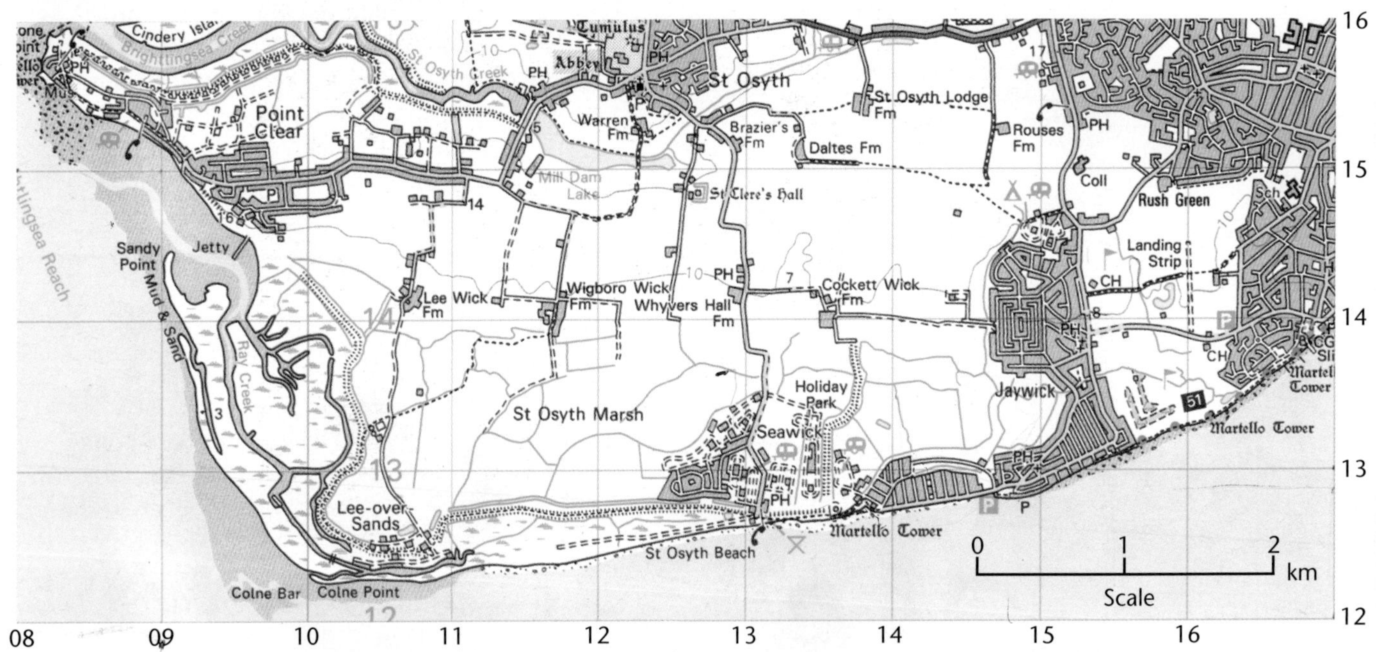


**Figure 5** An Ordnance Survey extract of Colne Point and Jaywick. Scale 1:50,000 Sheet 169

## Activity

**4 a)** Identify the landform shown in Figure 4.

**b)** Explain how this landform has been created by the process of longshore drift. You could use diagrams to help.

**5** Study Figure 5.

**a)** Give a four-figure reference for Sandy Point.

**b)** What is the straight line distance from Colne Point (100123) to the car park in Jaywick (147128)?

**c)** Give three pieces of map evidence to suggest that this coastline is used by tourists.

**6** Use the Ordnance Survey extract, Figure 5.

**a)** Give a six-figure reference for the road junction at A on Figure 6.

**b)** Suggest what can be seen at B on Figure 6.

## Part B: what coastal management strategies are available?

There are three coastal management strategies being used to protect the salt marshes and beaches of the Essex coastline:

- hard engineering such as building sea walls and rock groynes
- managed realignment – also known as managed retreat
- sediment nourishment of salt marshes and mud flats.

### Hard engineering

Sea defences such as timber or rock groynes and concrete sea walls can be built to protect the coast from erosion. New fish-tailed **groynes** and an artificial reef have recently been built at Jaywick, and they can be seen in Figure 6. Hard engineering is expensive. Groynes cost at least £200,000 each and sea walls cost about £5,000 per m. Sea level rise means that such defences would need to be constantly maintained, strengthened and eventually replaced with larger structures. For this reason hard engineering is usually used only where the land that is being protected is particularly valuable. Hard engineering can also disrupt the natural coastal processes causing problems at a neighbouring stretch of coastline.

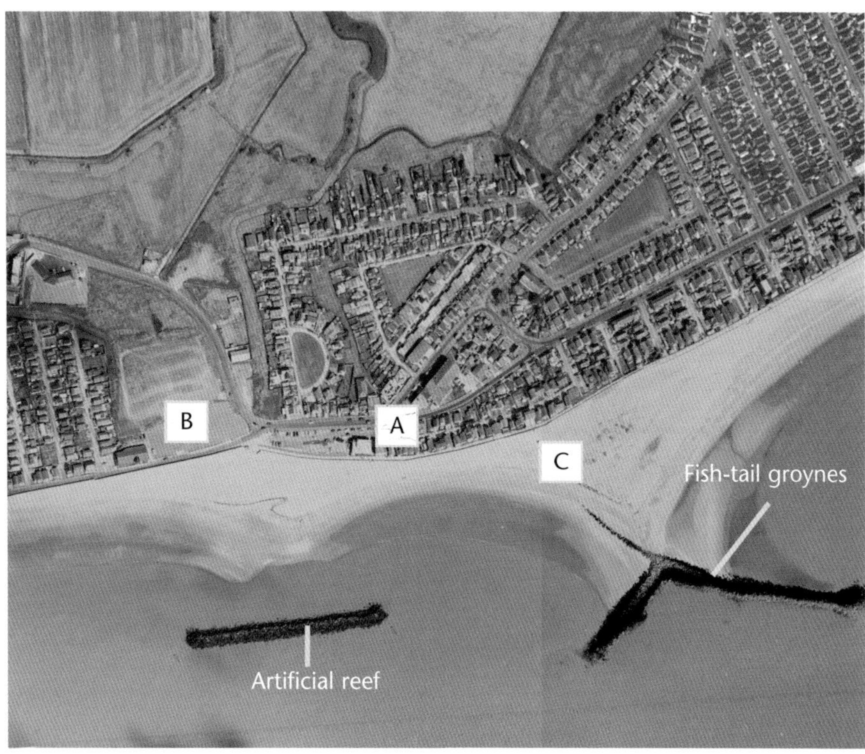


**Figure 6** An aerial photograph of Jaywick and its hard-engineering sea defences

### Activity

**7** Compare the width of the beach at C on Figures 5 and 6. What does this suggest about the success or otherwise of the hard engineering?

**8** Use Figure 6.
**a)** State the direction of longshore drift.
**b)** Explain how you can tell from the evidence in the photograph.
**c)** Suggest how the fish-tail groynes might affect coastal processes at Colne Point.

**9** Make a sketch of Figure 6. Label it to show how the hard engineering has protected this stretch of coastline.

### Sediment nourishment

Extra sediment is taken from the sea bed and dumped either in the estuary or on top of the mud flats. This extra sediment reduces the energy of the waves, providing a natural barrier to erosion. This method has very few negative effects unless too much sediment is placed on the mud flat. If this happens then molluscs that live in the mud can be killed and the food chain damaged.

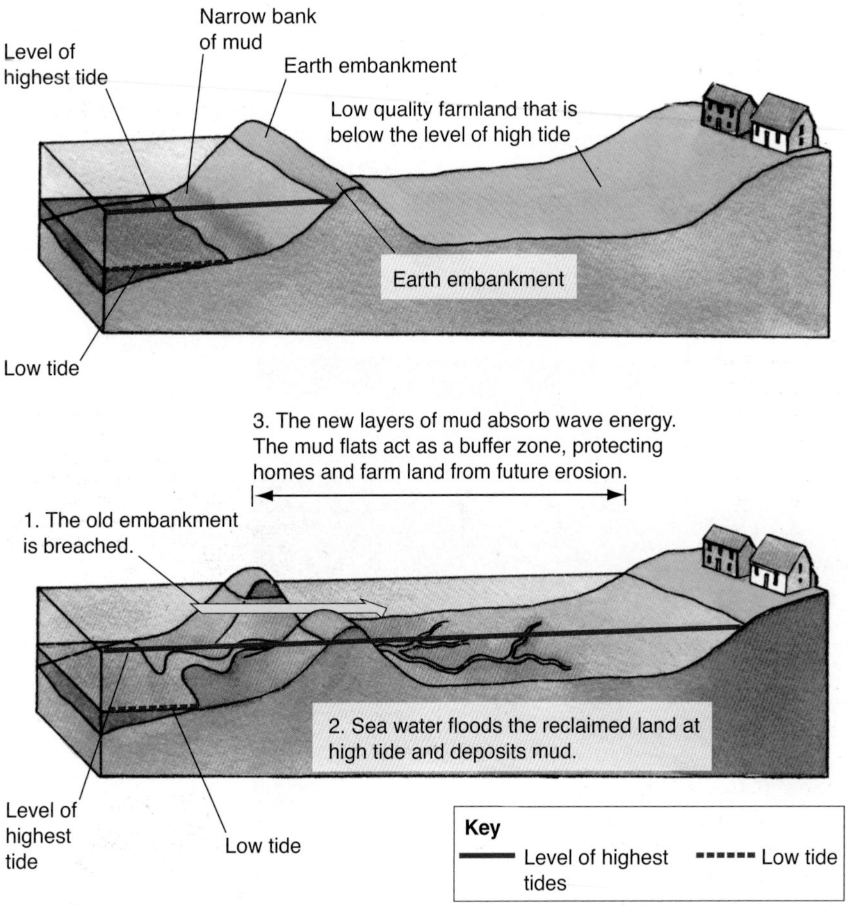

**Figure 7** How managed realignment protects the coast

### Managed realignment

This is a controversial management technique because it allows land to be flooded by the sea (see Figure 7). Sections of the old earth embankments are breached. This means that holes are made to allow the high tide to flood farmland. The invading sea water deposits mud, recreating mud flats and salt marshes that act as a natural buffer against erosion. These new salt marshes absorb wave energy and create a new habitat suitable for wading birds.

This technique has already been used near Tollesbury on the River Blackwater, and at Wallasea (see Figure 2 on page 125). Not everyone is convinced that this is a good strategy because no one can be sure what long-term effects realignment of the coast might have on coastal processes.

## Activity

**10** Use the information in part B. Copy and complete the following table. Make sure you describe and explain each advantage and disadvantage.

| | **Advantages** | **Disadvantages** |
|---|---|---|
| Hard engineering | Valuable homes are protected and local residents feel reassured. | |
| Sediment nourishment | | The process has to be repeated in a few years because ... |
| Managed realignment | | Loss of reclaimed land. Some people would object to this because ... |

## Part C: how should this stretch of coastline be managed in the future?

The Government believes that managed realignment is the most **sustainable** strategy for many parts of the Essex coastline. But not everyone agrees. The residents of Walton-on-the-Naze are concerned about the poor state of repair of their sea wall and groynes. They would like them to be repaired so that the erosion of the cliffs (known as 'the Naze') is slowed. Four points of view are explained below:

It's not only our town that is under threat. Erosion is damaging the local areas of natural beauty that attract visitors to the town. The cliffs themselves are a tourist attraction and a Site of Special Scientific Interest (SSSI) due to over 50 million years of geological history and the large number of fossils they contain. We should protect this natural heritage from the sea using hard engineering.

Local geologist

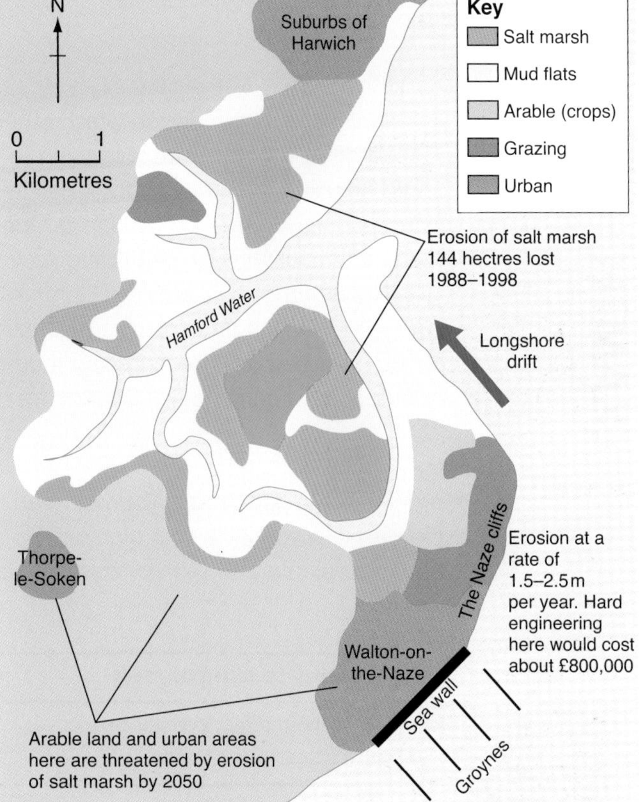


**Figure 8** The coastal processes affecting the Naze and Hamford Water

The cost of maintaining the sea defences along many parts of the Essex coast is greater than the benefits of those defences. The land is poor-quality farmland. It doesn't make sense to keep paying for the maintenance of structures like groynes.

Government (DEFRA) spokesperson

The only way that we can guarantee the protection of the Naze is with groynes. They trap sand and build up a beach which will then absorb the energy of the waves and protect the cliffs. We know that this works because the Victorians used them; the groynes they built not only slowed the rate of erosion but actually caused deposition, creating new land! But the wooden groynes have rotted away and the sand has been washed away leaving the cliffs very vulnerable. With nothing to protect them they're just being lost to the sea. This is very bad news for us.

Local resident

The erosion of the cliffs at the Naze supply sediment which is then moved northwards into Hamford Water by longshore drift. As sea levels rise it is very important that the mudflats of Hamford Water continue to be supplied with fresh sediment. These mudflats act as a natural barrier to wave energy that would otherwise cause flood damage and loss of land in the estuary.

County council spokesperson

### Activity

**11** Describe your plan to manage the coastline at Walton-on-the-Naze. You may include diagrams. You must also justify your plan, explaining why you think your management plan is the best course of action.

**EXAMTECHNIQUE**

## Getting the best mark for part C of this problem-solving exercise

Part C is your opportunity to suggest how this section of the Essex coastline should be managed.

Step 1

The first thing to do is to decide which of the three options has most advantages and least disadvantages. Are you going to recommend:

- hard engineering: maintain the existing line of the coast by building bigger, stronger sea defences at Walton-on-the-Naze and protect the local community
- sediment nourishment: depositing new sediment on the beaches at Walton-on-the-Naze and in the estuary of Hamford Water
- managed realignment: allowing the existing defences around Hamford Water to be breached and creating new mud flats that will make a buffer zone. This would protect a large area from future floods.

Step 2

In order to get a good mark, you will need to justify your plan. This means explaining why you think your plan will be successful. Make a copy of the following table and evaluate your plan by completing the comments.

| Key questions to ask yourself | Comments |
|---|---|
| How will my plan affect coastal processes on neighbouring sections of coastline? | |
| Is this plan sustainable? What are the long-term benefits or problems? | |
| Why is this plan better than the alternatives? | |

**Tip 1**

Consider how your plan will affect different communities. Coastal management schemes can have benefits for some communities while others feel their needs are being ignored. In order to get a good mark for this problem-solving exercise you need to consider the impact of your scheme on different communities.

For example, suppose you suggest strengthening the old sea wall and repairing the groynes at Walton-on-the-Naze.

*Strengthening the sea wall at Walton-on-the-Naze would benefit the local residents because …* (consider how the residents would feel). *It might also cause local house prices to … because …. Local businesses such as guesthouses would benefit because ….*

*By repairing the damaged wooden groynes …* (consider the effect of depositon on the beach here, and also the rate of erosion of the Naze cliffs). *This would also benefit the local community because …* (consider the effect on rates of erosion and how this might reduce the risk of flooding).

*However, by repairing the groynes at the Naze the amount of sediment transported northwards by longshore drift would be reduced. This means less sediment would be deposited in Hamford Water and rates of erosion of the salt marsh and mud flats here would accelerate. This would affect farming communities in this area by ….*

To conclude this justification you would need to explain why you think the needs of one community outweigh the needs of another.

# Unit 3 People and Place

## Chapter 1 The Big Picture

In 2005, New Orleans was flooded by a storm surge of water created by Hurricane Katrina. A total of 1,836 people were killed by Katrina. Much of the city is built below sea level. The city is built on the soft sands of a river delta and as these dry out the city gradually sinks. This subsidence, combined with rising sea levels, means that New Orleans is at increasing risk of more floods.

About 3.6 billion people (or 60 per cent of the world's population) live within 60 km of the coast. This is likely to rise to 6.4 billion (75 per cent of the world's population) by 2030.

Between 1900 and 2000 the world's sea levels rose on average by two mm per year. This is mainly due to the melting of ice on the world's continents, especially in Greenland and Antarctica.

Of the world's 23 mega-cities, sixteen are in coastal regions and are at risk from further sea-level rise. Many of these cities are in Less Economically Developed Countries (LEDCs) and are continuing to grow rapidly. This photograph was taken in Mumbai, the world's second largest city, during the floods in August 2005.

The Thames flood barrier was completed in 1982 to protect London from tidal surges of water coming up the river from the North Sea. Tide levels are rising in the Thames estuary by about six mm per year (60 cm in 100 years). A major flood would perhaps cause damage to the value of £30,000 million and would certainly cause many deaths.

This unit focuses on:

- the places where people live
- the quality of the urban and rural environment in which they live.

How will the quality of rural and urban lifestyles change? What is their geographical future?

## Global patterns of urban development

The United Nations estimates that by 2008 more than half of the world's population will be living in **urban** areas: larger towns and cities.

The **urban population**, which is the percentage of people living in towns and cities, has grown steadily since the 1950s:

- 30 per cent in 1950.
- 47 per cent in 2000.
- It is estimated that it will reach 60 per cent by 2030.

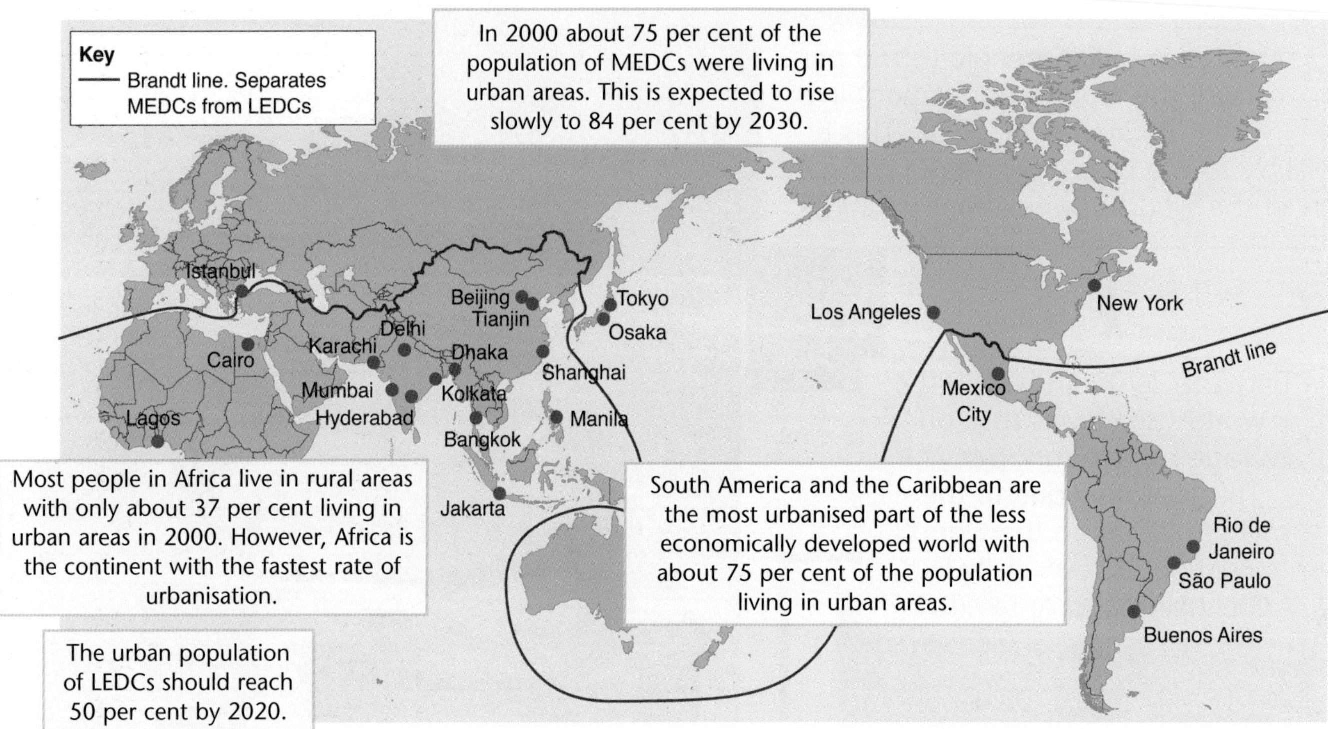


**Figure 1** Map showing the location of those cities which are forecast to be mega-cities by 2015

The process by which the population of a country becomes more urban and less rural is known as **urbanisation**. Urbanisation causes the physical and human growth of towns and cities. Urbanisation is caused by a combination of two factors:

- The migration of people from rural to urban areas.
- The **natural increase** of the urban population due to there being more births than deaths.

Urbanisation is currently much more rapid in the **Less Economically Developed Countries (LEDCs)** than in **More Economically Developed Countries (MEDCs)**. LEDCs tend to have faster-growing populations than MEDCs and they also have a larger number of people moving from rural to urban areas.

The urban areas of MEDCs grew rapidly during the Industrial Revolution. In the 1950s most of the world's largest cities, such as New York, Tokyo, Paris, London and Moscow, were in MEDCs. However, as cities have grown larger and become more crowded they can also become less comfortable places in which to live. Some people prefer to live in smaller towns, or even in the countryside, so they have moved out: a process known as **counter-urbanisation**. So the trend since the 1960s has been for some of the world's larger cities to lose some people while others move in. As a result the population growth of most large MEDC cities has slowed right down in comparison with many LEDC cities.

| Rank order | 1950 | Pop (m) | 1975 | Pop (m) | 2000 | Pop (m) | 2015* | Pop (m) |
|---|---|---|---|---|---|---|---|---|
| 1 | New York | 12.3 | Tokyo | 19.8 | Tokyo | 26.4 | Tokyo | 26.4 |
| 2 | | | New York | 15.9 | Mexico City | 18.1 | Mumbai (Bombay) | 26.1 |
| 3 | | | Shanghai | 11.4 | Mumbai (Bombay) | 18.1 | Lagos | 23.2 |
| 4 | | | Mexico City | 11.2 | São Paulo | 17.8 | Dhaka | 21.1 |
| 5 | | | São Paulo | 10.0 | New York | 16.6 | São Paulo | 20.4 |
| 6 | | | | | Lagos | 13.4 | Karachi | 19.2 |
| 7 | | | | | Los Angeles | 13.1 | Mexico City | 19.2 |
| 8 | | | | | Kolkata (Calcutta) | 12.9 | New York | 17.4 |
| 9 | | | | | Shanghai | 12.9 | Jakarta | 17.3 |
| 10 | | | | | Buenos Aires | 12.6 | Kolkata (Calcutta) | 17.3 |
| 11 | | | | | Dhaka | 12.3 | Delhi | 16.8 |
| 12 | | | | | Karachi | 11.8 | Manila | 14.8 |
| 13 | | | | | Delhi | 11.7 | Shanghai | 14.6 |
| 14 | | | | | Jakarta | 11.0 | Los Angeles | 14.1 |
| 15 | | | | | Osaka | 11.0 | Buenos Aires | 14.1 |
| 16 | | | | | Manila | 10.9 | Cairo | 13.8 |
| 17 | | | | | Beijing | 10.8 | Istanbul | 12.5 |
| 18 | | | | | Rio de Janeiro | 10.6 | Beijing | 12.3 |
| 19 | | | | | Cairo | 10.6 | Rio de Janeiro | 11.9 |
| 20 | | | | | | | Osaka | 11.0 |
| 21 | | | | | | | Tianjin | 10.7 |
| 22 | | | | | | | Hyderabad | 10.5 |
| 23 | | | | | | | Bangkok | 10.1 |

**Figure 2** Mega-cities: cities with a population greater than 10 million (m = million) * = projected

## Activity

**1** Use Figure 1 to complete the following:

**MEDCs have a *larger / smaller* proportion of people living in urban areas than LEDCs. Of the less economically developed regions:**

- **......................... is the most urbanised**
- **......................... is experiencing the most rapid urbanisation.**

**2** Use the text on page 132 to make your own definitions for **urbanisation** and **counter-urbanisation**.

**3** Explain the two factors that led to the more rapid urbanisation in LEDCs.

**4** Use Figure 1.

**a)** Describe the distribution (see page 143) of the world's mega-cities in 2015.

**b)** Use Figure 2 to draw graphs of the population growth in:

i) New York

ii) São Paulo.

**c)** Describe and explain the trend of each graph.

**5** Use the opening page of this chapter to explain why many climate scientists are concerned about the distribution of the world's urban population.

Unit 3

# Chapter 2
# Inequality in the urban environment

**KEY QUESTIONS**

- How is quality of life different from standard of living?
- How and why do quality of life and standard of living vary between different groups of people?
- Why do different groups of people live in different parts of a city?
- What factors help to determine what kind of housing people live in, and where this is located?

## How is quality of life different from standard of living?

**Standard of living** is a measure of the relative wealth of individuals or families. It can be measured using **Gross National Income (GNI)** or **GNP** figures. Knowing someone's level of qualifications or their occupation can also be an indicator of income. Where **unemployment** figures are high, standard of living is usually low.

**Quality of life** is a measure of the happiness and contentment of an individual or family. Quality of life can be influenced by a number of factors such as:

- Personal or family health. Long-term health problems such as asthma, heart disease, obesity, or HIV can have serious impacts on someone's enjoyment of their life.
- The quality of the environment. If the neighbourhood is noisy, congested with traffic, or suffers a high crime rate then an individual might describe their quality of life as relatively poor even if their income was quite high.

**Figure 1** How do our urban surroundings influence quality of life?

## How do we use quality of life and standard of living indicators?

Figure 2 provides evidence of variations in standard of living and quality of life that exist within England.

An understanding of these patterns is important so that the government can target those areas that need most support. For example, knowing that fewer people in the northern regions of England are successful in their attempt to stop smoking means that the National Health Service can target these areas with extra funds.

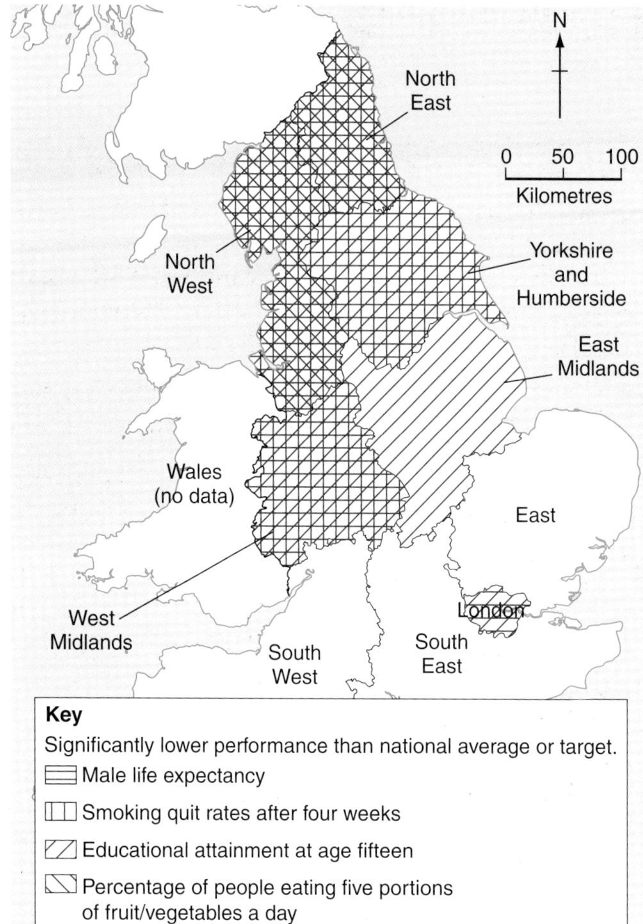


▲ **Figure 2** Regions of England with lower than average standard of living and quality of life using four indicators. Source: Association of Public Health Observatories (2006)

| | Infant mortality per 1,000 births | Adult male obesity (%) | Unemployment (% 2005) |
|---|---|---|---|
| Average for England | 5.4 | 20.8 | 4.6 |
| North East | 5.7 | 24.7 | 5.5 |
| North West | 5.8 | 20.3 | 4.8 |
| Yorkshire & Humberside | 6.4 | 22 | 4.2 |
| East Midlands | 5.3 | 23.2 | 4.3 |
| West Midlands | 6.6 | 22.2 | 4.6 |
| East | 4.4 | 19.5 | 3.9 |
| London | 5.7 | 18.2 | 6.7 |
| South East | 4.4 | 20.3 | 3.7 |
| South West | 4.8 | 18.9 | 3.5 |

◀ **Figure 3** Regional variations in quality of life and standard of living. Cells coloured red are significantly worse than the national average. Cells coloured blue are significantly better than the national average

### Activity

1 Study Figure 2. It provides four pieces of evidence that could be used as indicators to investigate inequality within urban areas.
   **a)** Work in pairs. For each indicator in the key, decide whether quality of life or standard of living is being measured. Explain your choice.
   **b)** Suggest two more indicators of standard of living, and four more for quality of life.
   **c)** Use the indicators you have come up with and those in Figure 2 to explain the difference between standard of living and quality of life.

2 **a)** Choose a suitable technique to either graph or map the data in Figure 3.
   **b)** Describe the regional patterns you see in Figures 2 and 3.

3 **a)** Summarise: which regions have the poorest and which the best quality of life?
   **b)** Evaluate: what data would be useful if you wanted to investigate regional variations in standard of living?

4 **a)** What connection, if any, exists between the unemployment figures in Figure 3 and the educational attainment indicator in Figure 2?
   **b)** Suggest reasons for this apparent connection.

# Investigating standard of living and quality of life in an MEDC: Newcastle-under-Lyme, Staffordshire

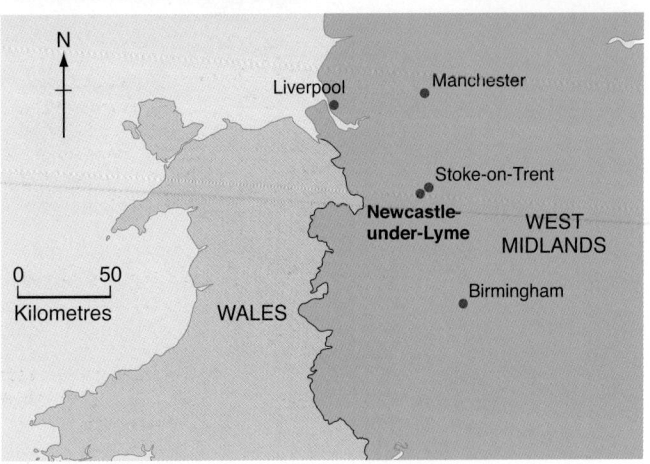


▲ **Figure 4** The location of Newcastle-under-Lyme

Newcastle-under-Lyme is a large town in Staffordshire in the West Midlands. It has a population of around 125,000 people. Our key enquiry questions are:

- How do quality of life and standard of living vary from one part of the urban area to another?
- Do these variations form any distinctive patterns? For example, are inner urban areas better or worse than suburban areas?
- Do different groups of people live in different parts of the urban area? For example, do some residential areas have more families and fewer retired people?

You can use similar enquiry questions to investigate inequality in your own local area.

**www.communityhealthprofiles.info/index.php**

This website describes quality of life in all local authorities in England. These Community Health Profiles describe key health data for each local authority commenting on whether the figures are above or below average.

**Figure 5** Fact file on Newcastle-under-Lyme ▶

Some key facts about standards of living and quality of life in Newcastle-under-Lyme compared with other urban areas in the West Midlands.

- Life expectancy varies considerably from one part of the town to another.
- GCSE examination results are significantly lower than the national average.
- There is a high rate of recorded violent crime, with nearly 3,000 incidents in a single year.
- The number of elderly people who are supported by family and voluntary organisations to live independently in their own home is significantly higher than the national average.
- It is estimated that less than twenty per cent of adults eat a healthy balance of fruit and vegetables, and a quarter of adults are obese.
- Deaths or serious injury due to traffic accidents are significantly lower than average.

| | | | Wards of Newcastle-under-Lyme | | | | |
|---|---|---|---|---|---|---|---|
| | Averages | | Inner urban areas | | | Suburban wards | Commuter village |
| **Percentages** | England | Newcastle-under-Lyme | Cross Heath | Silverdale | Town | Westlands | Loggerheads |
| Unemployed people aged 16–24 | 26 | 31 | 41 | 32 | 31 | 22 | 23 |
| People of working age with a limiting long-term illness | 13 | 16 | 20 | 20 | 15 | 12 | 13 |
| General health: good | 69 | 66 | 60 | 60 | 62 | 72 | 72 |
| General health: fairly good | 22 | 23 | 26 | 26 | 24 | 20 | 20 |
| General health: not good | 9 | 11 | 14 | 13 | 14 | 8 | 8 |

**Figure 6** Evidence of variations in standard of living and quality of life in Newcastle-under-Lyme. Source: 2001 Census

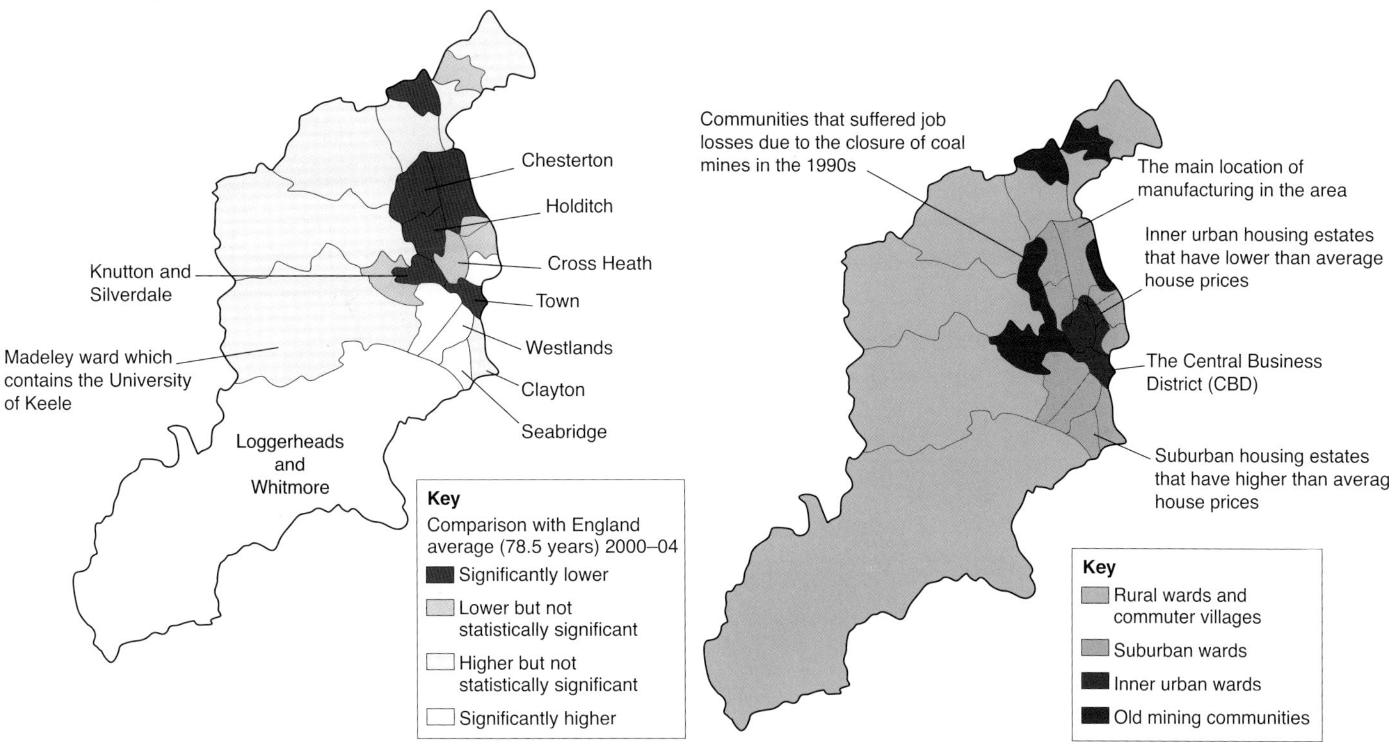


**Figure 7** Variations in life expectancy in Newcastle-under-Lyme

**Figure 8** A map of wards in Newcastle-under-Lyme

## Activity

**5** Use Figure 4 to describe the location (see page 154) of Newcastle-under-Lyme.

**6** Study Figure 5. Use it to make:
**a)** two positive statements about quality of life in Newcastle-under-Lyme
**b)** two negative statements about quality of life in Newcastle-under-Lyme.

**7** Use Figure 7 to describe the distribution (see page 143) of wards with:
**a)** significantly lower life expectancy
**b)** significantly higher life expectancy.

**8** Use Figures 6 and 7 to complete the table below which compares local averages to averages for England.

**9** **a)** Choose suitable techniques to produce a series of graphs to illustrate the data in Figure 6.
**b)** Summarise the main differences in quality of life between the inner urban, suburban and commuter village areas of Newcastle-under-Lyme.

| | **Cross Heath (inner urban)** | **Westlands (suburban)** | **Loggerheads (commuter village)** |
|---|---|---|---|
| Life expectancy | | Significantly higher | |
| Unemployed people (aged 16–24) | Significantly higher | | |
| People of working age with a limiting long-term illness | | Slightly lower | |
| General health: good | | | Slightly higher |

## Housing tenure in Newcastle-under-Lyme

Do different parts of Newcastle-under-Lyme have different patterns of **housing tenure**?

Housing tenure refers to the ownership of the home. The main categories are:

- owner occupied
- rented from a private landlord
- **social housing** which is rented from a not-for-profit organisation such as a housing association or the local authority.

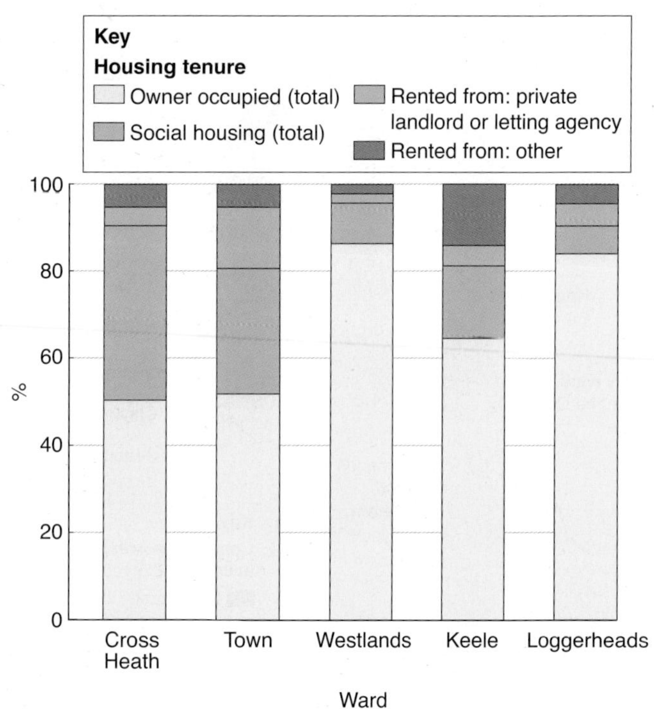


**Figure 11** Housing tenure in five wards of Newcastle-under-Lyme

### Activity

**10** Describe the housing in each photograph (Figures 9, 10 and 12) using these headings:
- Type (terraced, semi-detached, detached)
- Density
- Age.

**Figure 9** Town ward in Newcastle-under-Lyme's inner urban zone. OS map ref: 848456

**Figure 10** Baldwin's Gate is part of Loggerheads' ward. This is a commuter village on the western edge of Newcastle-under-Lyme's suburbs. OS map ref: 793402

**Figure 12** Westlands' ward is one of Newcastle-under-Lyme's suburban zones. OS map ref: 843448

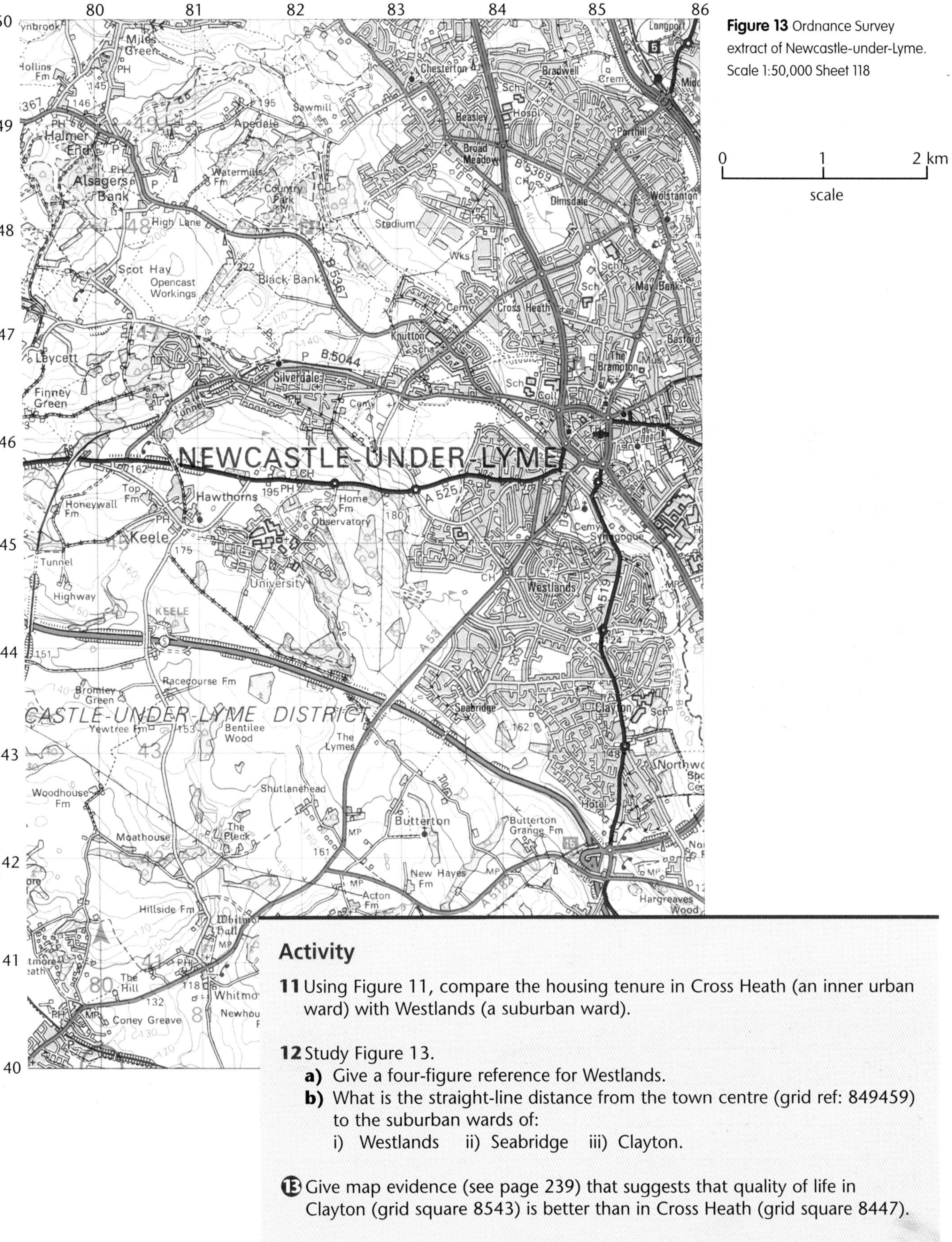


**Figure 13** Ordnance Survey extract of Newcastle-under-Lyme. Scale 1:50,000 Sheet 118

## Activity

**11** Using Figure 11, compare the housing tenure in Cross Heath (an inner urban ward) with Westlands (a suburban ward).

**12** Study Figure 13.

**a)** Give a four-figure reference for Westlands.

**b)** What is the straight-line distance from the town centre (grid ref: 849459) to the suburban wards of:

i) Westlands ii) Seabridge iii) Clayton.

**13** Give map evidence (see page 239) that suggests that quality of life in Clayton (grid square 8543) is better than in Cross Heath (grid square 8447).

## Who lives where in Newcastle-under-Lyme?

Do different groups of people live in different parts of Newcastle? Do some parts of the town have:

- more highly qualified residents (which would indicate a higher standard of living, as people with higher qualifications usually have better-paid jobs)?
- more families or more elderly residents than average?

**www.statistics.gov.uk** This is the official website of the UK National Census. Use the Neighbourhood Statistics link on the homepage to search the site using postcodes. The data in Figure 14 is available on this site.

| | Newcastle - under-Lyme | Inner urban wards | | Suburba n wards | Rural wards | |
|---|---|---|---|---|---|---|
| | Average | Cross Heath | Town | Westlands | Keele | Logger - heads |
| **Age groups** | | | | | | |
| 0–4 years | 5.25 | 6.42 | 3.95 | 5.12 | 1.03 | 4.86 |
| 5–15 years | 13.37 | 14.13 | 7.57 | 13.78 | 2.91 | 12.9 |
| 16–19 years | 5.33 | 5.8 | 5.03 | 4.37 | 24.78 | 4.33 |
| 20–44 years | 34.07 | 33.39 | 41.63 | 27.11 | 60.89 | 27.19 |
| 45–64 years | 25.08 | 23.1 | 19.85 | 28.05 | 6.43 | 33.37 |
| 65 years and over | 16.91 | 17.17 | 21.96 | 21.58 | 3.95 | 17.35 |
| **People aged 16–74 with:** | | | | | | |
| No qualifications | 34.32 | 46.15 | 28.95 | 21.97 | 3.05 | 22.93 |
| Highest qualification attained level 3 (equal to A level) | 8.81 | 5.92 | 13.22 | 8.06 | 67.39 | 7.83 |
| Highest qualification attained level 4/5 (equal to a degree) | 15.49 | 9.57 | 22.16 | 32.16 | 19.47 | 25.67 |

**Figure 14** Age structure and qualifications in five wards in Newcastle-under-Lyme

### Activity

**14** Use Figure 14 to complete the following table:

| Compared with Newcastle-under-Lyme average | Cross Heath | Town | Westlands | Keele |
|---|---|---|---|---|
| % of population of school age (5–15) | Similar | | | |
| % of population younger adults (20–44) | | | | Significantly higher |
| % of population aged 65 and over | Slightly higher | | Significantly higher | |
| % of adults with no qualifications | Significantly higher | | | |
| % of population with a degree | | | | |

**15** Use evidence from Figures 11 and 14 to compare Cross Heath (an inner urban ward) to Westlands (a suburban ward).

**16** Choose three pieces of evidence from Figures 11 and 14 that suggest that Keele ward contains a university.

## Going Further

### How education standards shape our cities

Parental choice over education for their children has become a significant factor that determines who lives where in the modern UK city. For many parents the standard of local education is an important factor when choosing the location of their family home. The **catchment areas** of successful primary or secondary schools become desirable areas in which to live. As more parents try to buy houses in the catchments of these schools, house prices begin to rise. The opposite trend may also be true: the catchments of less successful schools are less desirable to parents, and house prices in these areas remain at lower levels.

**www.upmystreet.com**
You can use this website to find data such as the school performance statistics and average house prices shown in Figure 15 in your own urban area.

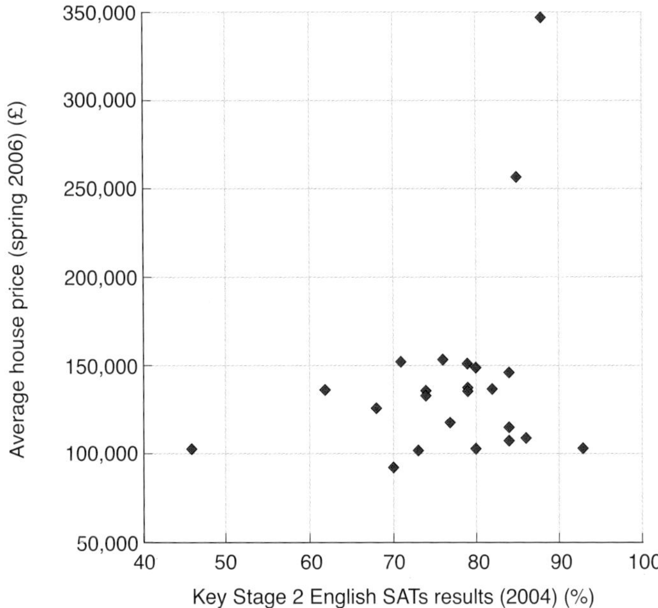


**Figure 15** Scattergraph to show the relationship between house prices and Key Stage 2 English SATs results in Newcastle-under-Lyme

**17** Study Figures 15 and 16. Working in groups:

**a)** Investigate the links between:
- house price and deprivation score
- house price and primary school score.

**b)** Suggest reasons for the links you have found. Remember that this region was affected by the loss of jobs in coal mining and manufacturing during the 1980s and 1990s.

| Ward | Average house price (£) (spring 2006) | KS2 English SATs results (2004) |
|---|---|---|
| Talke | 92,563 | 70 |
| Knutton and Silverdale | 93,568 | 38 |
| Holditch | 101,815 | 73 |
| Bradwell | 103,062 | 93 |
| Chesterton | 103,464 | 46 |
| Silverdale and Parksite | 103,529 | 80 |
| May Bank | 108,046 | 84 |
| Ravenscliffe | 108,956 | 86 |
| Wolstanton | 115,033 | 84 |
| Porthill | 117,686 | 77 |
| Cross Heath | 126,467 | 68 |
| Audley and Bignall End | 133,906 | 74 |
| Clayton | 135,658 | 74 |
| Kidsgrove | 136,502 | 62 |
| Butt Lane | 136,502 | 79 |
| Madeley (Keele community) | 137,205 | 82 |
| Town | 138,079 | 79 |
| Thistleberry | 146,335 | 84 |
| Newchapel | 148,826 | 80 |
| Westlands | 151,168 | 79 |
| Halmerend | 152,082 | 71 |
| Seabridge | 153,184 | 76 |
| Loggerheads | 256,000 | 85 |
| Baldwin's Gate | 346,000 | 88 |

**Key**

| | | |
|---|---|---|
| Lowest quality of life | | Significantly higher levels of deprivation |
| | | Slightly higher levels |
| | | Slightly lower levels |
| Highest quality of life | | Significantly lower levels of deprivation |

**Figure 16** House prices and Key Stage 2 English results in Newcastle-under-Lyme

# Chapter 3
# Investigating access to urban services

**KEY QUESTIONS**

- How are different services distributed in an urban area?
- How and why does access to services vary between different groups of people?

## What do we mean by urban services?

One advantage of living in a large urban area is that you can get access to a range of useful services:

- Leisure and sports facilities such as swimming pools or tennis courts.
- Cultural venues such as museums, galleries and theatres.
- Health services such as clinics and hospitals.
- A range of schools, colleges and universities providing parents with choice.
- Places of worship for a variety of faiths.
- Specialist shops and services such as travel agents and solicitors.
- A variety of public transport services including bus, train and underground.

This chapter examines the distribution of some services in the city of Barcelona, Spain. It also investigates why some groups of people in Barcelona have better access to these services than others.

**Figure 1** The location of Barcelona

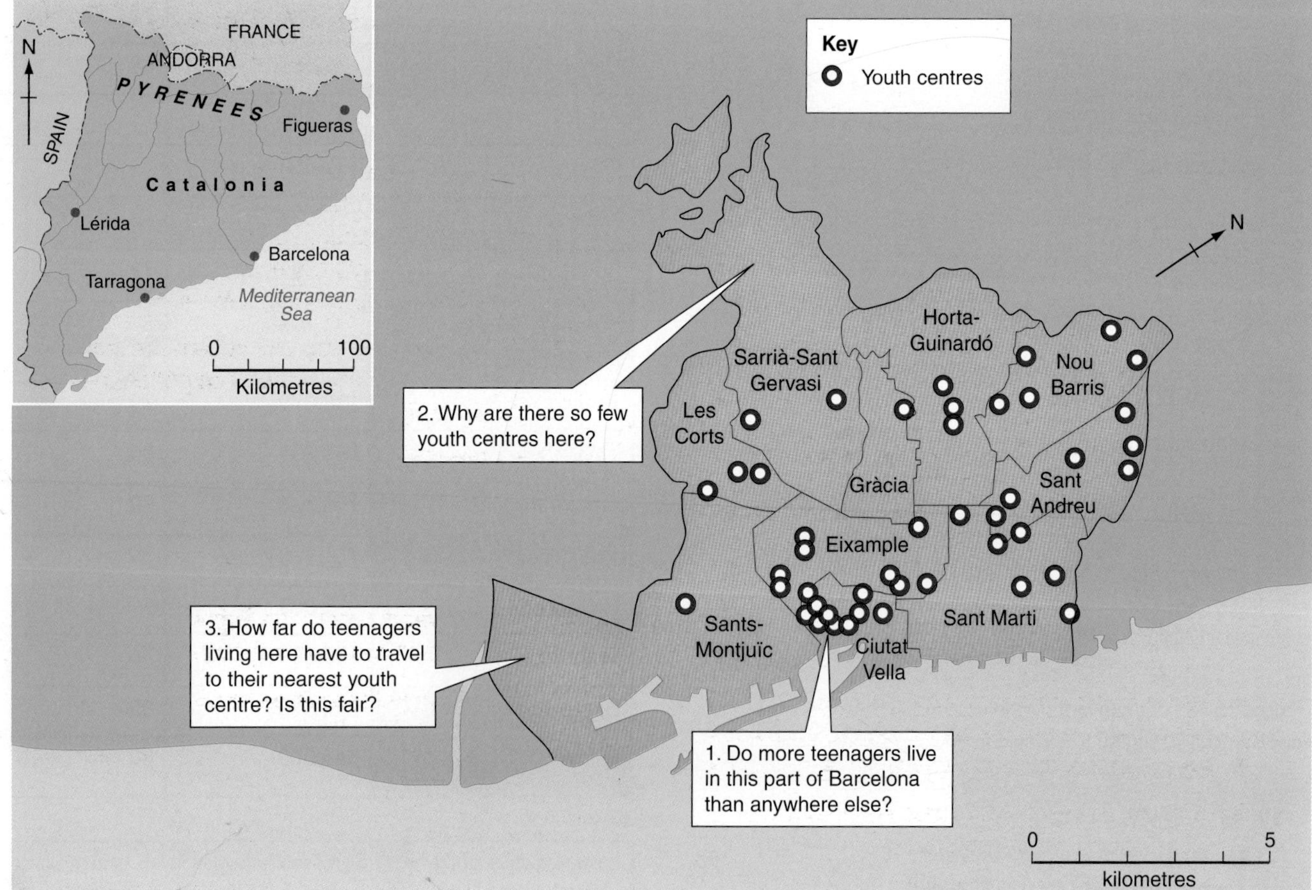


**Figure 2** Youth centres in Barcelona (see www.bcn.es/english/ihome.htm)

**Activity**

**1** Suggest two reasons why some districts have more youth centres than others.

## Barcelona, Spain – Does everyone have equal access to urban services?

People living in larger cities such as Barcelona have more choice of services than people living in the countryside: but do all city dwellers have equal access to urban services? In this case study we will see that some groups of people have better access to urban services than others. This may be for one of two reasons:

- The services are not distributed evenly through the urban area. So, for example, people living in a central district may have better access to theatres and museums than people living in a distant suburb of the city.
- Some services are more expensive than others, and not all groups of people can afford them.

### Activity

**2** Match the four distribution patterns shown in Figure 3 to the following terms:
- random
- regular
- linear
- clustered

**3** Use Figure 2 to complete this description of the distribution of youth centres in Barcelona:

**There is a ............ pattern in the city centre with a large group of youth centres in ..................... The rest of the youth centres have a ........... pattern with very few centres in districts such as .......... and ............ whereas districts such as ............ have more.**

**4 a)** Match the following services to their likely distribution pattern:
- motorway service stations • clustered
- high street banks in a town • regular linear
- primary schools in a large town • regular

**b)** Suggest reasons why these services are distributed in this way.

**EXAMTECHNIQUE**

### Describing distributions

To describe a distribution is to describe how similar things are spread across a map. Geographers are interested in the distribution of natural features such as forests, volcanoes or habitats, as well as human features such as settlements, hospitals or sporting facilities and other urban services.

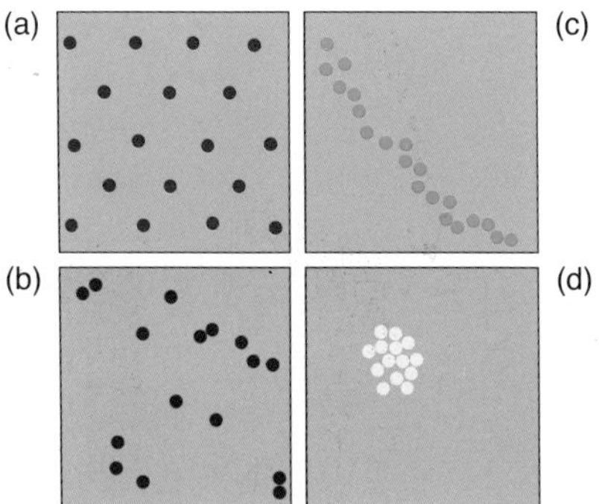


**Figure 3** Distribution patterns

Describing a distribution requires you to do two things.

1. You need to describe where on the map the features are located. For example, a lot of the youth centres marked on Figure 2 are in the Ciutat Vella (or old city of Barcelona), whereas there are very few in Sants-Montjuïc.
2. You need to describe any pattern the features might make. These distribution patterns are shown in Figure 3:
   - **Regular**, where the features are more or less equally spaced.
   - **Random**, where the features are scattered across the map at irregular distances from each other.
   - **Clustered**, where the features are grouped together into only one part of the map.

   In addition to these three main patterns, some features make a **linear** pattern if they all fall along a line.

## Multicultural Barcelona and the distribution of services for ethnic groups

Barcelona is a large city with a population of more than 1.5 million people. The surrounding districts are also urban, so its overall size is greater than four million people. The city grew rapidly during the 1970s and 1980s, attracting migrants from Spain and abroad. Like many large European cities, it has a diverse multicultural population, and the city has sizeable populations of people descended from:

- Mexico and other Spanish-speaking Central and South American countries
- parts of Asia, especially Pakistan and China
- various African countries, but especially Morocco
- other European countries.

**Figure 4** Halal butchers in El Raval provide a service for the Muslim population of the district

Barcelona's ethnic groups tend to be concentrated in the **inner urban** districts of the city. The district of El Raval, in the Ciutat Vella (the old city centre), has a sizeable immigrant population: 27.6 per cent of the population are foreign migrants compared with 7.2 per cent for Barcelona as a whole. Muslims from Morocco and Pakistan may choose to live here because they have better access to particular services that are also clustered in this part of Barcelona. For example, Ciutat Vella has six of Barcelona's ten mosques, and three of these are in El Raval. The district also has many shops catering for the Muslim population such as halal butchers and stores offering internet or telephone connections to all parts of the globe. It also has video rental stores that specialise in Asian films.

However, an alternative explanation for the concentration of Moroccans and Pakistanis in El Raval is that this is one of the cheapest districts of Barcelona in which to live. Many immigrants from these countries do poorly paid work and cannot afford to live in other, more expensive parts of the city.

### Activity

**5** Describe the distribution (see page 143) of mosques in Figure 5. Make sure you use the relevant words from the following list:
- regular
- random
- linear
- clustered
- distribution.

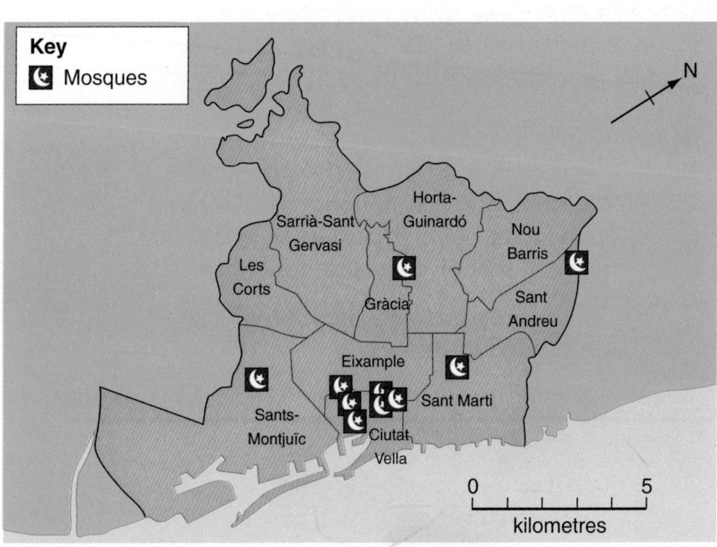


**Figure 5** The distribution of mosques in Barcelona

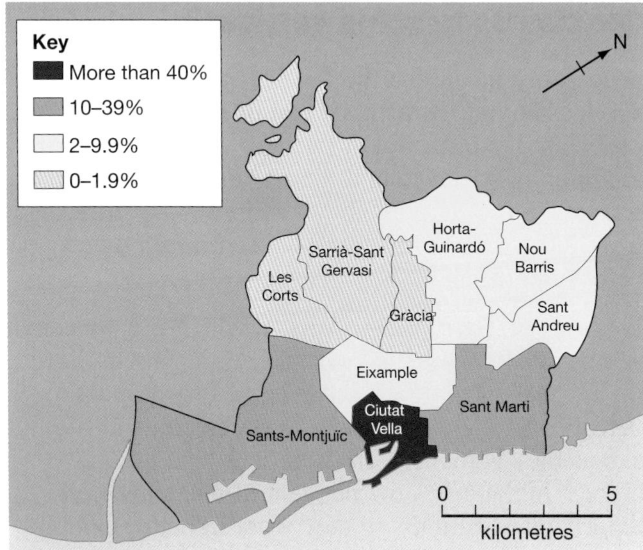


**Figure 6** Pakistani and Moroccan population of Barcelona (% of total in each district)

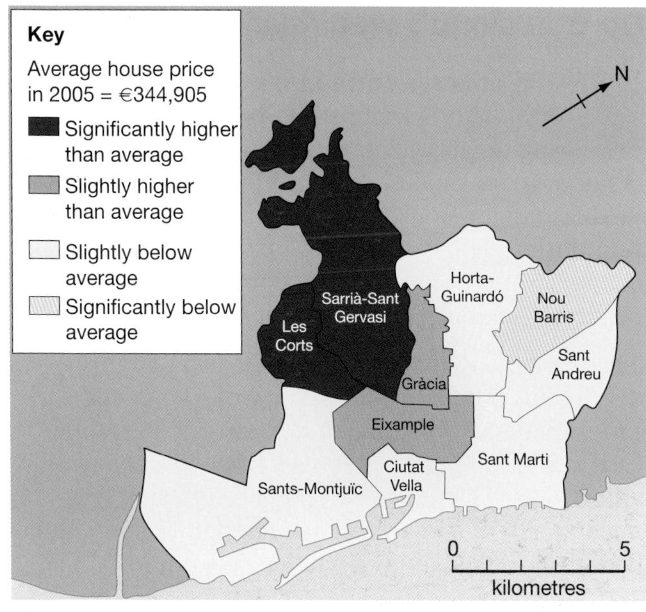


**Figure 7** Average house prices (euros) 2005

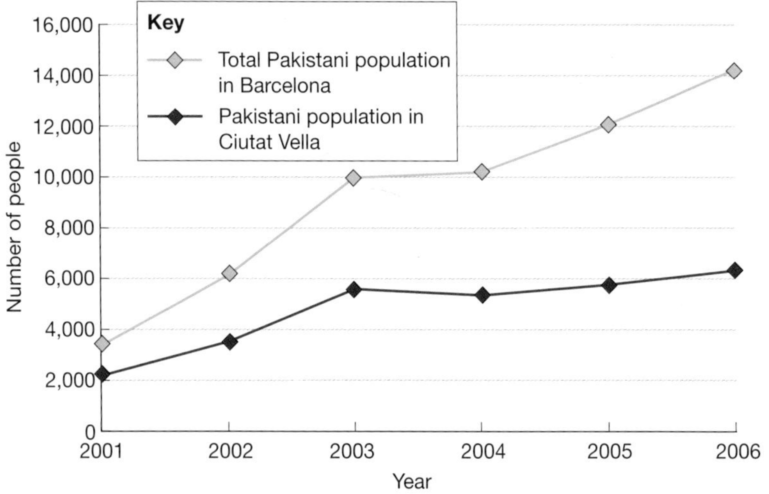


**Figure 8** The Pakistani population of Barcelona

| | Moroccan population in Ciutat Vella | Total Moroccan population in Barcelona |
|---|---|---|
| 2001 | 3,019 | 7,165 |
| 2002 | 3,645 | 9,751 |
| 2003 | 4,061 | 11,985 |
| 2004 | 4,247 | 13,594 |
| 2005 | 4,390 | 14,508 |
| 2006 | 4,468 | 15,522 |

**Figure 9** The Moroccan population of Barcelona

## Activity

**6** Explain why there are so many mosques in Ciutat Vella.

**7** Give three reasons why Pakistani and Moroccan immigrants might choose to live in El Raval.

**8** Use Figures 6 and 7.
**a)** Compare the distribution of Barcelona's Muslim population with the pattern of house prices.
**b)** What does this suggest about the income of Pakistani and Moroccan immigrants?

**9** Study Figure 8.
**a)** Describe the trend shown on both lines.
**b)** Use the graph to explain whether Barcelona's Pakistani population is getting more or less concentrated into Ciutat Vella.

**10 a)** Use the data in Figure 9 to draw another pair of lines on a line graph.
**b)** Compare this graph with Figure 8. What are the main similarities and differences?

## Do Barcelona's wealthier districts have better access to some services?

El Raval is an inner urban district within the Ciutat Vella (or old city). The district has narrow streets set out during the medieval development of the city, so it is not easy for modern traffic. Most of the housing is in six- to eight-storey apartment buildings. The **population density**, at 34,445 people per km$^2$, is about four times greater than London's average population density of 8,860 people per km$^2$.

There are many indicators that suggest that this district has both a lower standard of living, and a lower quality of life, than other parts of Barcelona. El Raval has the second-lowest **life expectancy** of all districts. The number of people suffering from malaria, AIDS and tuberculosis is significantly higher here than in the city as a whole. This does not necessarily mean that the district has poor healthcare services compared with the rest of Barcelona. It is probably due to the fact that these diseases are more common in Africa than in Spain, and the district has a large Moroccan population. Most people suffering from these diseases would have contracted them before migrating to Spain.

By contrast, Sarrià-Sant Gervasi, which is a western suburb of Barcelona, is home to residents who have the highest standard of living in the city. Population densities here are the lowest in Barcelona and life expectancy is highest. House prices here are the highest in the city. 36.7 per cent of residents have higher qualifications, so they work in better-paid jobs.

| | Density (persons per km$^2$) 2004 | Life expectancy 2006 | Persons with higher qualifications 2006 | Immigrant population (% 2006) | Average house price (euros, 2005) |
|---|---|---|---|---|---|
| Ciutat Vella | 23,943 | 73.2 | 11.4 | 15.7 | 286,520 |
| Eixample | 34,863 | 79.7 | 23.9 | 17.1 | 396,863 |
| Sants-Montjuïc | 8,246 | 78.4 | 11.1 | 12.6 | 288,366 |
| Les Corts | 13,718 | 80.4 | 26.9 | 3.6 | 433,577 |
| Sarrià-Sant Gervasi | 6,900 | 80.5 | 36.7 | 6.3 | 663,814 |
| Gràcia | 28,477 | 79.2 | 21.6 | 6.6 | 345,031 |
| Horta-Guinardó | 14,197 | 79.0 | 12.1 | 7.3 | 284,729 |
| Nou Barris | 20,572 | 78.2 | 6.2 | 8.8 | 230,588 |
| Sant Andreu | 21,504 | 79.1 | 10.5 | 6.3 | 287,058 |
| Sant Marti | 20,192 | 78.9 | 10.6 | 11.4 | 314,813 |
| Barcelona | 15,635 | 78.5 | 16.5 | 100* | 344,905 |

**Figure 10** Standard of living and quality of life indicators for Barcelona's main districts

* 100% of the immigrants living in the city live in Barcelona. This includes 4.6 per cent who have no fixed address

**www.bcn.es/english/ihome.htm**
This is the local government website for Barcelona, and some of the pages are in English. Particularly useful from the home page are links to the BCN map and statistics. The BCN map is a great example of a **Geographical Information System** (GIS). It is an interactive street map of the city. As well as street plans at various scales you can switch on or off a large number of layers of information that locate the city's community, cultural and sports facilities.

EXAMTECHNIQUE

## Making comparisons

Compare is a common command word in the Avery Hill Geography examination. You could be asked to compare two climate charts in unit 1 or two hydrographs in unit 2. In unit 3 you could be asked to compare two contrasting districts of a city, such as El Raval and Sarrià-Sant Gervasi.

The text on page 146 describes some of the features that give El Raval (a district within Ciutat Vella) a low quality of life such as the densely crowded housing and the high incidence of disease. It then goes on to describe the high standard of living in Sarrià-Sant Gervasi. However, no direct comparison has been made. If this text were an answer to the question 'Compare two districts of Barcelona' then it would score a very low mark!

In order to compare these two places successfully you must link a statement about one to the other with a connective in the same sentence. Connectives are words such as 'however', 'whereas' and 'similarly' (more are given in Figure 12). For example:

Ciutat Vella has an average life expectancy of 73.2 years, which is the lowest in Barcelona, *whereas* life expectancy in Sarrià-Sant Gervasi is 7.3 years higher and is the highest in the city.

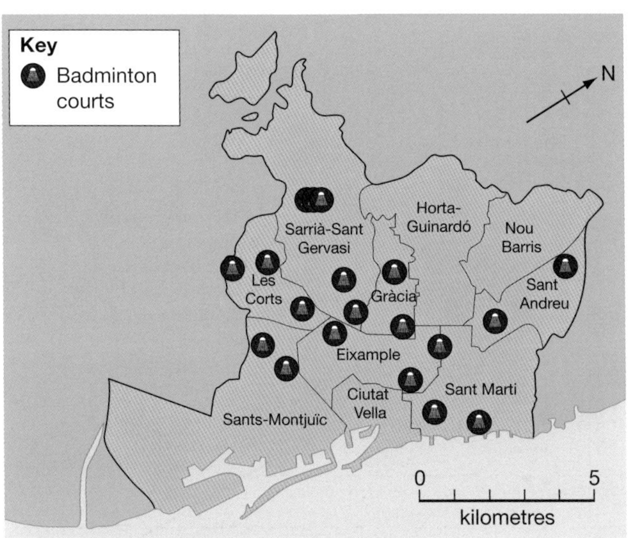


**Figure 11** Distribution of badminton courts in Barcelona

**Connectives to highlight difference**

... unlike ...
... whereas ...
... though ...
... conversely ...
... is much greater than ...
... is much smaller than ...
... is significantly larger than ...

**Connectives to highlight similarity**

... like ...
... similarly ...
... equally ...
... identically ...
... likewise ...
... in common with ...

**Figure 12** Connectives that can be used for comparison

## Activity

**11** Use Figure 11.

**a)** Describe the distribution (see page 143) of badminton courts in Barcelona.

**b)** List the districts which have no badminton courts. Using Figure 10, state whether each of these districts has house prices that are above or below Barcelona's average.

**c)** Assuming that customers have to pay a membership or court fee to play badminton, explain why the badminton courts are located only in certain districts.

**d)** What groups of people have poor access to these sports facilities?

**12** Study Figure 10. Choose one column that shows standard of living and one that shows quality of life. Explain the difference between these two concepts.

**13** Use Figures 10 and 12.

**a)** Compare the quality of life in Les Corts with Sarrià-Sant Gervasi.

**b)** Compare the standard of living in Eixample with Nou Barris.

## Going Further

### Using scattergraphs to make connections

Figure 15 divides each of the main districts of Barcelona into smaller statistical zones (rather like wards in a UK city). It provides four pieces of evidence that could be used to investigate inequality within the city.

Geographers are interested in the way in which factors such as immigration, education, healthcare and housing density are interconnected. Is it true, for example, that districts with a higher percentage of people with higher qualifications also have longer life expectancies? This might be because people who have experienced higher education have:

- higher incomes and can therefore afford private healthcare
- better understanding of healthcare issues such as the need for a balanced diet and to moderate smoking and drinking.

Geographers usually express such ideas as a **hypothesis**: a statement that can be proved or disproved using the available evidence. In this case our hypothesis might be: **Districts with a higher percentage of people with higher qualifications also have longer life expectancies.**

This hypothesis can be tested in several ways using the data in Figure 15. One of the most effective ways is to draw a scattergraph where two sets of data that might be connected are plotted on the same graph, as in Figures 13 and 14.

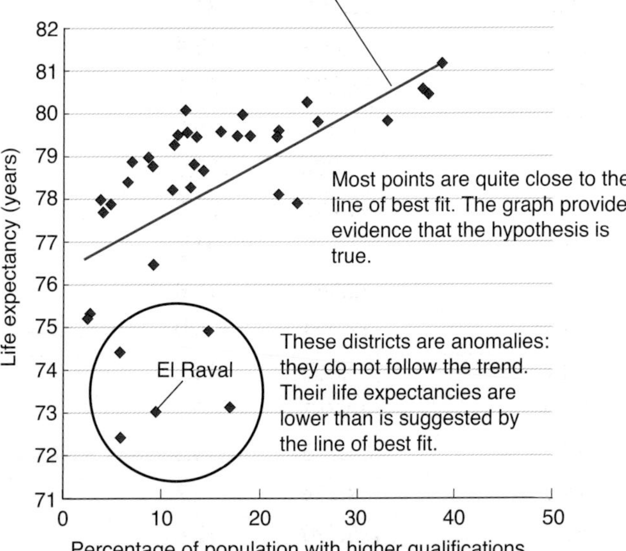


**Figure 13** Scattergraph showing the positive relationship between life expectancy and percentage of the population with higher qualifications

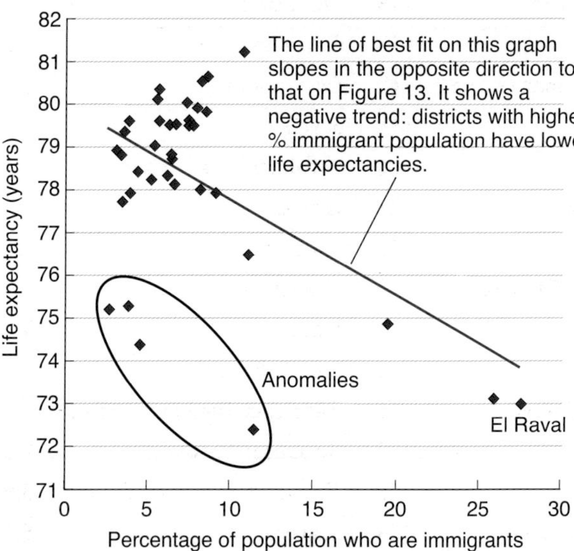


**Figure 14** Scattergraph showing the negative relationship between life expectancy and the percentage of the population who are immigrants

**14** Define the terms **hypothesis** and **anomaly**.

**15** Study Figure 14.

**a)** What hypothesis is tested by this scattergraph?

**b)** Does the graph provide better or worse proof of a connection than Figure 13?

**c)** Explain why three districts are shown as anomalies.

**16** Study Figure 15.

**a)** Suggest another hypothesis.

**b)** Test your hypothesis by drawing a scattergraph.

**c)** What conclusion do you reach?

| District | | Statistical zone | Foreign born (%) | Life expectancy (years) | Density per km² | Higher qualifications (%) |
|---|---|---|---|---|---|---|
| Ciutat Vella | 1 | Barceloneta | 11.5 | 72.4 | 10,308 | 5.8 |
| | 2 | Parc | 19.5 | 74.9 | 17,854 | 14.6 |
| | 3 | Gòtic | 26.0 | 73.1 | 19,714 | 16.9 |
| | 4 | El Raval | 27.6 | 73.0 | 34,445 | 9.4 |
| Eixample | 5 | Sant Antoni | 7.8 | 79.5 | 45,038 | 17.8 |
| | 6 | Esquerra Eixample | 8.6 | 79.8 | 36,605 | 25.8 |
| | 7 | Dreta Eixample | 8.1 | 79.9 | 18,811 | 32.9 |
| | 8 | Estació Nord | 7.6 | 79.6 | 30,787 | 21.7 |
| | 9 | Sagrada Familia | 7.6 | 79.5 | 47,642 | 18.9 |
| Sants-Montjuïc | 10 | Poble Sec | 11.2 | 76.5 | 45,948 | 9.2 |
| | 11 | Montjuïc | 4.7 | 74.4 | 143 | 5.7 |
| | 12 | Zona Franca-Port | 4.5 | 78.4 | 2,344 | 6.4 |
| | 13 | Font de la Guatlla | 6.5 | 78.7 | 21,586 | 14.1 |
| | 14 | Bordeta-Hostafrancs | 6.9 | 79.5 | 30,603 | 11.6 |
| | 15 | Sants | 6.5 | 78.8 | 39,805 | 13.2 |
| Les Corts | 16 | Les Corts | 5.8 | 80.3 | 22,161 | 24.6 |
| | 17 | Pedralbes | 10.9 | 81.2 | 4,606 | 38.4 |
| Sarrià-Sant Gervasi | 18 | Sant Gervasi | 8.3 | 80.5 | 18,297 | 37.1 |
| | 19 | Sarrià | 8.7 | 80.6 | 7,809 | 36.5 |
| | 20 | Vallvidrera-Les Planes | 9.2 | 77.9 | 286 | 23.6 |
| Gràcia | 21 | Gràcia | 6.8 | 79.5 | 40,751 | 21.5 |
| | 22 | Vallcarca | 6.7 | 78.1 | 14,315 | 21.8 |
| Horta-Guinardó | 23 | Guinardó | 5.8 | 79.6 | 32,067 | 15.8 |
| | 24 | Horta | 3.5 | 78.8 | 17,924 | 9.0 |
| | 25 | Vall d'Hebron | 5.3 | 78.2 | 4,860 | 10.9 |
| Nou Barris | 26 | Vilapicina-Turó de la Peira | 5.5 | 79.0 | 33,712 | 8.7 |
| | 27 | Roquetes-Verdum | 4.0 | 77.9 | 29,140 | 4.8 |
| | 28 | Ciutat Meridiana-Vallbona | 3.9 | 75.3 | 4,014 | 2.7 |
| Sant Andreu | 29 | Sagrera | 5.6 | 80.1 | 35,620 | 12.4 |
| | 30 | Congrés | 3.9 | 79.6 | 33,166 | 12.5 |
| | 31 | Sant Andreu | 3.7 | 79.3 | 28,486 | 11.2 |
| | 32 | Bon Pastor | 2.8 | 75.2 | 5,727 | 2.4 |
| | 33 | Trinitat Vella | 8.3 | 78.0 | 9,836 | 3.7 |
| Sant Marti | 34 | Fort Pius | 7.5 | 80.0 | 26,364 | 18.0 |
| | 35 | Poblenou | 6.3 | 78.3 | 8,364 | 12.8 |
| | 36 | Barris Besòs | 3.6 | 77.7 | 25,675 | 3.9 |
| | 37 | Clot | 6.4 | 79.5 | 42,986 | 13.5 |
| | 38 | Verneda | 3.2 | 78.9 | 30,907 | 7.0 |

**Figure 15** Investigating inequality in Barcelona

# Chapter 4
# Changing the city

**KEY QUESTIONS**

- How are urban areas changing?
- Who makes decisions about these changes and which groups benefit from them?
- Why do some people have more power than others to influence planning decisions for housing and service provision?

## How are urban areas changing?

Cities are growing and changing fastest in Less Economically Developed Countries (LEDCs). The process by which the population of a country becomes more urban and less rural is known as urbanisation. Urbanisation causes the physical and human growth of towns and cities. The pace of urban growth in many LEDC cities is so fast that the city's **infrastructure** cannot keep pace with the demand from new residents. As a consequence many LEDC cities fail to provide an adequate quality of life with many city dwellers lacking:

- suitable housing
- a piped water supply
- sewers and safe levels of **sanitation**
- paved roads or street lighting
- electricity connected to the home.

In many places city dwellers live in homes that have not been planned by the city council. This may be a shelter on the pavement of an Indian city, or a corrugated iron shack in Nairobi, Kenya. In either case, the house was not planned so it has no sewer or connection to the water supply. It does not formally exist and in most cases the land on which it was built does not belong to the resident. That is why these properties are often referred to as:

- squatter settlements or shanty towns
- **informal settlements**
- spontaneous settlements.

**Figure 1** Cities in LEDCs are growing fast. Many are being improved using self-help projects. This project is in Madagascar

## Self-help

The residents of informal settlements usually have no **security of tenure**. In other words, they have no legal right to live there and could be evicted at any time. It is this insecurity, as well as poverty, that prevents people from improving their homes. However, after they have been established for some years, and the threat of eviction has gone, informal settlements are gradually improved. These improvements are often made by the residents themselves with advice and practical support from the local council or a **Non-Governmental Organisation (NGO)**. This type of urban change is called a **self-help** project.

### WHERE THE SIDEWALKS END:
### HOW THE POOR COMBAT POVERTY DAILY

*Molly O'Meara Sheehan*

On city maps, the location of this settlement – called 'Mtumba' by the 6,000 people who live there – shows up as prime habitat for rhino and giraffe. That's because this unsanctioned community lies on the edge of Nairobi National Park. Mtumba is only one of the many slums around Nairobi. In fact, more than half of the residents of Kenya's capital city cannot afford to live in 'formal' housing, and have been forced to find shelter in slums like this one.

'We can't depend on the government for anything,' says Castro as we walk through the settlement. He points out a water tap – one of two small spigots that supply water for the entire settlement. But no city water is piped here. Instead, these taps are fed by private companies that truck in tanks. And they sell their water at a premium. As of yet, no company has seen fit to establish any sort of business setting up toilets or sewers. Instead the 6,000 people who live here share three flimsy pit latrines.

Informal communities have certain advantages. Rents are lower than in formal housing. There are no property taxes. Residents can skirt cumbersome zoning laws that separate housing from businesses, and set up shop inside their homes or just outside. Mtumba's commercial strip boasts rows of brightly painted storefronts, each about one metre wide. There are produce stands, coffee shops, a 'movie house' showing videos, a barber shop, and an outfit that collects old newspapers.

But ... slums are often located in a city's least-desirable locations – situated on steep hillsides, on flood plains, or downstream from industrial polluters – leaving residents vulnerable to disease and natural disasters.

'Land is the key to implement any project for development,' says a Mtumba woman who is involved in the community's self-run school. She explains that the people of her community have difficulty convincing themselves – let alone anyone else – to invest in water, toilets, or any sort of improvement. Why bother if the neighbourhood could be bulldozed the next day? Indeed, a central obstacle to any sort of 'self-help' in many slums is that in the eyes of the law the residents do not belong on the land where they live.

**Figure 2** Extract from *Global Urban Development* magazine, describing the Mtumba informal settlement in Nairobi, Kenya

### Activity

**1** Define the terms **informal settlement** and **self-help project**.

**2** Discuss Figure 1. If you were designing an enquiry into this settlement what other questions would you want to ask?

**3** Read Figure 2 carefully.
- **a)** Explain two advantages of informal settlements.
- **b)** Explain why the location of informal settlements is often hazardous.

**4** Who is making decisions about Mtumba informal settlement? Use Figure 2 to explain what each of the following groups is doing:
- **a)** The residents.
- **b)** Officials of the city authority such as planners.
- **c)** Local businesses.

**5** Explain why insecurity of tenure is likely to reduce quality of life for urban dwellers.

## Contrasting approaches to urban poverty in Kenya

We have seen that various groups make decisions about Kenya's informal settlements. Sometimes these groups have different ideas about how urban areas should change, and this can lead to conflict.

Amnesty International is an international NGO. It has accused the Kenyan government of the forcible eviction of people from informal settlements in both Mombassa and Nairobi. Amnesty International claims that shanty homes have been bulldozed. Possessions have then been burned to prevent people from rebuilding shanty housing elsewhere. There may be a number of reasons for this controversial action:

- Property developers want the land to build planned houses which can be sold for a profit.
- Government officials are concerned that informal settlements look untidy and prevent foreign tourists visiting the country.
- Police believe that shanty towns protect criminals such as drug dealers.

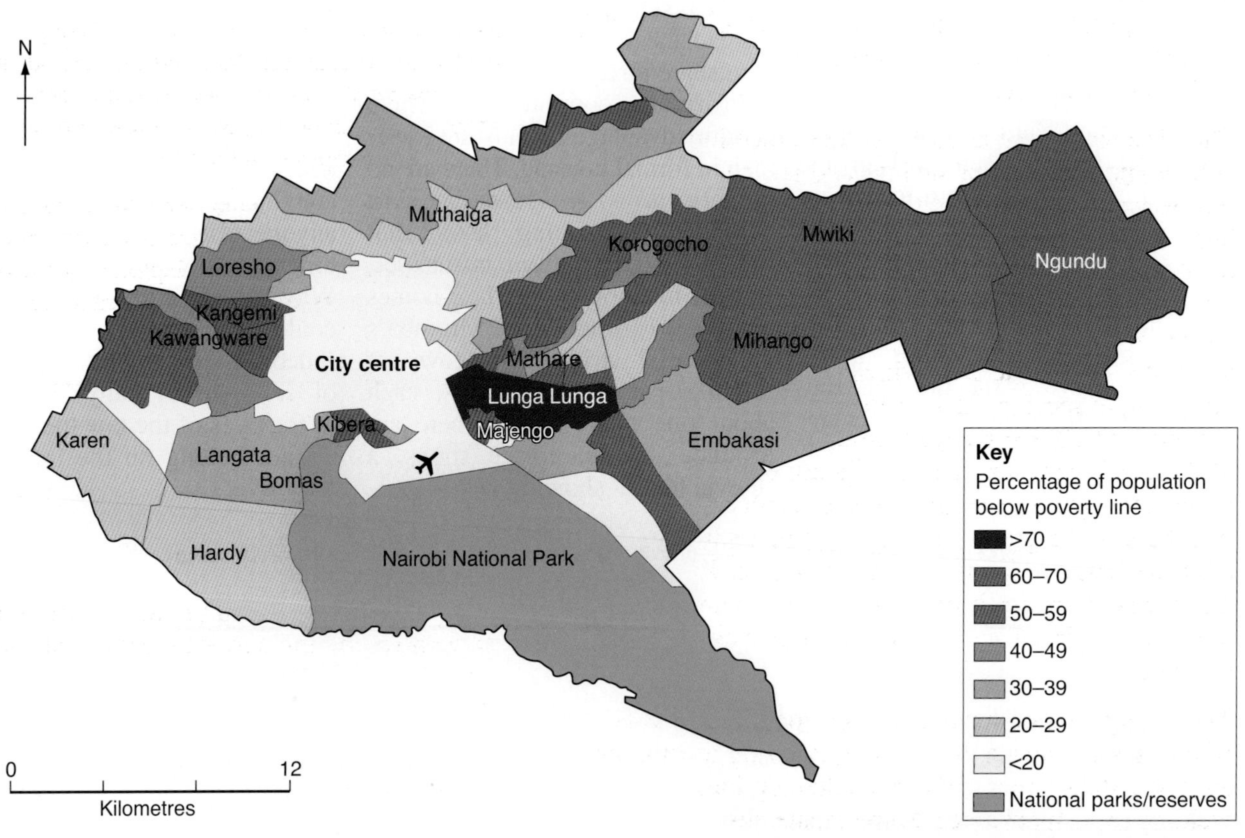


**Figure 3** Map of poverty in Nairobi

### Activity

**6** Use Figure 3 to describe the distribution (see page 143) of districts where:
  **a)** more than 50 per cent of the population lives below the poverty line.
  **b)** more than 70 per cent of the population lives below the poverty line.

**7** If shanty homes are bulldozed suggest what will happen to the residents.

## Self-help through micro-credit schemes

The Population Council is an international, not-for-profit NGO. In Kenya the council decided to introduce a **micro-credit** scheme for young women. The scheme is called TRY.

If you earn less than US$1 a day, how can you save even small amounts of money so that you can start your own business? Traditional banks are unlikely to lend you any money because you do not own a house or have some other guarantee that you can repay the loan. So micro-credit loans are now being used to support new businesses in the world's poorest communities. Micro-credit is where small loans are given to enterpreneurs who are too poor to qualify for traditional bank loans.

The TRY micro-credit scheme provides small loans to young women living in the squatter settlements of Nairobi. The girls receive basic financial training and are then grouped into teams of five. Each girl agrees to save a minimum of 50 Kenyan shillings (about US$0.65) each week.

The girls meet once a week. At these meetings they collect and record their savings and are given business advice. Many of these young women become great friends and use the meeting as an opportunity to share concerns about their relationships with partners or parents as well as their money worries. After saving for eight weeks, each team of five girls decides which two of its members are going to receive the first loan. These loans are in the order of 10,000 Kenyan shillings (US$130). Making this decision can be difficult, but it is based on the strength of each girl's business plan. Other members of the group can only receive their loans after the first two loans have been paid back. This arrangement creates a strong sense of responsibility: none of the girls wants to let down other members of the group.

The young women have used their loans in all sorts of businesses such as hairstyling, tailoring or running a market stall. Other girls have taken up jobs in welding or as mechanics. Some create new businesses, others expand existing businesses.

Not only has the scheme helped poor young women to set up businesses and earn money, it has also helped them to save. Before joining the scheme each girl had average savings of just US$43. After three years each member has average savings of US$95.

## Going Further

### The Grameen Bank

The Grameen Bank (which means 'Bank of the Villages') was founded in 1983 by Muhammad Yunus. It makes micro-credit loans to the poorest people of Bangladesh. It has been so successful that it has inspired the development of micro-credit schemes in many other developing countries, including Kenya. Muhammad Yunus was awarded the Nobel Peace Prize in 2006.

**www.grameen-info.org/**
The official Grameen Bank website gives more information about micro-credit loans in Bangladesh.

**www.grameenfoundation.org/**
The website of a non-profit making organisation set up to reproduce the success of the Bangladesh Grameen Bank in other countries.

**1** From the home page www.grameen-info.org/ click on the link to the Grameen Bank and click the side link to 'Ten Indicators'. What do these indicators tell you about the way in which poverty is measured in Bangladesh compared to the UK?

**2** Use the Grameen Foundation website to produce a map of countries in which micro-credit schemes are supported by the Foundation. Explain why micro-credit schemes are necessary in relatively wealthy countries such as the USA.

### Activity

**8** Define the term **micro-credit**.

**9** Suggest why micro-credit schemes loan money to women and the poorest members of society.

## Event-led urban regeneration in South Africa

By staging the Olympic Games in Barcelona (1992) the city authority created a massive urban regeneration project. It is estimated that US$8 billion was invested in new infrastructure such as roads and sports facilities, and new housing over a six-year period. This kind of urban change normally takes decades. Since then, this type of **event-led regeneration** project has been used successfully in Sydney, Australia (2000 Olympics). It is hoped that staging the football World Cup in South Africa in 2010 will help to regenerate ten urban areas.

The benefits for South African cities:

- New sports facilities. While cricket and rugby are mainly played by white South Africans, football is the favourite sport of black South Africans. By developing new football stadiums the government is creating sports facilities which will be used by South Africans for many years after the 2010 World Cup.
- New jobs. In the short term the regeneration project will create thousands of jobs for local people in construction. This should have a **positive multiplier** effect (see page 236): the extra jobs will mean extra income which means extra spending and local investment.
- New image. South Africa is hoping to create a positive image among visiting fans and in the media. If people think that South African cities are attractive, exciting places, then they may return here on holiday or even invest money in local businesses.

**Figure 4** The World Cup will create world class sporting facilities for future South African footballers (in yellow and green)

### Activity

**10** Use Figure 5 to describe the location of:
**a)** Cape Town
**b)** Pretoria.

**11** Use Figure 5 to describe the distribution of National Parks in South Africa.

**12** Use Figure 5 to create an itinerary for a football fan visiting South Africa in 2010. The fan wants to see matches at three different stadiums and visit a National Park. Give directions for the fan, making sure you clearly describe the location of each place that is to be visited.

**13** Explain the advantages of event-led regeneration:
**a)** before the event
**b)** after the event.

**14** The South African government was originally going to improve existing rugby stadiums. In 2006 it changed its mind and decided to build brand-new football stadiums, even though this would cost more money. Suggest the reasons it might have had for this decision.

EXAMTECHNIQUE

## Describing locations

To describe a location means to be able to pinpoint somewhere on a map. Describing a location on an Ordnance Survey map can be done easily by giving a grid reference. But describing a location on a map that has no grid lines requires a different technique. To describe the location of places on Figure 5, which has no grid lines, you will have to use other significant places on the map, places that really stand out such as Pretoria, Lesotho or Kruger National Park, as landmarks to guide the viewer to the place you are describing.

First, you need to give a broad indication of place by describing in which part of the map the viewer should be looking. Always use points of the compass, such as 'in northern South Africa' rather than 'at the top of the map'. Second, you should use a combination of two facts to pinpoint a specific location:

- Distance from a landmark using km.
- Direction from a landmark using points of the compass.

### Question

Describe the location of Polokwane.

### Answers

1 Polokwane is in northern South Africa.

2 It is approximately 200 km north-east of Pretoria and 200 km west of Kruger National Park.

## Describing distributions

To describe a distribution is to describe how similar things are spread across a map. Geographers are interested in the distribution of natural features such as forests, volcanoes or habitats, as well as human features such as settlements, hospitals or sporting facilities.

Describing a distribution requires you to do two things. First, you need to describe where on the map the features are located. Second, you need to describe any pattern the features might make: regular, random or clustered (see page 143).

### Question

Describe the distribution of World Cup cities in South Africa.

### Answers

1 Six of the ten cities that are going to host the World Cup are in northern South Africa, with two in central and eastern regions and two in the south.

2 The cities are scattered fairly randomly across South Africa, although there is a cluster of World Cup cities around the capital Pretoria.

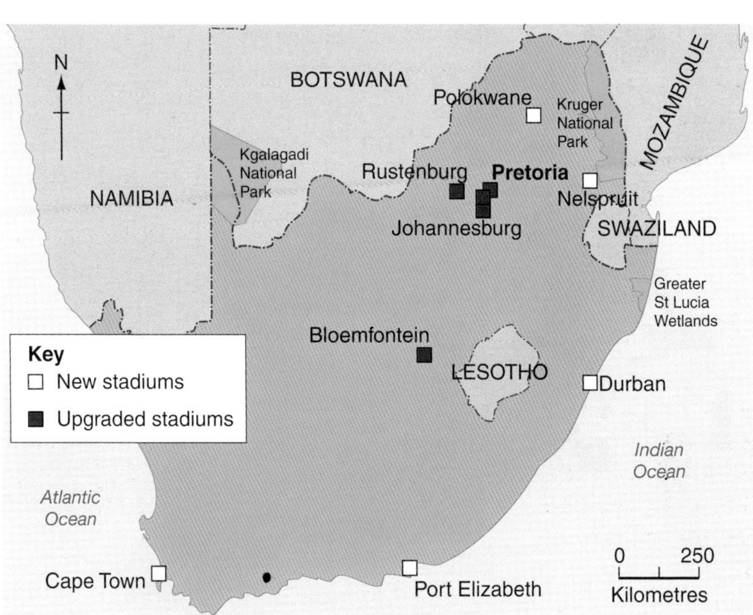


**Figure 5** The location of the 2010 World Cup football grounds

## Investigating urban change in Johannesburg

Johannesburg is South Africa's biggest city. It has a population of more than 1.5 million. On the edge of the city is the settlement of Soweto. Soweto is a black township with another one million people. It grew up during the apartheid era when black Africans were forced to live in locations separate from white South Africans. Approximately twelve per cent of the housing in Soweto is informal.

Quality of life in Soweto for many residents is poor. The population has grown quickly and the housing density is very high. There is little space for leisure activities for the half a million children who live here. The township lacks sufficient basic services such as piped water, sanitation and waste collection.

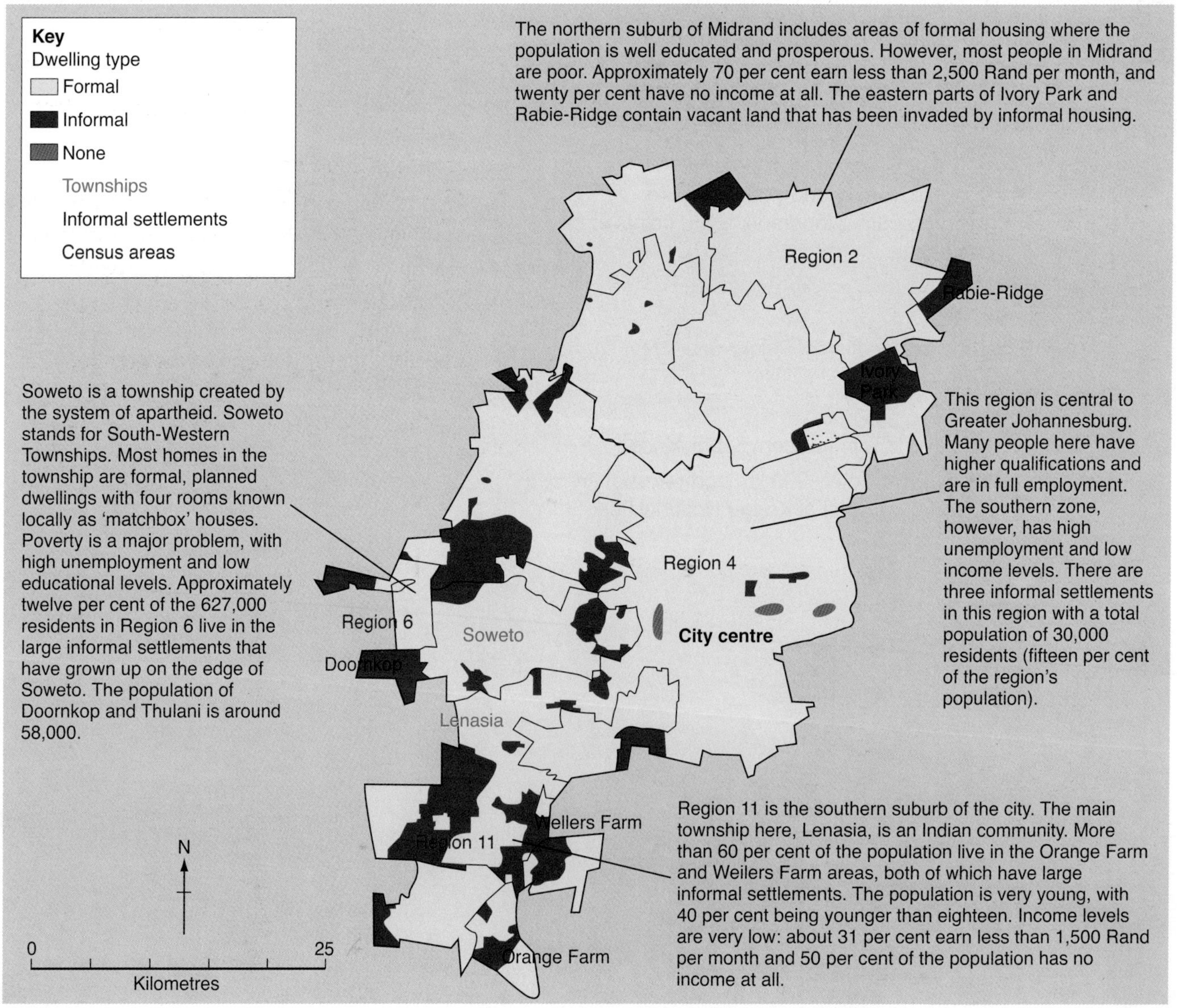

**Key**
Dwelling type
Formal
Informal
None
Townships
Informal settlements
Census areas

The northern suburb of Midrand includes areas of formal housing where the population is well educated and prosperous. However, most people in Midrand are poor. Approximately 70 per cent earn less than 2,500 Rand per month, and twenty per cent have no income at all. The eastern parts of Ivory Park and Rabie-Ridge contain vacant land that has been invaded by informal housing.

Soweto is a township created by the system of apartheid. Soweto stands for South-Western Townships. Most homes in the township are formal, planned dwellings with four rooms known locally as 'matchbox' houses. Poverty is a major problem, with high unemployment and low educational levels. Approximately twelve per cent of the 627,000 residents in Region 6 live in the large informal settlements that have grown up on the edge of Soweto. The population of Doornkop and Thulani is around 58,000.

This region is central to Greater Johannesburg. Many people here have higher qualifications and are in full employment. The southern zone, however, has high unemployment and low income levels. There are three informal settlements in this region with a total population of 30,000 residents (fifteen per cent of the region's population).

Region 11 is the southern suburb of the city. The main township here, Lenasia, is an Indian community. More than 60 per cent of the population live in the Orange Farm and Weilers Farm areas, both of which have large informal settlements. The population is very young, with 40 per cent being younger than eighteen. Income levels are very low: about 31 per cent earn less than 1,500 Rand per month and 50 per cent of the population has no income at all.

Region 2
Rabie-Ridge
Ivory Park
Region 4
City centre
Region 6
Soweto
Doornkop
Lenasia
Weilers Farm
Region 11
Orange Farm
N
0 25
Kilometres

**Figure 6** The distribution of informal housing in Johannesburg

However, some improvements are being made. In the 1980s water supply in Soweto was very poor. The iron pipes carrying water were rusted and between 50 and 60 per cent of water was wasted in leaks. Many districts were able to have water only at night. Obviously, this was a major health concern. Gradually the situation has improved. Many new water pipes have been laid, and township roads have been paved. The local authority employed local people to do the work, so Sowetans benefited from extra jobs as well as improved services.

**Figure 7** The township of Soweto is home to one million people

## Activity

**15** Use Figure 6 to describe the location (see page 154) of Soweto.

**16** Use Figure 6 to describe the distribution (see page 143) of informal settlements in Johannesburg.

**17** Explain how each of the following would affect quality of life:
- **a)** High population density
- **b)** Irregular water supply
- **c)** Unpaved roads.

**18** If you have access to a computer, use the internet to research and find definitions for the following terms:
- **a) socio-economic group**
- **b) housing tenure**
- **c) apartheid**
- **d) township.**

Read the advice that follows on how to find definitions.

## Using the internet to find definitions of geographical terms

Using the internet to research the meaning of a term is easy.

1. Use a search engine such as Google™.
2. Type in 'define': in the dialog box, and the word you want to define (see example on the right).
3. View the sites that are returned in your web search (see below). Some sites are more reliable than others. For example, university and government sites tend to be factual and accurate, whereas weblogs often contain opinions that may not be factually correct.

Definitions of **quality of life** on the Web:

- The overall enjoyment of life. Many clinical trials measure aspects of a patient's sense of well-being and ability to perform various tasks to assess the effects that cancer and its treatment have on the patient.
  nydailynews.healthology.com/nydailynews/15836.htm
- The level of enjoyment and fulfillment derived by humans from the life they live within their local economic, cultural, social, and environmental conditions. The Jacksonville Community Council defines quality of life as the "feeling of wellbeing, fulfillment, or satisfaction resulting from factors in the external environments." Quality of life, in this sense, is most directly measured using subjective indicators. ...
  indicators.top10by2010.org/glossary.cfm

## Will Johannesburg meet its target?

The South African government has the aim of replacing all informal housing with low-cost social housing by 2014. The United Nations (UN) estimates that, in 2001, 33 per cent of South Africans were living in slum housing. This is a term not usually used by geographers, but it obviously means that this housing is inadequate. The UN does not believe that South Africa can achieve its target. Despite building 200,000 low-cost houses every year, they estimate that another 2.4 million will still be needed in 2014.

The Johannesburg City Authority is much more positive about progress. They claim that residents of Johannesburg (or Jo'burg) already have the highest standard of living in South Africa. Their report on change in the city (see Figure 8) makes very positive reading.

# Jo'burg advertises its successes

*February 15, 2006 By Ndaba Dlamini*

### The City is drawing attention to successes attained over the past five years through a media campaign currently underway.

THE City of Johannesburg has made positive strides over the past five years in its efforts to deliver quality services to its citizens. To highlight some of these achievements, it is running an advertising campaign in various media.

It focuses on:

- The tarring of roads, in particular in Soweto, where 232 km of roads were tarred over the past three years at a cost of Rand 74 million. In addition, the city maintains 30,000 km of roads annually.
- The upgrading of the water supply, namely that through Operation Gcin'amanzi the City has delivered water to and upgraded water supplies to 98 per cent of its households.
- Increasing the number of street lights – in the past five years the City has installed and upgraded 16,427 street lights, making it a safer place for all its citizens.
- Job creation, namely that in the past eight years more than 316,000 jobs have been created in Jo'burg, which is more than in any other major city in South Africa. In addition, while South Africa's economy has grown by 2.9 per cent since 1996, Jo'burg's has grown by an exceptional 4.5 per cent. Jo'burg is booming!
- The building of new and upgrading of existing parks – in the last five years Jo'burg has spent Rand 31 million on its parks. With more than six million trees, it is now the biggest man-made forest in the world, and the City employs more than 2,000 people to maintain these trees and parks every day.
- Increased metro police presence, which has risen by 331 per cent in the past five years.
- Housing – in the past five years the City has facilitated housing for 8,000 families.

**Figure 8** Extract from the official Johannesburg website (www.joburg.org.za)

### Activity

**19** Study Figure 8. Explain how each of the initiatives described in the article has affected quality of life.

**20** Explain why the Johannesburg City Council has done much more than just provide low-cost housing.

**21** Write a 250-word newspaper article about urban improvement in South Africa. The article must have a positive point of view.

## Going Further

### The Millennium Development Goals and urban change

The United Nations is a major international not-for-profit NGO. It has no direct control over the way governments act (for example, it cannot prevent evictions of shanty towns in Kenya), but it does support other NGOs who then implement self-help and micro-credit schemes.

The UN also has a vision of how urban areas need to change. It has set a **Millennium Development Goal**: to have achieved a significant improvement of the lives of at least 100 million slum dwellers by 2020.

- Less than 35 per cent of cities in the developing world have their wastewater treated.
- In cities of the developing world, one out of every four households lives in poverty. 40 per cent of African urban households and 25 per cent of Latin American urban households are living below the locally defined poverty lines.
- One out of every four countries in the developing world have constitutions or national laws which prevent women from owning land and/or taking mortgages in their own names. Customary or legal constraints to women owning land or property are highest in Africa, the Arab States, Asia and Latin America.
- 37 per cent of the population in cities of the developing world are employed within the informal sector.
- 71 per cent of the world's cities have building codes with anticyclone and anti-seismic building standards based on hazard and vulnerability assessment.

**Figure 9** Why do urban areas need to change? A web extract from www.unhabitat.org

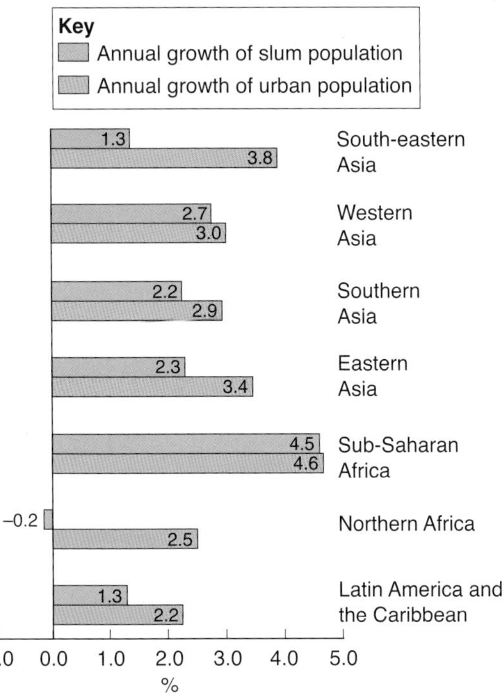


**Figure 10** Annual percentage growth of urban and slum populations between 1990 and 2001

**22** Study Figure 10. Make two lists in rank order from highest to lowest:

**a)** Growth rate of urban populations.

**b)** Growth rate of slum populations.

**23** Study Figure 9. Use it to produce a snappy 300-word news report. Focus on three key urban issues that need change.

**24** Discuss the Millennium Development Goal target to have achieved a significant improvement of the lives of at least 100 million slum dwellers by 2020. Suggest eight ways in which a geographer could measure whether or not the target has been met.

# Chapter 5
# Rural–urban interactions in Africa

**KEY QUESTIONS**

- What are the reasons for the movement of people from rural to urban areas?
- What are the impacts of rural to urban migration on rural communities?
- Are rural African communities sustainable?

## Why do people migrate in sub-Saharan Africa?

More than half of the world's population now lives in cities. The countries which have the highest percentage of rural populations are in **sub-Saharan Africa** (Africa south of the Sahara) so this chapter will focus on how these societies are changing.

People move for a variety of reasons. Conflicts and natural disasters may force people to move, in which case the migrants may be described as **refugees**. Figure 1 of the Darfur region in Sudan shows one tragic example of this refugee movement. However, in most cases people migrate out of choice rather than because of violence or disaster. People generally move because they want to improve their standard of living by finding a better-paid job. A migrant who moves in order to find work is described as an **economic migrant**. Many migrants also expect that moving to the city will improve their quality of life, perhaps by giving them better access to clean water or healthcare facilities.

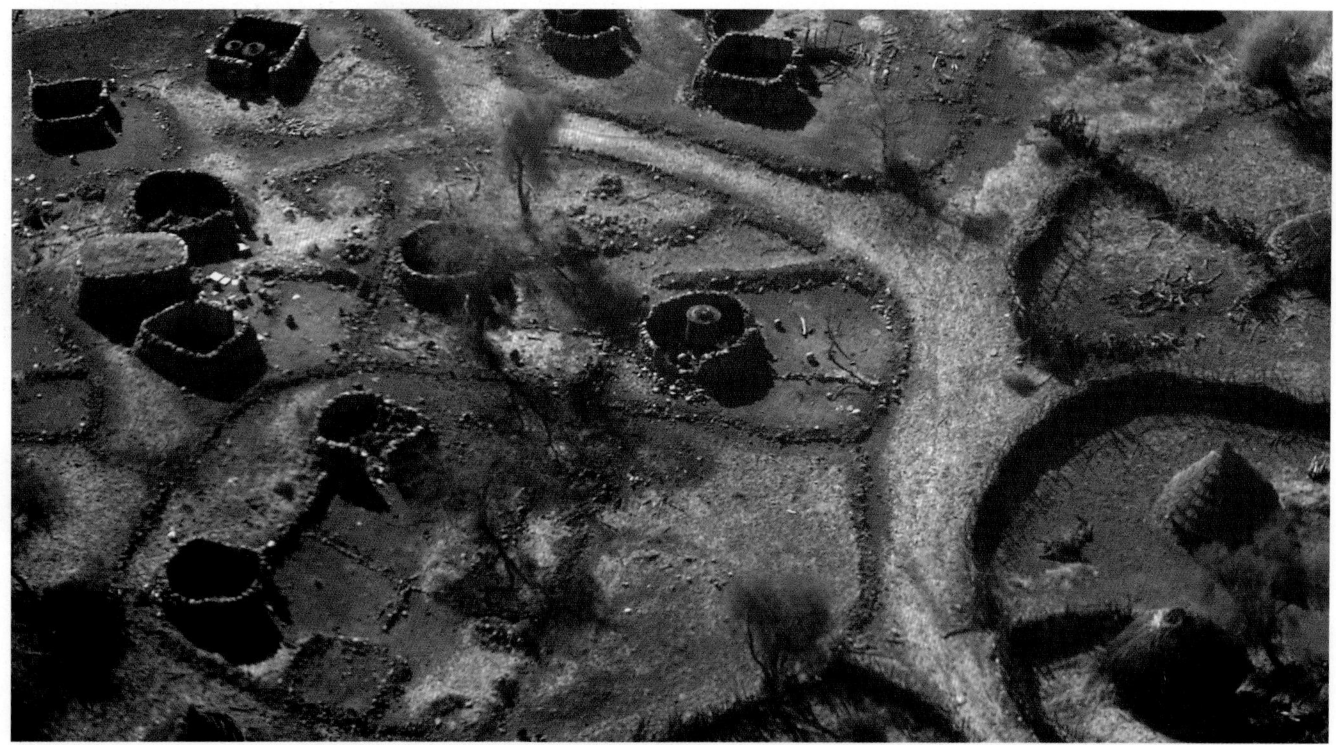

**Figure 1** The roofs of these circular homes have been burnt by soldiers and the villagers have become refugees

## Investigating rural to urban migration in South Africa

Gauteng is South Africa's most urban province and contains three major cities of more than one million people: Johannesburg, Pretoria and Soweto. By contrast, the largest city in the neighbouring province of Limpopo has only 90,000 people and more than 90 per cent of the population lives in rural areas. In this case study we will investigate the reasons for migration between Limpopo and Gauteng, and also examine the effects of this migration on rural communities.

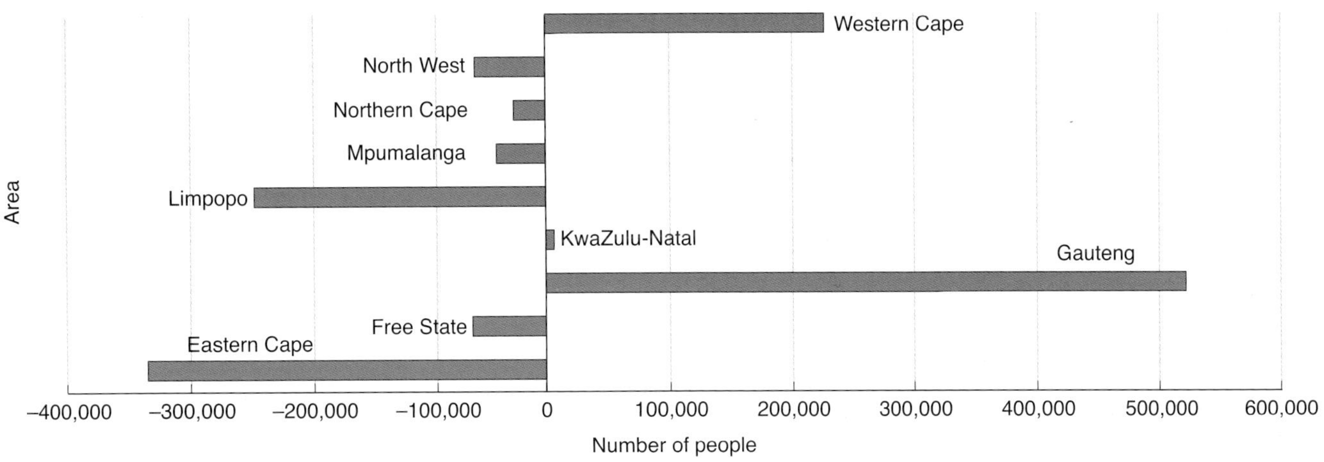


**Figure 2** Total population gains and losses due to migration in 2005

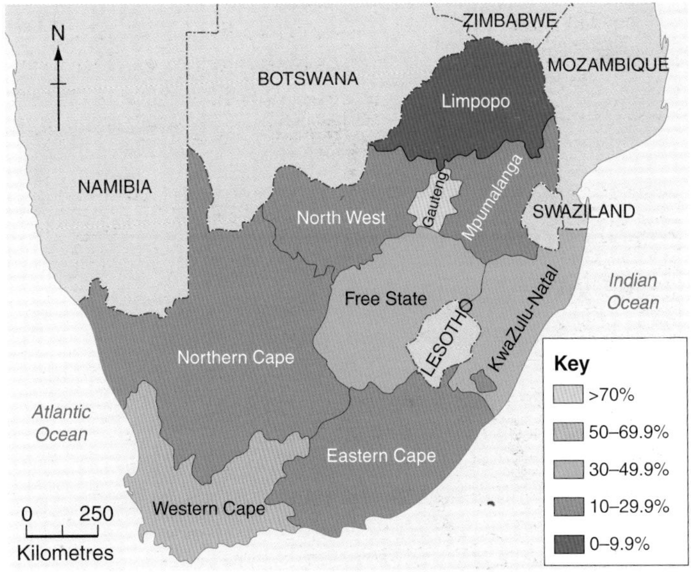


**Figure 3** Urban population in South Africa's provinces (estimate based on population living in settlements greater than 20,000 people)

## Activity

**1 a)** Define the terms **refugee** and **economic migrant.**

**b)** Explain the difference between **quality of life** and **standard of living**.

**2** Use Figures 2 and 3 to complete the following:

**The two most urban provinces are:**

**i) .......... which gained .......... migrants during 2005 and;**

**ii) ......... which gained ....... migrants in 2005.**

**The more rural provinces, such as .......... gained / lost population during the year.**

**3** Study Figure 4. Choose from the following phrases to describe the flow of migrants from Limpopo:

**Most migrants migrate short / long distances. Most / all migrants move to provinces that are less rural than Limpopo. Some / many migrants move to the most urban provinces of South Africa.**

**4** Based on the evidence in Figures 2, 3 and 4:

**a)** suggest why so few migrants move from Limpopo to Western Cape

**b)** suggest which regions are losing migrants to Western Cape and give reasons for your answer.

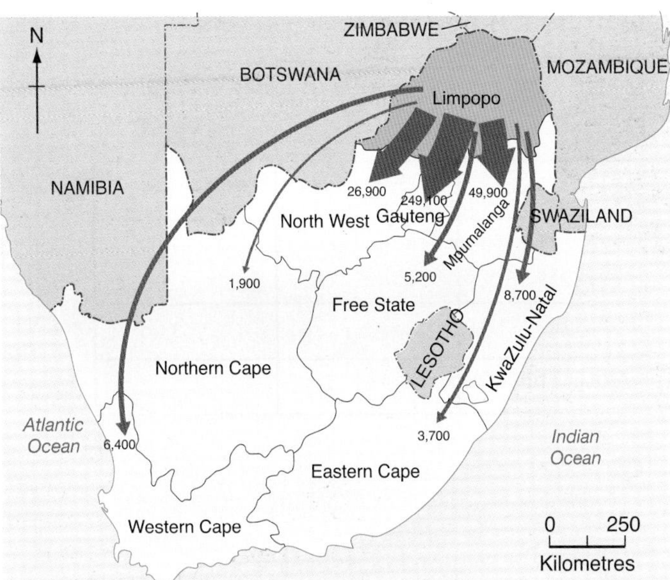


**Figure 4** Migration from Limpopo province during 2005

## What are the push/pull factors for rural to urban migration in South Africa?

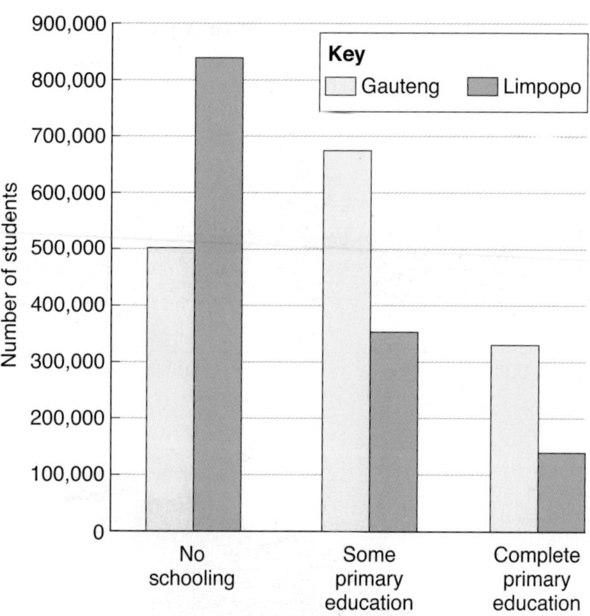


**Figure 5** Comparing education in Limpopo with Gauteng

People living in rural areas such as Limpopo are attracted by the jobs and better opportunities available in cities such as Johannesburg. The possibility of better healthcare and schools for their children are **pull factors** that encourage migrants to leave their rural homes. At the same time, migrants are often dissatisfied with life in the countryside. Few rural houses have a connection to the national electricity grid. Most people do not own an electric cooker, let alone a computer or television. Lack of money, poor job opportunities and relatively low quality of life are all **push factors** that can force people to move away from rural areas.

People living in the province of Limpopo rely on either farming or tourism for their income. The region has a seasonal wet/dry tropical **climate** and a **savanna ecosystem**. Rural population densities are relatively high and farm sizes small.

Most households in Limpopo earn a little less than 1,000 Rand a month, whereas average household income in Johannesburg is 7,175 Rand a month. The **poverty line** in South Africa is defined at 1,100 Rand (about US$150) a month. Of people in Limpopo, 60 per cent live below this poverty line compared with only twenty per cent of people in Gauteng province.

The percentage of Johannesburg residents who:

- own an electric stove in the home: 77.86 per cent
- own a fridge or freezer: 87.26 per cent
- own a dishwasher: 5.24 per cent
- own a vacuum cleaner: 31.35 per cent
- own a television: 89.53 per cent
- own a hi-fi or music centre: 73.61 per cent
- own a personal computer: 17.86 per cent
- have a telephone connection: 57.65 per cent
- have eaten in a restaurant in the last month: 44.1 per cent
- bought a take-away meal in the last month (from a permanent establishment, not a street hawker): 55.26 per cent
- hired a video or DVD in the last month: 13.65 per cent.

**Figure 6** Some lifestyle statistics for Johannesburg, drawn from the annual All Media Products Survey (AMPS)

### Activity

**5** Use Figure 5. How many students in each province:
**a)** have no schooling
**b)** complete primary education?

**6** Explain how each of the following might be push factors that contribute to migration from rural areas of Limpopo.
- The rural areas are densely populated.
- Rainfall is low and unpredictable.
- Rural communities are isolated from services such as schools and healthcare.

**7** List the reasons for rural to urban migration using this table:

| | Push factors | Pull factors |
|---|---|---|
| Economic reasons | | |
| Education | | |
| Quality of life | | |

**8** Study Figure 6 taken from a South African website. Suggest how the internet and advertising might accidentally encourage further migration into Johannesburg.

## What are the consequences of rural to urban migration?

What effect does migration have on the rural areas that the migrants leave behind? Does the loss of so many people cause economic and social problems in the countryside? Or does migration create benefits for rural areas? Research suggests that the consequences of migration are very complex. They include:

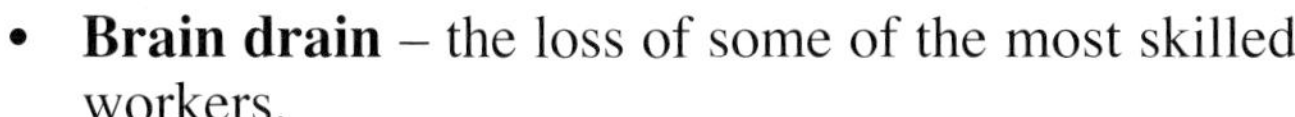

- **Brain drain** – the loss of some of the most skilled workers.
- **Remittances** – the money sent back by workers to support their families.
- Information and ideas – new technologies and skills learned in the city flow back into the country where they are used to support local businesses.

**www.statssa.gov.za/census2001/digiatlas/index.html**
This site uses **Geographical Information Systems (GIS)** to display an online atlas of South Africa. It uses data from the most recent census which can be displayed in either map or graph form.

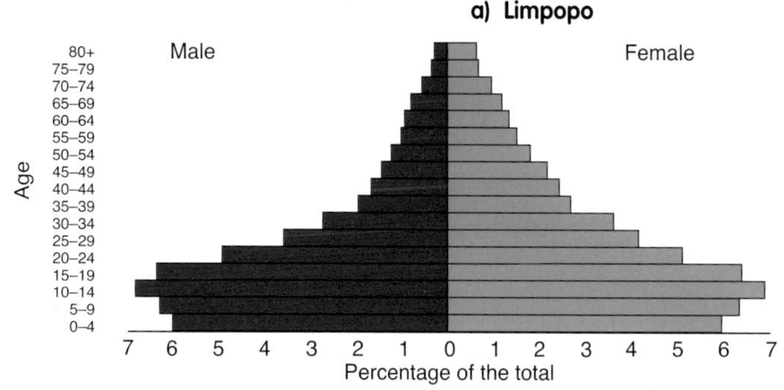


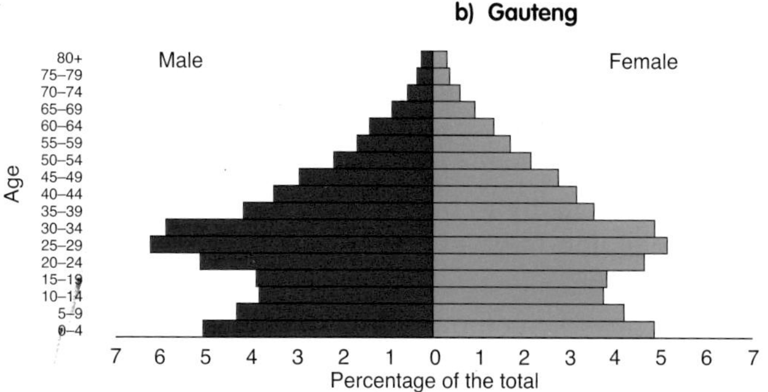


**Figure 7** Population pyramids for a) Limpopo (a rural province) and b) Gauteng (a neighbouring urban province)

### Activity

**9** Compare the population pyramids in Figure 7. Focus on the differences/similarities in the following parts of each graph:

**a)** The percentage of the population aged 0 to nineteen.

**b)** The percentage of the population aged 25 to 34.

**c)** The balance between males and females.

**10** Use Figure 8 to suggest reasons for the differences you noticed between the population pyramids.

**11** Explain whether each of the following is an advantage or disadvantage to a rural area that is losing migrants:

**a)** brain drain

**b)** remittances

**c)** information and ideas.

Studies in South Africa show that:

- those aged between fifteen and 35 are the most likely to migrate
- more males migrate than females, but an increasing number of females are migrating
- female migrants are slightly younger than male migrants
- circular migration (see page 164) is more common than permanent migration
- some rural migrants move to large urban areas such as Johannesburg, but many rural migrants move to smaller towns
- an increasing number of rural migrants move to other rural areas.

**Figure 8** Key points of migration in South Africa

## Circular migration

Many migrants do not make a permanent move to the city. It is common for people to leave the countryside when there are few farming jobs and return at busier times of the year, for example, at harvest. This temporary form of rural to urban migration is known as **circular migration**.

Circular migration brings both benefits and problems to rural communities. Migrants earn money which can be sent to the rural family and invested in improving the farm: repairing terraces and in tree-planting schemes. Circular migrants also reduce demand on village food and water supplies. This is particularly helpful in Limpopo which has a long dry season.

However, circular migration is almost certainly one of the reasons for the spread of AIDS and other sexually transmitted diseases. Studies in South Africa suggest that migrants are three times more likely to be infected with HIV than non-migrants. A returning migrant who is unaware that he or she is HIV positive could then infect a partner in the rural home. It is more difficult to treat rural AIDS sufferers because of their isolation from health clinics.

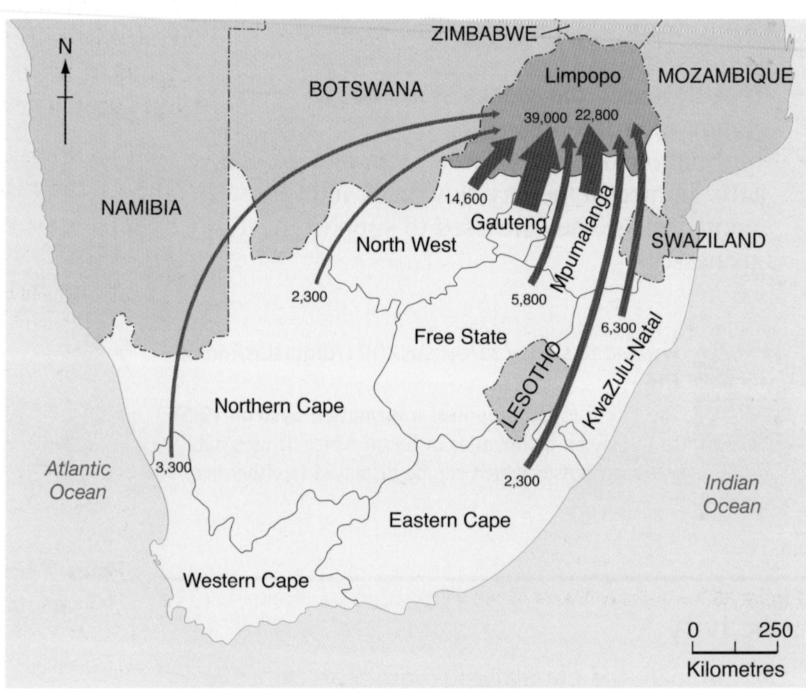


**Figure 9** Migration into Limpopo, 2005

### Activity

**12** Define **circular migration**.

**13** Use Figure 9.

**a)** How many migrants returned from provinces that are mostly urban?

**b)** Compare this map with Figure 4 on page 161. What are the similarities and differences?

**14** Use the text and your own ideas to complete the following table about the advantages and disadvantages of circular migration:

| | Advantages to the rural area | Disadvantages to the rural area |
|---|---|---|
| Economic | | |
| Social | | |

**15** Explain why circular migration is likely to be more beneficial to rural areas than permanent migration.

## A case study of rural–urban interaction in Ghana

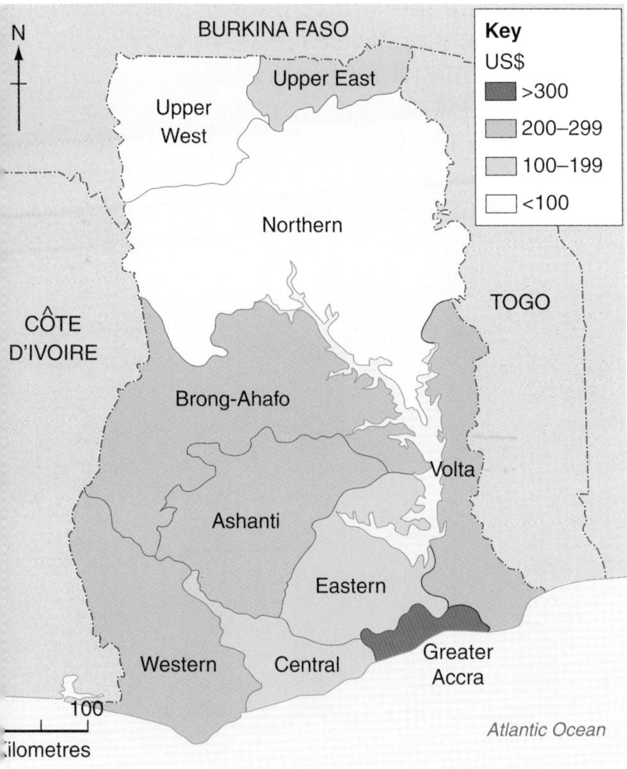


**Figure 10** The regional pattern of income in Ghana (latest survey 2000)

Ghana has fewer large cities than South Africa, and a larger percentage of its population lives in rural areas. As in South Africa there is a big gap between urban and rural incomes. This gap is one cause of rural to urban migration in Ghana.

Not only is there a gap between rural and urban incomes, but there is also a growing north–south divide in Ghana. Northern Ghana is very rural whereas the south of the country is more urban. Incomes in the more urban southern regions of the country are 2.4 times higher than in the more rural north. The reasons for this include:

- The south has more cities and better transport so industry has grown faster there.
- The south is more accessible to tourists and has benefited from the growth of tourism during the 1990s.
- The north has unreliable patterns of rainfall which make farming more difficult than in the south.

### Activity

**16** Describe the distribution (see page 143) of regions in Ghana where average incomes were above US$200 in 2000.

**17** Give two reasons for higher incomes in the more urban south of Ghana.

**Figure 11** A street market in Accra

**Figure 12** Village life in rural Ghana

## What are the push/pull factors that influence migration in Ghana?

The northern regions of Ghana face severe problems such as poverty, lack of job opportunities (especially for women), and lack of safe drinking water. The region has a harsh climate and farming is an unreliable way of making a living. The lack of decent roads and public transport makes it difficult for rural families to get to local towns to visit friends, go to the shops, or get medical attention. There is a severe shortage of teachers in the northern regions of Ghana. In rural northern Ghana, the **infant mortality rate (IMR)** is twice as high as in urban areas in the south. Malaria, acute respiratory infections, diarrhoea, malnutrition and measles are still the five main causes of death in young children.

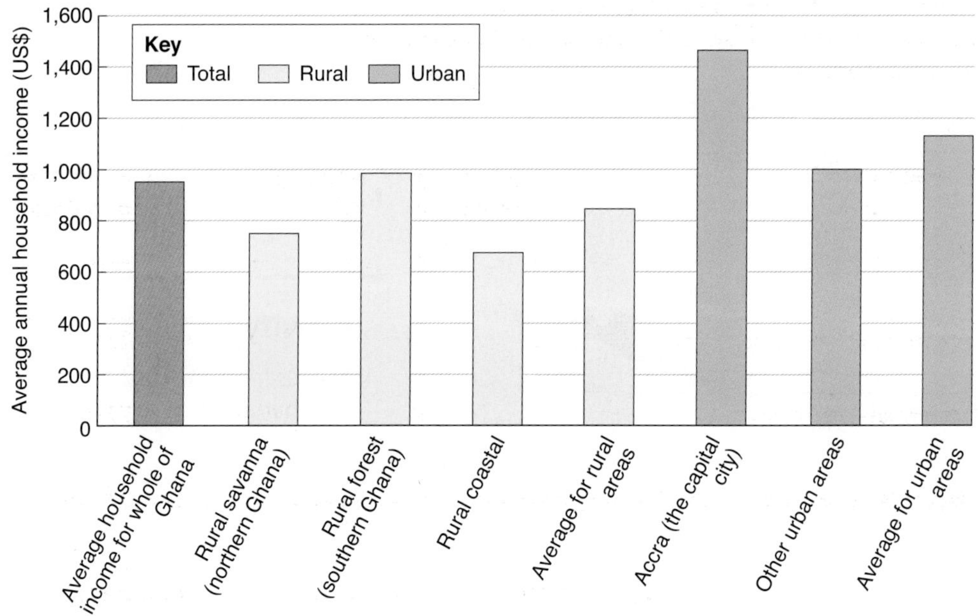


**Figure 13** Average household incomes in urban and rural parts of Ghana (last survey 2000)

### Activity

**18** Use Figure 13 to compare the average household incomes:

**a)** in Accra with those in other urban areas

**b)** in Accra with rural areas.

**19** Suggest how each of the following factors contributes to the high infant mortality rates in the north of Ghana:

**a)** poor transport networks

**b)** low family incomes.

**20** Produce a 150-word report explaining the push and pull factors that might cause someone to leave northern Ghana to live in Accra.

## Going Further

### Do men and women have equality in rural areas of Ghana?

**Gender inequalities** are those inequalities that exist between men and women. For example, in Ghana fewer girls than boys attend primary or secondary school. Poor families believe it is more beneficial for their sons to be educated. They expect their daughters to help out with chores around the home. As a consequence, many young mothers are not as well educated as they should be and struggle to care for their own children when they are taken ill. It can be proved that there is a connection between poverty, poor education for girls, and higher rates of infant mortality.

Most rural girls do not complete a formal education so they find it difficult to find formal (waged) occupations. More than 90 per cent of women therefore work in the **informal sector** of the economy such as growing food crops or selling foodstuffs on market stalls by the roadside. Because these women are illiterate and have very low, irregular incomes they find it difficult to qualify for loans that would help them improve their business.

| Type of work | Percentage of working population (1992) | | | Percentage of working population (1999) | | |
|---|---|---|---|---|---|---|
| | Male | Female | All | Male | Female | All |
| Formal (waged) employment | 20.7 | 7.5 | 13.6 | 23.0 | 6.2 | 13.8 |
| Informal employment | 79.3 | 92.5 | 86.4 | 77.0 | 93.8 | 86.2 |

**Figure 14** Gender inequality: people working in the formal and informal sectors of the economy in Ghana

| | Upper west | Upper east | Northern | Total in Ghana |
|---|---|---|---|---|
| Percentage of boys out of school | 40.0 | 35.1 | 32.8 | 15.6 |
| Percentage of girls out of school | 26.8 | 45.4 | 42.7 | 18.4 |

**Figure 15** Children out of school (six to eleven years) in the northern regions of Ghana compared with the average for Ghana

**21** Explain what is meant by the informal sector of the economy.

**22** Give three examples of ways in which women in Ghana suffer gender inequality.

**23** Use Figure 15 to compare the percentage of girls out of school in the three regions with:

**a)** the percentage of boys out of school in the same regions

**b)** the percentage of girls out of school in the whole of Ghana.

**24** Suggest the kinds of projects that are needed in rural Ghana to reduce the current gender inequalities.

# Chapter 6
# Conflicting demands on Europe's countryside

**KEY QUESTIONS**
- How do urban and rural areas interact and why do people move from urban to rural areas?
- How are rural communities changing?
- How and why does change within rural communities sometimes lead to conflict?

## How do urban and rural areas interact?

The migration of people from larger cities into towns and villages in the countryside is a process known as counter-urbanisation. This process has created enormous change in the rural areas of many More Economically Developed Countries (MEDCs), especially in western Europe. This chapter focuses on rural areas in the UK where change is causing conflict between established residents and incomers.

**Figure 1** Types of interaction between rural and urban places in the UK

| | |
|---|---|
| **Leisure** | Rural and coastal areas are increasingly used for day trips, adventure activities and short holidays by people who live in urban areas. |
| **Commuting** | Many people who live in small rural towns commute to jobs in larger cities. |
| **Retirement** | Some rural areas, for example parts of North Wales, Dorset and Cornwall, attract retired people who spent their lives working in urban areas. |
| **Resources** | The countryside produces food and most of the UK's renewable energy from wind farms. Since 93 per cent of the UK's population live in urban areas, most of this consumption is in towns and cities. |
| **Waste** | Most landfill sites are in rural locations but take waste from our cities. |

**Figure 2** Negative image of rural life: sheep and cattle were killed and burned to control the spread of foot-and-mouth disease in 2001

**Figure 3** Positive image of rural life: the Shropshire Bedlams are a Morris side who perform traditional country dances. Country traditions such as this help to create supportive communities. Outsiders might also view this as evidence that rural life is lived at a slower pace than the urban 'rat-race'

### Why do people want to move to the country?

Cities are often seen as stressful places in which to live and work. The cost and difficulty of commuting through rush-hour traffic, the lack of open space and places for children to play in safety, the noise, pollution and rising crime are all given as reasons for leaving the city. These negative views about city life are known as push factors. By contrast, life in a smaller town or village has many attractions. People are attracted to the peace and quiet, access to open countryside can reduce stress and tension, and lower numbers of cars may seem safer for parents who have young children. These positive features are known as pull factors and they attract people to move to rural areas.

## How has technology contributed to change in the countryside?

The move from town to country first became popular in the UK in the 1960s and 1970s. This was a period of rising car ownership and expansion of the motorway network. It became possible to **commute** from a home in the country to a job in the city. Since then, massive changes in communication technology have made it possible for increasing numbers of people to work from a home in the country. Writers, researchers and business consultants can spend most of the working week at a computer at home and need to commute to the office only for the occasional meeting. This type of work is known as **tele-working** or tele-cottaging.

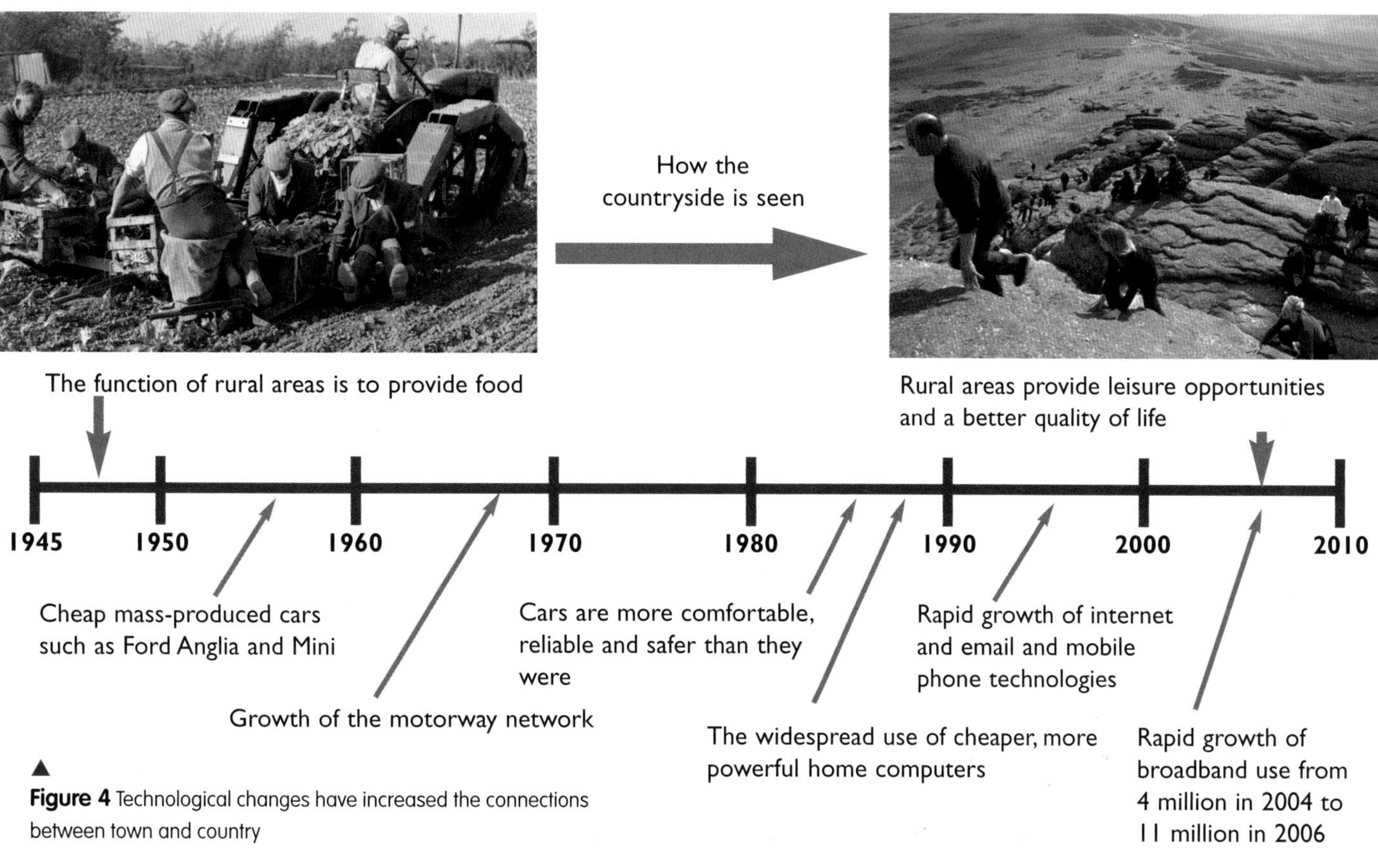


▲ **Figure 4** Technological changes have increased the connections between town and country

### Activity

**1** Study Figure 1. Working in pairs, list all the ways that the connections between urban and rural places might benefit:
- **a)** rural areas
- **b)** urban areas.

**2 a)** Explain what is meant by push factors and pull factors.
**b)** Suggest the push and pull factors that might be considered by each of the following groups of people:
- i) Someone who has just retired from a job in the city.
- ii) A student who has just completed A levels in a rural school.

**3** Study Figure 4. Use it to explain how technology has allowed:
- **a)** greater commuting
- **b)** greater use of the countryside for leisure
- **c)** more opportunities to move to the country and work from home.

**4** Using Figure 4, suggest how you imagine the countryside might change twenty years from now.

## How are rural populations changing in South Shropshire?

Each year the rural regions of England and Wales receive some migrants and lose others. In some regions more people move into the region than leave it, a situation known as **net in-migration**. In these regions, such as the commuter belts around London and in South East England, rural populations are rising and rural towns are experiencing **suburban sprawl**.

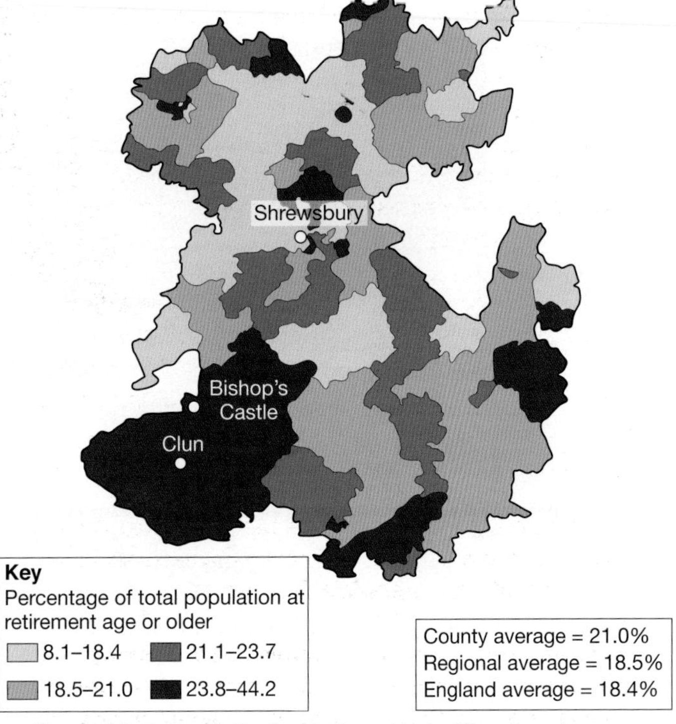


**Figure 5** Patterns of retirement in Shropshire in different wards

In South Shropshire, in the West Midlands, the number of people moving into rural areas is balanced by a similar number of people moving out. The total population of rural South Shropshire is not changing much. However, newcomers to rural life often have social and economic (or **socio-economic**) backgrounds that are different from the local people they replace, so the socio-economic character of South Shropshire is gradually changing. As we shall see later, this socio-economic change can lead to conflict as newcomers clash with established residents.

### Who is moving into South Shropshire and who is moving out?

The relatively high quality of life in the countryside appeals to a wide range of people from young professionals through families to the retired. What these people have in common is the ability to pay the relatively high prices of rural homes.

The countryside doesn't appeal to everyone. Many teenagers living in the countryside move into urban areas when they leave school. The lack of jobs, leisure facilities, shops, theatres and cinemas in the countryside are push factors, while the chance to go to university and the greater choice of jobs are pull factors for moving to a city. In addition, the cost of buying a house in the countryside is likely to prevent young people on lower incomes from staying in a rural area.

Rural communities in South Shropshire.

An urban community of 96,000 in central Shropshire.

This large region includes South Shropshire and Shrewsbury. However, more than 90 per cent of the region is classed as urban.

| Age | Clun % | Bishop's Castle % | Shrewsbury % | West Midlands % |
|---|---|---|---|---|
| 0 to 9 | 9.2 | 10.3 | 11.7 | 12.6 |
| 10 to 19 | 9.4 | 11.2 | 13.1 | 13.3 |
| 20 to 29 | 5.1 | 8.8 | 10.3 | 12.1 |
| 30 to 44 | 19.4 | 19.5 | 22.0 | 21.9 |
| 45 to 59 | 24.6 | 22.9 | 20.3 | 19.1 |
| 60 to 74 | 22.1 | 17.5 | 14.3 | 13.6 |
| 75 + | 10.0 | 9.8 | 8.4 | 7.4 |

**Figure 6** Population structures in rural and urban wards of Shropshire in the West Midlands (Source: 2001 Census)

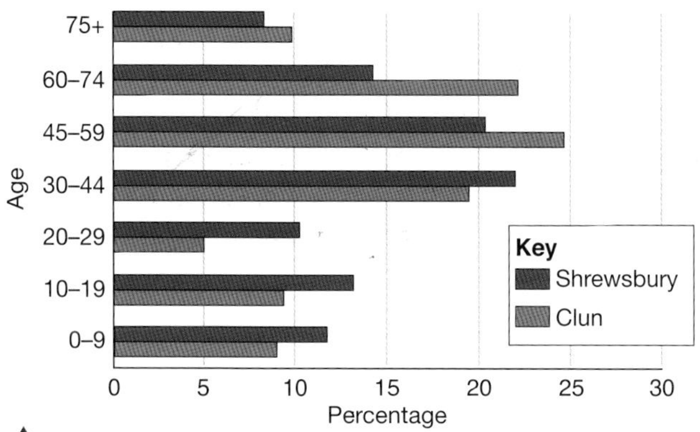


**Figure 7** Comparing population structures in Shrewsbury and Clun

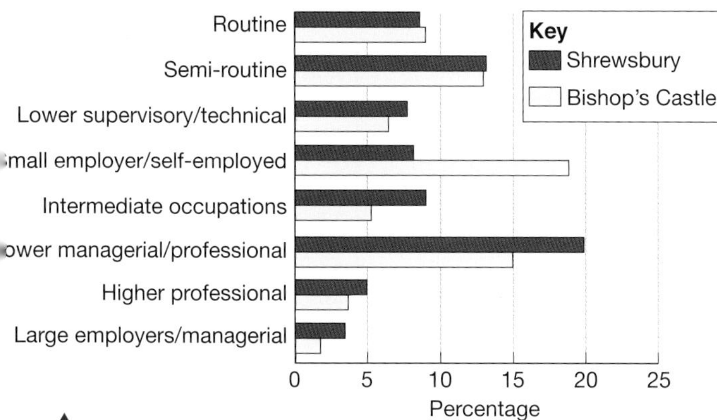


**Figure 8** Comparing occupations in Shrewsbury and Bishop's Castle (Source: 2001 Census)

| | **Bishop's Castle** | **West Midlands** |
|---|---|---|
| Total population | 2,474 | 5,276,308 |
| Percentage white | 99.8 | 88.7 |
| Percentage mixed – white and Asian, white and black African or black Caribbean | 0.2 | 1.4 |
| Percentage Asian or Asian British | 0 | 7.3 |
| Percentage black or black British | 0 | 2.0 |
| Percentage Chinese or other ethnic group | 0 | 0.6 |

**Figure 9** Comparing ethnic population of Bishop's Castle and the West Midlands (Source: 2001 Census)

## Activity

**5** Use Figure 5 to describe the location (see page 155) of
  **a)** Bishop's Castle
  **b)** Shrewsbury.

**6** Use Figure 5 to describe the distribution (see page 143) of wards that have more than 23.8 per cent retired population.

**7** Use Figure 7.
  **a)** Compare the population structure of Clun with that of Shrewsbury.
  **b)** Suggest two reasons for the differences you have noticed.

**8** Use Figure 8.
  **a)** Compare occupations in Bishop's Castle with Shrewsbury.
  **b)** Use this evidence to explain why some younger adults are leaving South Shropshire.

**9** Draw up a table like the one below. Add to the push and pull factors that cause movements in and out of rural areas like Shropshire.

| **Retired professionals moving out of larger towns and into the countryside** | | **Young adults moving out of the countryside and into larger towns** | |
|---|---|---|---|
| **Push factors** | **Pull factors** | **Push factors** | **Pull factors** |
| | Peace and quiet | Few full-time jobs | |

**10** Study Figure 9.
  **a)** Explain what this data tells us about the ethnic origin of people who migrate into Bishop's Castle.
  **b)** Suggest why so few Asian and black Afro-Caribbean people move into the countryside.
  **c)** Suggest why this might cause problems for the UK's multicultural society unless things change.

## Change can lead to conflict: the lack of affordable homes

- Is it true that many young rural people can no longer afford to stay in the countryside because there is a lack of **affordable homes**?
- Is it true that too little new social housing is being built and that the sale of owner-occupied housing to newcomers is forcing up the price of rural homes?

Newcomers to a rural area often commute to a full-time job outside the rural area, whereas local residents may work locally. Commuters may do their shopping in a large retail park on the edge of the city where they work because by the time they get home the village shops have closed for the day. The result is that, as a village attracts more commuters, its shops may get fewer customers. Village pubs close and are converted to homes, bus services are axed, and local shops and banks may also close. The rise of internet banking has also badly affected small rural branches.

**Figure 10** The primary school in Sarn, mid Wales, closed in 2006

| Percentage of the rural population with access to: | 2000 | 2004 | 2005 |
|---|---|---|---|
| Banks and building societies (within 4 km) | 66 | 64 | 60 |
| Cashpoints (within 4 km) | 85 | 85 | 90 |
| Post offices (within 2 km) | 90 | 85 | 85 |
| Primary schools (within 2 km) | 88 | 85 | 87 |

**Figure 11** Changing rural services (Source: Commission for Rural Communities report 2005)

Very few new houses are built because planners do not want houses built in the countryside on greenfield sites.

Demand from second-home owners increases.

There are few council houses left in rural areas because of the Right-to-Buy schemes introduced in the 1980s.

The price of rural housing goes up.

The supply of houses for sale is low.

Local people, especially young adults or those on low incomes, cannot afford to buy houses in the countryside.

Too little social housing for people on lowest incomes.

People on lowest incomes move out.

**Figure 12** Rural housing issues

### Activity

**11** Use Figure 11.
- **a)** Produce a graph to show what is happening to rural services.
- **b)** Give two different reasons for the closure of some rural banks and building societies.

**12** Study Figure 12. Identify two main causes for the lack of affordable housing in rural areas.

| | Rural areas | | | Urban areas | | |
|---|---|---|---|---|---|---|
| | Private sector | Social housing | All new housing | Private sector | Social housing | All new housing |
| 2003 | 37,600 | 2,400 | 40,100 | 47,200 | 7,100 | 54,300 |
| 2004 | 36,000 | 2,400 | 38,400 | 50,900 | 7,300 | 58,200 |
| 2005 | 36,700 | 2,800 | 38,500 | 55,900 | 9,000 | 64,800 |
| | | | Change* –3.90% | | | Change* +19.40% |

**Figure 13** New houses built in England. * = the percentage change (between 2003 and 2005) in the total number of new housing built. A minus number indicates less new houses were built in 2005 than in 2003

| Average rural house prices in West Midlands (£s) | | |
|---|---|---|
| **Location of houses** | **2000** | **2004** |
| Hamlets and isolated houses | 190,856 | 302,657 |
| Villages | 160,331 | 247,712 |
| Rural suburbs | 107,551 | 173,598 |
| Urban, up to population of 10,000 | 80,176 | 134,983 |

**Figure 14** The rising cost of buying houses in the country is pricing many locals out of the market

| Sparsity (population density) | Settlement type | Owned (%) | Social rented (%) | Private rented (%) |
|---|---|---|---|---|
| Less sparse | Small rural towns <10,000 | 67 | 21 | 10 |
| | Rural suburbs | 77 | 15 | 7 |
| | Villages | 78 | 10 | 9 |
| | Hamlets and isolated dwellings | 78 | 5 | 13 |
| Sparse (most rural parts of England) | Small rural towns <10,000 | 70 | 16 | 12 |
| | Rural suburbs | 68 | 18 | 12 |
| | Villages | 73 | 11 | 13 |
| | Hamlets and isolated dwellings | 71 | 5 | 19 |

**Figure 15** Housing tenure in rural England

## Activity

**13** Study Figures 13 and 15.

**a)** Compare the amount of social housing built in rural areas with that built in urban areas.

**b)** Compare the percentage of social housing available in hamlets with that in small rural towns.

**14** Use Figures 13, 14 and 15 to produce a short report on the rural housing issue. Include:

**a)** three graphs

**b)** evidence that supports or rejects the view that there is a lack of affordable rural housing.

## The second homes issue

The lack of affordable housing in rural areas is often linked to the sale of rural houses as **second homes** or holiday cottages. When a rural house is sold to be used as a second home at weekends or during holidays there are two effects:

1 One less house is available to local people. As we have seen, increasing demand for rural homes forces up rural house prices.
2 Even more village services are likely to close. Owners of second homes may spend only a few weeks of each year in their village home, so have little use for village services.

### Which parts of England and Wales are affected by the second homes issue?

Figure 17 suggests that there are many different views about the function of the UK's countryside. This is partly because rural areas in the UK are so varied:

- Many small towns in the south-east have become commuter villages.
- Large parts of the south-east and east are used for growing cereal crops.
- Many coastal areas in the south-west are used for tourism.

Most second homes tend to be in the most scenic parts of England, especially in Devon, Cornwall, Cumbria and parts of Yorkshire. These areas are shown in Figure 18 on page 175.

Within these large regions there is huge variation. The average number of second homes for England is 0.6 per cent, but this rises to as much as 12.6 per cent among isolated homes and tiny hamlets in north-west England. The Lake District National Park has an unusually high number of second homes. In the area surrounding the village of Hawkshead, seen in the centre of Figure 17, it is estimated that 40 per cent of all homes are second homes or holiday cottages.

**Figure 16** An extract from the lyrics of *Country Life* by folk group Show of Hands ▶

*And the red brick cottage where I was born*
*Is the empty shell of a holiday home.*
*Most of the year there's no one there,*
*The village is dead and they don't care.*
*Now we live on the edge of town.*
*Haven't been back since the pub closed down.*
*One man's family pays the price*
*For another man's vision of country life.*

▲ **Figure 17** What is the countryside for?

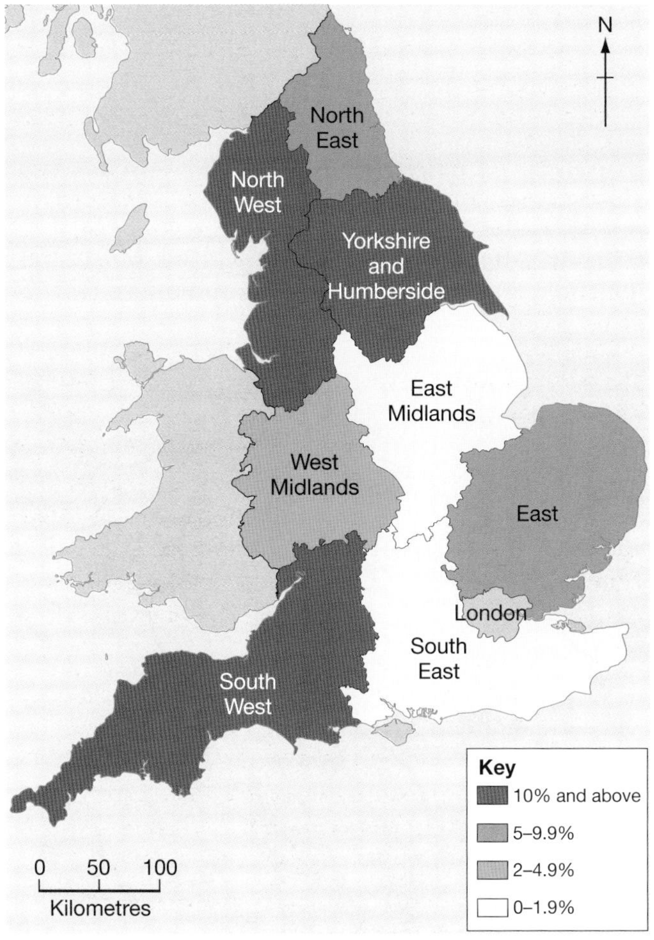


**Figure 18** The percentage of homes in hamlets and isolated villages that are unoccupied because they are either second homes or rented out as holiday homes

## Activity

**15** Describe and explain the point of view expressed in the song lyrics in Figure 16.

**16** Suggest why some rural areas have more second homes than others. Consider the effect of:
**a)** distance from larger cities
**b)** the attractiveness of the countryside.

**17** Use an atlas or the internet to find a map of England's National Parks. Compare this map with Figure 18.

**18** Discuss Shropshire's strategy to deal with second homes. Suggest:
**a)** Why a discount might be fair.
**b)** Reasons why the discount should be removed.

## Dealing with the second homes issue

All homeowners have to pay Council Tax on their main home: this is a tax that pays for a range of local services such as police, waste collection and local community facilities such as sports centres. However, many second homeowners get a substantial discount from their Council Tax bill for their second home. This is often a 50 per cent reduction in the bill, meaning a saving of £400 or more a year.

In 2007 there are estimated to be 100,000 second homes in rural parts of England. If the owners of these second homes were made to pay the full Council Tax it would raise an extra £400 million.

In Shropshire, a decision was made in 2003 to reduce the discount on the Council Tax for second homeowners from 50 per cent to ten per cent. During the period 2004–2007 this raised an extra £500,000 a year which was spent on local services. In South Shropshire, in which 2.6 per cent of the houses are second homes, this raised an additional £226,185 a year. The money has been spent on 80 different projects in South Shropshire, with payments of a few hundred pounds to several thousand pounds a year being made. The scheme is considered to be so successful that the project is being extended from 2007–2010. One of the projects to benefit most has been the SpArC project in Bishop's Castle. The SpArC project houses a small theatre space and a modern gym complex. It means that local people no longer have to travel to places such as Shrewsbury, which is 25 miles away, to access local sports and leisure services.

**Figure 19** Students from the local college work with professional actors in the Sports and Arts in the Community (SpArC) project

# Chapter 7
# Sustaining rural communities at the edge of Europe

## KEY QUESTIONS

- Why do people move between rural and urban areas?
- How is technology helping to support communities in isolated rural regions?
- Can isolated rural communities survive? Can they be made to be sustainable?

Iceland

## Impacts of migration

In this case study we will investigate patterns of migration in Iceland. Most rural areas in Iceland are losing population, a process known as **depopulation**. How can isolated rural communities be given a sustainable future?

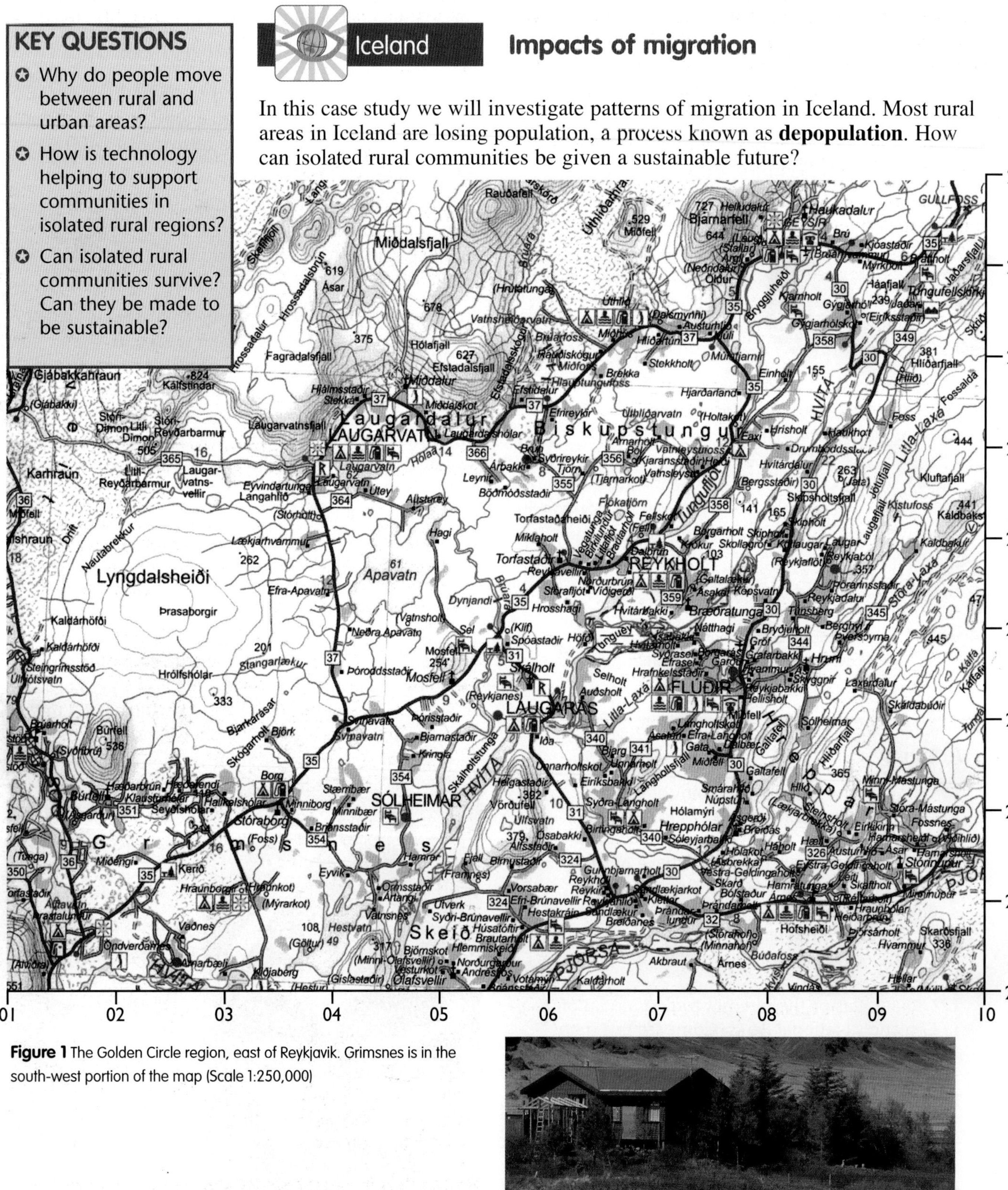


Figure 1 The Golden Circle region, east of Reykjavik. Grimsnes is in the south-west portion of the map (Scale 1:250,000)

Figure 2 There are more than 1,500 holiday homes like this in Grimsnes

## How is counter-urbanisation affecting Iceland?

Iceland has only one major city, the capital Reykjavik. Many wealthy residents of Reykjavik own second homes in the countryside so they can get away from the city at the weekend. This is a form of counter-urbanisation. Most second homes are located in the 'Golden Circle' region: a rural area about one hour's drive to the east of Reykjavik. This area contains many of Iceland's most popular attractions such as Geysir and Gullfoss (see page 112).

The construction of second homes and the growth of tourism are changing this rural community and these changes could create conflict. Locals could feel swamped by newcomers: Grimsnes, just one housing development in the Golden Circle, has more than 1,500 holiday homes but has only 356 permanent residents.

The recreational use of rural areas by visitors from Reykjavik is also causing conflict. Off-road driving in the rural regions of Iceland is popular, but the tyre tracks and deep ruts are scarring the landscape. The Environment and Food Agency of Iceland is so concerned about this damage that most off-road driving has been banned since 1999.

**Figure 3** The construction of new holiday homes in Selfoss (grid ref: 0120 in Figure 1) creates valuable local employment

### Activity

**1** Use Figure 1.
- **a)** Give a four-figure grid reference for Geysir (north-east corner of the map).
- **b)** Use the map to give directions and approximate distances to travel from Grimsnes to Geysir.
- **c)** Give four pieces of evidence that the area is heavily used by tourists.

**2** Describe two ways in which counter-urbanisation could create conflict in Iceland's rural regions.

**3** Suggest the arguments for and against the building of more second homes and holiday homes in Grimsnes.

**4** Study Figure 4. Give three reasons why soils in Iceland are at great risk of erosion.

**5** Suggest why it is necessary to protect Iceland's wilderness regions.

**Figure 4** Illegal off-road driving in Skaftafell National Park has left these tyre tracks

## Rural depopulation

Reykjavik's population is 114,000 and a further 74,000 people live within its outer suburbs. Two-thirds of all Iceland's population (300,000 people) lives within 40 km of Reykjavik's city centre. This number continues to grow as migrants leave the remote rural regions of Iceland. The pull factors include better jobs and much better urban services.

Other regions of Iceland have no large cities. The sparsely populated rural areas in the north-west, north and east are too isolated from Reykjavik to be affected by counter-urbanisation and commuting. Each year the rural regions of Iceland receive some migrants and lose others. In some regions more people leave the region than move in, a situation known as **net out-migration**. The loss of people by migration, combined with low birth rates, is causing **rural depopulation**.

### Activity

**6** Define **pull factors.**

**7** Give two reasons for the loss of population in remote rural areas.

**8** Study Figure 5.
**a)** Describe the distribution (see page 143) of regions which have lost most people.
**b)** Describe which parts of Iceland are gaining population.
**c)** Explain the pattern you have identified in answers a) and b).

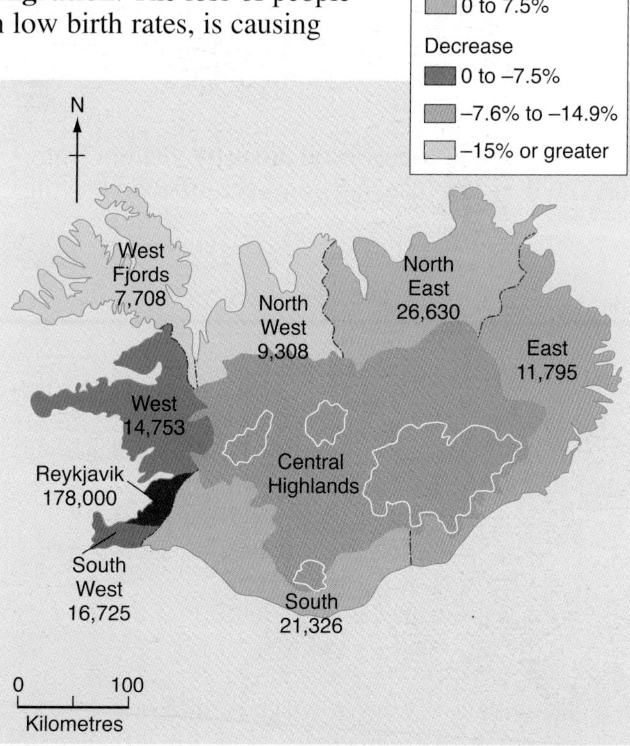


**Figure 5** Regional population and migration (gains or losses) for the regions of Iceland (2001)

### Depopulation in the West Fjords

The West Fjords is the rural region of Iceland that has been hardest hit by depopulation. In the period from 1986 to 2003 net out-migration from the West Fjords averaged 27 people per 1,000 population. More women than men are leaving these regions, especially in the age range twenty to 49.

The West Fjords is the most remote part of Iceland from Reykjavik. The region covers an area of more than 12,000 km$^2$ (similar in size to the West Midlands, England) but has a total population of only 7,900 (the population of the West Midlands is 2.69 million). The many sea inlets or **fjords** make the coastline very long and inland it is mountainous. In addition the roads are poor, with many single-track and unmade surfaces, so journey times are slow. The weather can be hazardous; in 1995 two separate avalanches of snow killed 34 people.

The traditional economy of the West Fjords is in decline. Fishing has always been the biggest employer, but the government has cut the number of fish that can be caught in order to conserve fish stocks in the sea. Sheep farming is the second-biggest employer, but it is unprofitable and unpopular among the young.

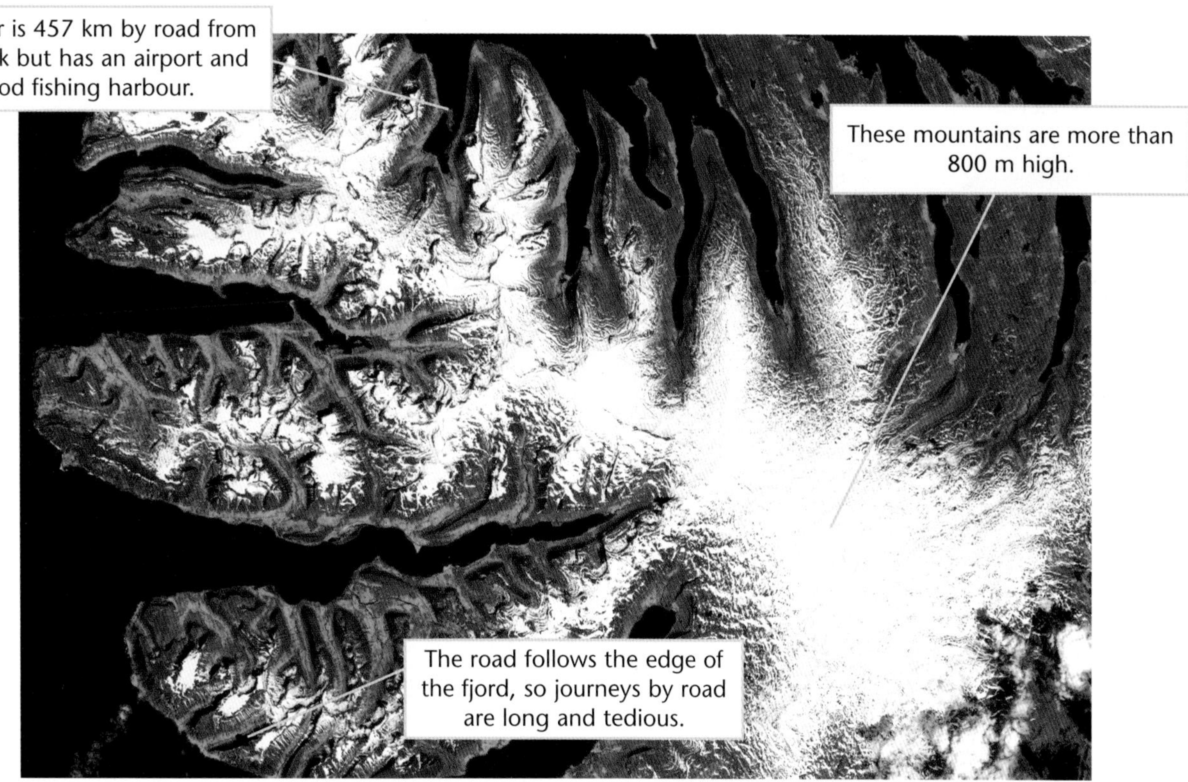


**Figure 6** A satellite image of the inaccessible West Fjords

**Figure 7** Isafjordur is the West Fjords region's largest settlement. It has a population of 2,700 people

| Employment | West Fjords | Reykjavik |
|---|---|---|
| Agriculture, fishing and mining | 43 | 3 |
| Manufacturing | 20 | 26 |
| Services | 37 | 71 |

**Figure 8** Employment (percentages) in West Fjords compared to Reykjavik (2003)

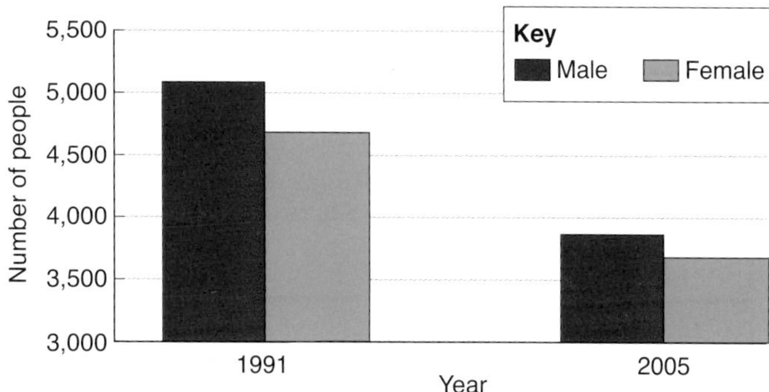


**Figure 9** Population decline in the West Fjords (1991 and 2005)

## Activity

**9** Use the text on page 178 and Figures 6 and 7 to create a list of the push factors that might be causing migration from the West Fjords.

**10** Use Figure 8.

**a)** Compare the employment pattern in West Fjords with that in Reykjavik.

**b)** Explain how this could be further evidence of push and pull factors.

**11** Use Figure 9 to compare the population of West Fjords in 2005 with that in 1991.

## Are Iceland's remote rural communities sustainable?

The migration of people from rural areas to Reykjavik is causing serious concern. If rural populations become too small then essential services such as schools and doctors' clinics become increasingly inefficient and expensive to sustain. If a doctor's surgery closes, local people find that they are further and further away from healthcare. Rural communities could become **unsustainable** and have no future.

A similar process has been happening in rural communities in other regions of the Arctic, such as Alaska, Greenland and Norway. As in Iceland, most migrants are young adults and more women than men migrate. In some of these regions the young men who remain in the rural area are experiencing severe social problems such as alcoholism and relatively high suicide rates.

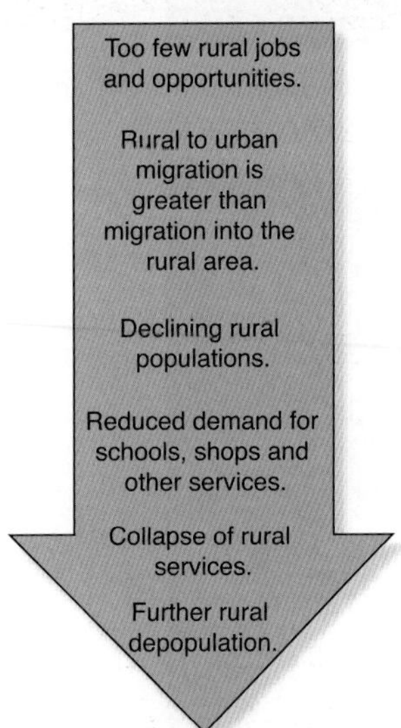


▲ **Figure 10** How rural depopulation creates unsustainable communities

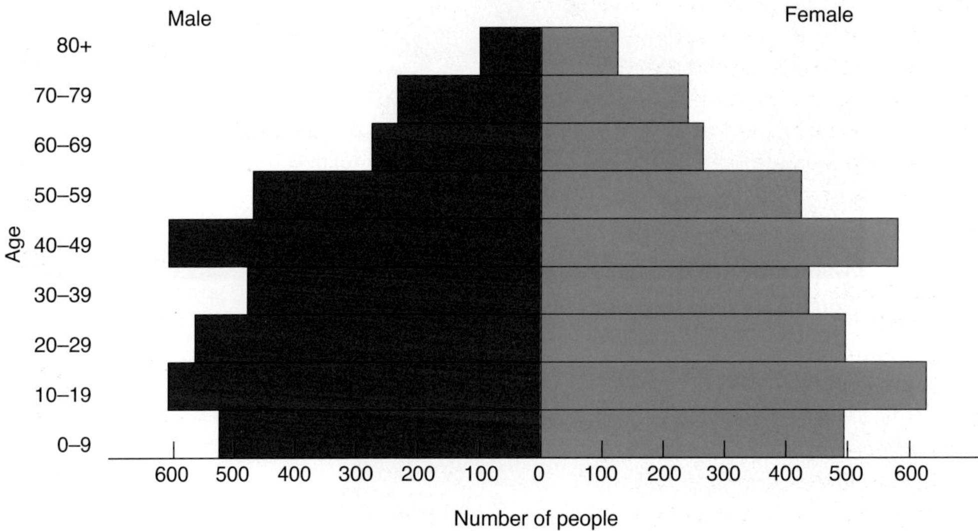


**Figure 12** A population pyramid for the West Fjords in 2005

| | |
|---|---|
| 1986 | 14.1 |
| 1987 | 17.8 |
| 1988 | 31.1 |
| 1989 | 27.7 |
| 1990 | 18.4 |
| 1991 | 23.4 |
| 1992 | 9.8 |
| 1993 | 16.0 |
| 1994 | 28.6 |
| 1995 | 47.9 |
| 1996 | 40.7 |
| 1997 | 44.6 |
| 1998 | 39.4 |
| 1999 | 43.5 |
| 2000 | 29.1 |
| 2001 | 21.2 |
| 2002 | 23.0 |
| 2003 | 16.7 |

**Figure 11** Net out-migration from West Fjords 1986 to 2003. Figures are per thousand population

### Activity

**12** Study Figure 10.

**a)** Identify the main cause of rural depopulation.

**b)** Explain how closure of services can be both a cause and an effect of depopulation.

**13 a)** Choose a suitable technique to graphically represent the data in Figure 11.

**b)** Is the depopulation issue getting worse? Describe the pattern shown on your graph.

**14** Suggest what you think could be done to reduce the impacts of depopulation.

**15** From what you have learned about the West Fjords, suggest why more women than men migrate from rural areas of the Arctic.

**16 a)** Describe the main features of the population pyramid, Figure 12.

**b)** Explain how Figure 12, provides evidence of the age and sex of migrants who have left the West Fjords.

## Going Further

### How can new technology help rural communities?

The growth of the mobile phone network and greater use of the internet have allowed rural communities better access to information and services such as education courses from their home. This will help to reverse the negative impacts that have been made by the closure of rural services such as schools, libraries and shops. Mobile phone coverage in Iceland is excellent, even in the most isolated areas, and internet connection is actively encouraged by the government. As a result, the number of students using distant learning methods, such as web-based courses and video-conferencing, almost trebled between 1998 and 2001. The government believes that these technologies will reduce rural isolation and depopulation.

**17** Use Figure 13 to compare Iceland's mobile phone subscriptions with:
- **a)** Romania
- **b)** Finland.

**18** Use the data in Figure 13 to suggest how mobile phone subscription might be an indicator of both quality of life and standard of living.

**19** Investigate the following hypothesis:

*The Scandinavian countries, which have the most rural and isolated populations in Europe, were the quickest European countries to develop their mobile networks.*

To structure this investigation you could:
- **a)** put the countries in Figure 13 into rank order, starting with the country with the highest mobile subscriptions in 2000
- **b)** use an atlas to identify which parts of Europe have the highest subscriptions
- **c)** consider alternative explanations for any pattern you discover. This might include researching the Gross National Income for the countries in Figure 13.

| Selected EU members | 2000 | 2001 | 2002 | 2003 |
|---|---|---|---|---|
| Czech Republic | 42 | 68 | 84 | 95 |
| Denmark | 63 | 74 | 83 | 89 |
| Germany | 59 | 68 | 72 | 79 |
| Greece | 54 | 73 | 85 | 81 |
| Spain | 61 | 73 | 82 | 90 |
| Italy | 73 | 89 | 93 | 98 |
| Latvia | 17 | 26 | 39 | 52 |
| Lithuania | 14 | 29 | 47 | 62 |
| Luxembourg | 70 | 93 | 107 | 120 |
| Hungary | 30 | 49 | 68 | 78 |
| Austria | 76 | 82 | 84 | 88 |
| Poland | 17 | 25 | 36 | 46 |
| Portugal | 65 | 81 | 83 | 90 |
| Slovenia | 57 | 76 | 77 | 87 |
| Slovakia | 21 | 41 | 56 | 68 |
| Finland | 72 | 81 | 87 | 91 |
| Sweden | 72 | 81 | 89 | 98 |
| **Non EU members** | | | | |
| Bulgaria | 9 | 20 | 32 | 45 |
| Romania | 9 | 20 | 23 | 32 |
| Iceland | 77 | 88 | 91 | 97 |
| Norway | 75 | 84 | 86 | 91 |

**Figure 13** The rise of mobile phone subscriptions in Europe. Figures refer to number of subscriptions per 100 people. Source: Eurostat

## Creating sustainable rural communities

Iceland's government wants to create sustainable rural communities. They believe that new industries such as tourism must be encouraged in order to **diversify** the rural economy. They are encouraging both Icelandic and **trans-national companies (TNCs)** to invest in rural communities. Foreign investors locating in a rural region of Iceland will experience a number of advantages:

- Business taxes in Iceland are lower than almost anywhere else in Europe.
- Energy is also cheap because Iceland uses **renewable resources** such as **hydro-electric power (HEP)** and geothermal (heat from the ground) rather than oil.
- Foreign film-makers who want to shoot their new film in Iceland are offered a refund of twelve per cent of all production costs.

Regional Development Agencies promote development in each of Iceland's rural areas. Their aim is to reduce inequalities between the rural areas and Reykjavik. The West Fjords Development Agency is attempting to attract high-tech industries such as data-processing or specialised food-processing or fishing-related industries. One example is an Irish company which has located a seaweed processing factory in West Fjords, employing ten full-time staff.

### Can sustainable futures be created from tourism?

Iceland has a fast-growing tourist industry based on its natural resources and wildlife. Farmers are diversifying their income by converting farms and outbuildings into holiday accommodation. Bed-and-breakfast type accommodation is now widespread in rural Iceland, but the tourist season is short because of the climate (see page 10).

The West Fjords has much to offer tourists interested in the natural environment:

- sea or river fishing
- bird-watching
- whale-watching from the harbour at Isafjordur
- kayaking, horse riding and hiking in the summer and skiing in winter.

Iceland has a long tradition of whale-hunting, but a television and radio poll in 2003 showed that 71 per cent of Icelanders would support an end to whaling if jobs could be created in nature-based tourism instead. A number of whalers and fishermen have switched from whaling to taking tourists on whale-watching trips. Whale-watching creates jobs and can continue without damaging the environment, so it is an example of a **sustainable development** for rural communities in Iceland.

**Figure 14** Whale-watching could help to sustain rural communities

◀ **Figure 15** A minke whale caught by a whaling boat from Isafjordur in 2003. Source: Greenpeace

| Year | Number of tourists |
|---|---|
| 1995 | 2,200 |
| 1996 | 9,700 |
| 1997 | 20,540 |
| 1998 | 30,330 |
| 1999 | 32,250 |
| 2000 | 45,400 |
| 2001 | 60,550 |
| 2002 | 62,050 |

**Figure 16** The growth in the number of whale-watching tourists in Iceland ▶

i) Specialised agriculture and breeding

ii) Ecotourism

a) Excellent water supply

iii) Remote data processing (using the internet to transfer and process databases, software and spreadsheets)

b) Knowledge of fisheries-related industries

c) Unused industrial and farm buildings

iv) Film production

d) Relatively cheap, renewable sources of electricity

e) Long coastline with sheltered fjords

v) Production of fresh water and marine foods (e.g. fish farming)

vi) Industry that requires up to 30 megawatts of power

f) Highly educated and skilled workforce

g) Magnificent and clean environment

vii) Fisheries-related industry

viii) Activity and adventure holidays

h) Excellent mobile communications and high usage of home computers

**Figure 17** The resources of the West Fjords, and industries that could be developed as the economy diversifies

## Activity

**20 a)** Choose an appropriate graphical technique to represent the data in Figure 16.
**b)** Describe the trend of your graph.

**21** Suggest the point of view of each of the following to both whale hunting and whale-watching:
**a)** A member of Greenpeace in the UK.
**b)** The owner of a whaling boat in Isafjordur.
**c)** The owner of a hotel in Isafjordur.

**22** Explain why it is important for the rural economy of Iceland to diversify.

**23** Study Figure 17.
**a)** Match the West Fjords' resources (a)–h)) to potential industries that could be attracted to the region (i)–viii)).
**b)** Use your list to describe how you think the West Fjords should diversify its economy. Suggest the possible advantages of your scheme compared with alternative types of diversification.

# Chapter 8
# Problem-solving exercise

## Creating sustainable rural communities in South Africa

**Your enquiry ...**

What is the quality of life for this South African family?

Why are they cooking on a wood stove?

Do they have electric light?

Do they know what they are missing in the city?

Can this rural community survive?

We saw in chapter 5 that many rural South Africans are leaving their homes and migrating to the city. In this chapter we will examine in more detail the quality of life for rural families living in Limpopo in the northern part of South Africa. Are these rural communities sustainable? Do they have any future? Can you design a plan that will help to give communities like this a better quality of life and make rural life more sustainable?

**Your decision ...**

How can this family have a better quality of life and a better future without moving to the city?

**Figure 1** Cooking over an open wood fire in a traditional rural home in Limpopo province

### Part A: what is it like to live in Limpopo, South Africa?

Limpopo is the most rural of South Africa's nine provinces and most people have farm occupations. The province also has stunning scenery and wildlife so some people are employed in tourism. Most tourists visit the Kruger National Park, although Africa's big five (elephant, lion, cheetah, giraffe and rhinoceros) can be seen in several other parts of the province.

Limpopo's largest city is Polokwane (formerly Pietersburg). With a population of 90,000, this city is similar in size to some of England's smaller county towns, such as Shrewsbury in Shropshire.

### Quality of life in Limpopo

Most farm workers in Limpopo are poorly paid; many earn less than US$1 a day. The average household income is below 1,000 Rand (US$140), so 60 per cent of families live below the poverty line. Many farm workers do not have security of tenure, in other words, they do not have full legal rights to live in their own home. Other kinds of work are scarce and unemployment is high. Recent surveys suggest that only 23 per cent of the population between the ages of fifteen and 65 have formal employment.

Almost twenty per cent of the houses in Limpopo are traditional timber frame and thatch huts, and in some districts, such as Mutale in the north of the province, this percentage rises to almost 50 per cent. These homes can be very uncomfortable. The roofs leak in the rainy season and they are badly ventilated so smoke from cooking stoves is trapped inside the building. People prefer to live in 'formal' concrete block houses.

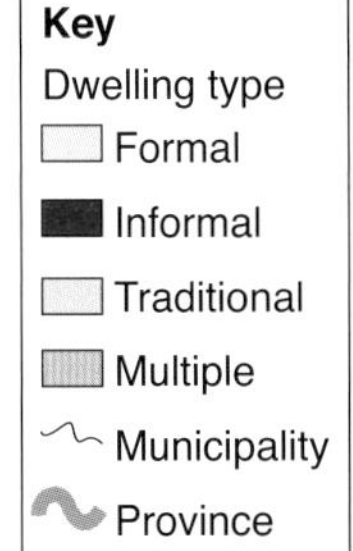

**Figure 2** The distribution of traditional housing in Limpopo

**Figure 3** Traditional housing in Limpopo. This household benefits from electricity provided by a photovoltaic cell

## Activity

**1** Use Figure 1 to complete the following description:

**Limpopo is located in the … of South Africa. To the … it shares borders with Botswana and …. It also shares a border with … in the ….**

**2** Use Figure 2 to describe the location (see page 155) of the district of Kruger.

**3** Describe the distribution (see page 143) of traditional homes in Limpopo.

**4** **a)** Explain what is meant by push and pull factors.

**b)** Explain three push factors that cause migration from Limpopo.

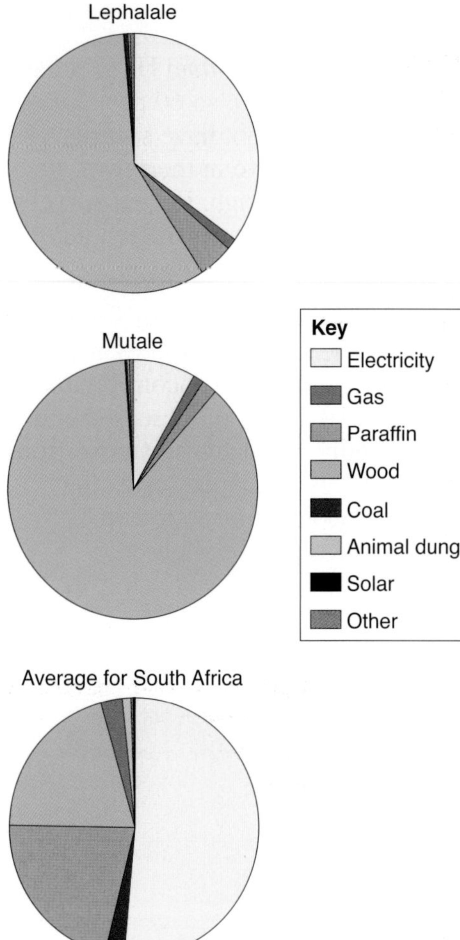


**Figure 4** The percentage of homes using electricity or other energy sources for cooking

## Part B: how can rural standards of living be improved?

There are a large number of strategies being used to improve the **standard of living** and quality of life in rural areas of Limpopo. This part of the chapter examines four such strategies.

### Rural electrification

Since 1994 South Africa has been extending the supply of electricity to both **urban** and rural communities. By 2000 about 70 per cent of households had an electricity supply, but the network extended to more urban homes than rural ones. As you can see in Figure 4, large parts of Limpopo were still using wood stoves for cooking in 2001. The use of wood burning stoves for cooking causes health problems such as eye and chest irritations. The inhalation of wood smoke is also linked to the development of some cancers.

The South African government aims to extend the electricity supply into rural areas so that 85 per cent of homes have a supply by 2010. In many places this is done by extending the national grid of power cables. However, in some more remote areas **off-grid electricity** is being supplied by using car batteries or photovoltaic cells.

This strategy has obvious benefits. Women's health benefits because they no longer have to cook on wood stoves. Rural schools can start to invest in televisions and computers. Lighting in rural areas means that children can do their homework in the evening. However, studies have shown that rural electrification does not always create the benefits that might be expected. The poorest households cannot afford to pay their electricity bills and continue to use wood stoves after electricity has been connected. In one study, 44 per cent of households had still not purchased an electric stove three years after electrification.

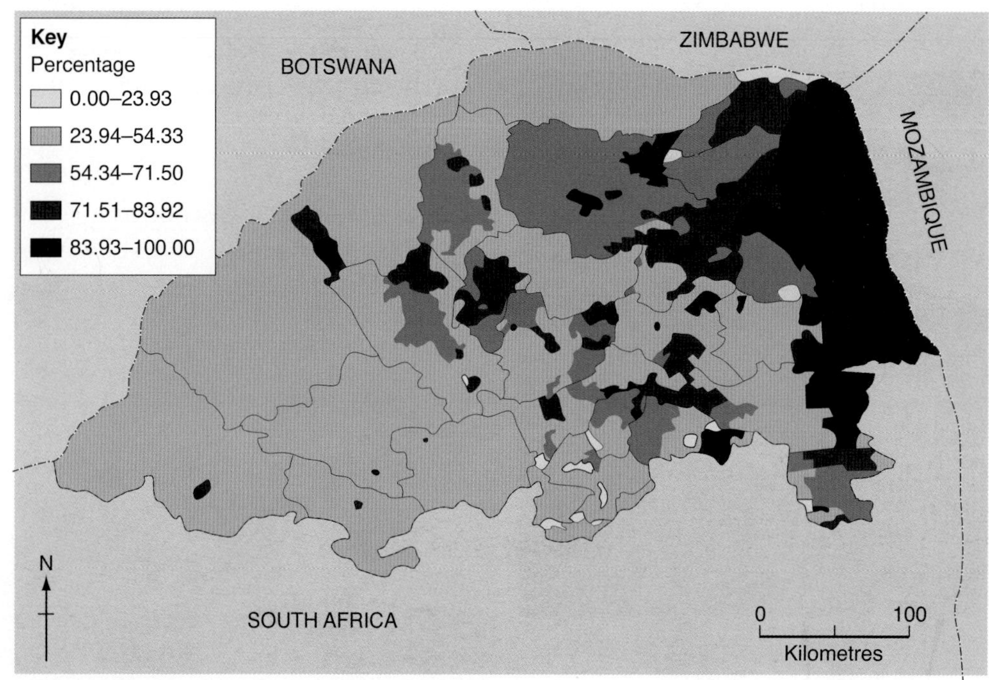


**Figure 5** Percentage of households in Limpopo with access to piped water

## Improving rural water supplies

Many isolated rural communities in Limpopo still collect water from rivers or pools where the water can be dirty and cause ill health. Rural houses can be adapted for **rainwater harvesting** by collecting rainwater from the roof in a large rainwater tank. However, at the moment, only 3,100 houses in Limpopo have this system.

| Main water supply | Lephalale | Mutale | Limpopo | South Africa |
|---|---|---|---|---|
| Piped water to the dwelling | 19.9 | 3.1 | 9.4 | 32.3 |
| Piped water inside yard | 39.2 | 18.4 | 29.0 | 29.0 |
| Piped water to community stand <200 m | 19.0 | 23.6 | 15.9 | 10.7 |
| Piped water to community stand >200 m | 17.3 | 32.9 | 23.7 | 12.4 |
| Other (includes boreholes, rivers, pools) | 4.6 | 22.0 | 22.0 | 15.6 |

**Figure 6** The percentage of homes with a piped water supply compared with other sources of water

### Activity

**5** Use Figure 5 to describe the distribution (see page 143) of districts where more than 71.51 per cent of households are connected to a piped water supply.

**6** Use Figure 4.
**a)** Compare the use of energy sources for cooking in Lephalale with the average for South Africa.
**b)** Which district, Lephalale or Mutale, needs the rural electrification project most? Justify your choice.

**7** Explain why lack of electricity and piped water are a possible cause of rural to urban migration.

**8** Explain the benefits of rural electrification for:
**a)** women
**b)** children.

**9** Use Figure 6.
**a)** Produce pie charts to represent the data.
**b)** Which district, Lephalale or Mutale, most needs better water supplies? Justify your choice.

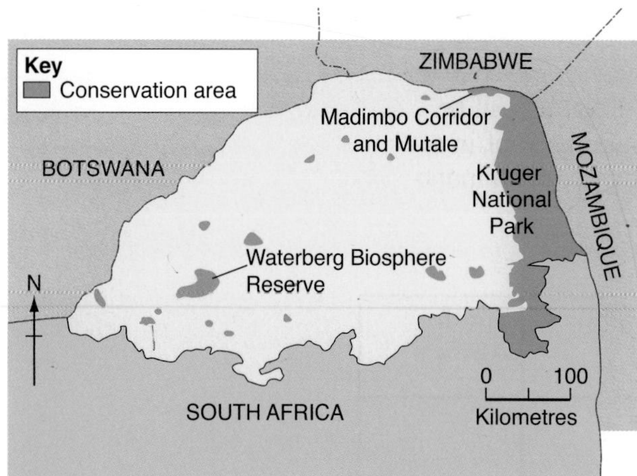


**Figure 7** Conservation areas in Limpopo

## Creating more jobs in ecotourism

There is an urgent need to diversify the rural economy by creating new jobs that are not connected to farming. Tourists already visit Limpopo. Most visit the Kruger National Park in the east of the province. Other areas of Limpopo could benefit, including:

- The Madimbo Corridor and Mutale in the north
- the Waterberg Biosphere Reserve in Laphalale in the west of the province.

The Waterberg Biosphere Reserve was created in 1999. 77,000 people live in the reserve. It is a large area where the dry climate makes farming difficult and incomes are low. Farmers are gradually switching to **ecotourism**. Tourists pay to stay with local families or in luxury lodges. Local people are employed to act as guides and wardens. The reserve contains 75 mammal species (including the big five) and 300 species of bird. A limited amount of hunting is allowed. Tourists pay large sums to shoot impala and other wild animals. This money is then used to pay for conservation projects such as breeding programmes, habitat conservation and anti-poaching patrols.

The Madimbo Corridor is a narrow strip of land between the district of Mutale and Zimbabwe. Many hippo and crocodile live in its rivers and pools. The area is on a migration route for elephants and buffalo between Zimbabwe and the Kruger National Park. The creation of a conservation project and jobs in ecotourism would benefit wildlife and create badly needed jobs.

### Activity

**10** Use Figure 7 to describe the distribution of conservation areas in Limpopo.

**11 a)** Explain what is meant by the phrase 'diversify the rural economy'.

**b)** Explain what could happen to districts like Mutale if the economy is not diversified.

**12** Explain how a new ecotourism project would:

**a)** improve standards of living

**b)** conserve wildlife.

**Figure 8** Hunting for wild animals is strictly limited. This tourist will have paid a high price for the right to shoot game in Limpopo. Tourist fees are divided between local communities and conservation groups

### Creating more jobs in mining

Limpopo is rich in mineral deposits. Some are already mined, but many new jobs would be created if new mining operations were permitted. The Madimbo Corridor, for example, has deposits of diamonds. These diamonds could be mined creating hundreds of jobs, but conservationists worry that this would prevent the development of tourism.

Meanwhile, in Lephalale district, to the immediate west of the Waterberg Biosphere Reserve, Kumba Coal (a trans-national mining company) would like to develop a new open-cast coal mine. The Waterberg area already produces eight per cent of South Africa's coal, but the region contains huge reserves that are yet to be mined: approximately 44 per cent of the country's coal reserves are in Waterberg. A new mine is being proposed that would produce approximately three million tonnes of coal a year for the next twenty years.

## Part C: how can rural communities have a sustainable future?

- Some of the strategies discussed in Part B are more appropriate to some groups of people than others. You should consider who benefits most from each of these schemes.
- You also need to create a plan that will be achievable: you can't do everything at once so you will need to think about your priorities.
- It would be sensible to focus your resources on just one rural community. So consider which schemes are most appropriate for Mutale, and which would work best in Lephalale.

## Activity

**13** Use what you have learned so far to complete each of the following tables:

| Group of people | Strategies that create most benefits |
|---|---|
| Those who do the household chores, especially women and children | |
| School children | |
| Farmers | |
| Isolated rural communities | |
| The population of larger rural towns such as Polokwane and Lephalale | |

| Scheme | Main advantages | Main disadvantages |
|---|---|---|
| Rural electrification | | Some households cannot afford electricity bills or electric stoves |
| Improving water supplies | | Few if any |
| Ecotourism projects | | Would prevent mining operations nearby |
| Mining | | Would prevent tourism locally until the mining operation was complete |

**14** Produce a development plan for a rural district of Limpopo. You must justify your plan to show how it will create a sustainable future for this rural area.

EXAMTECHNIQUE

## Getting the best mark for part C of this problem-solving exercise

In section C of paper 3/4 you will be asked to prepare a plan to show how you think a particular issue could best be tackled. You will be marked on how well you justify this plan: this means you need to explain why you think your plan is a good one.

### Step 1

The first thing to do is to decide which of the schemes has most advantages and least disadvantages. Are you going to recommend:

- speeding up the rural electrification programme and/or the supply of piped water?
- encouraging the development of rural ecotourism projects?
- exploring for further deposits of minerals and creating more mining and industrial jobs?

You could suggest a combination of these approaches or ideas of your own, such as improved school facilities.

### Step 2

In order to get a good mark, you will need to justify your plan. This means explaining why you think your plan will be successful.

| Key questions to ask yourself | Comments |
|---|---|
| How does my plan meet the needs of particular groups of people? | Will the women and children who do chores, such as collecting firewood and cooking, benefit? |
| Does my plan improve quality of life? | Will people have healthier and happier lifestyles as a result of your plan? |
| What are the advantages of my plan for the rural economy or the environment? | Does your plan create jobs for unemployed young men? Will wildlife be conserved? |
| Is my plan sustainable? In other words, will it create lasting benefits? | Will people be happier to stay in Limpopo as a result of your plan? |

**Tip 1**

### Think about the short- and long-term benefits of your plan

The aim of this problem-solving exercise is to create a rural development plan that will be sustainable. In other words, you need to prove that your plan will have lasting benefits. You could structure your answer around two headings:

1 The benefits that might be created in the first few months of your plan. These are the **short-term benefits** or advantages.

Example:
**Short-term benefits:**
If the rural electrification project was speeded up in the Mutale region the immediate or short-term benefits would be ... (consider health benefits for women, and educational benefits for children).

2 The benefits that might be created over the next ten or more years. These are the **long-term benefits**.

Example:
**Long-term benefits:**
If this region had better water and electricity supplies it would be more appealing to foreign tourists. Such people expect to be able to have hot showers and air-conditioning. So, in the longer term (over the next ten years or so) the benefits of rural electrification would be ...

# Unit 4 Work and Development

## Chapter 1 The Big Picture

This unit is about the global economy. Flows of people, ideas, money and goods are making an increasingly complex global web that links people and places from distant continents together. We call this process **globalisation**.

## The factors that drive globalisation

**Example:** avocados grown in Mexico will be flown to a UK supermarket. This improves customer choice but **food air miles** have an impact on carbon emissions.

**Trade:** Improved technology and cheap aviation fuel mean that fresh food can be flown from distant places to our supermarkets.

**Example:** local people demonstrating about the falling water levels in their wells after this soft-drinks company opened a bottling plant in Kerala, India.

**Trans-national companies:** Large companies open branches in several different countries throughout the world.

**Ideas and communication:** The growth of communication technology such as the internet, mobile phones and satellite television has vastly improved global interconnection.

**Culture:** Certain styles of music, television and film are now shown around the world.

**Example:** films made in Hollywood, USA, advertised in an Asian street. But will local styles of music and entertainment survive?

**Example:** African countries which have few telephone landlines have used mobile technology to leapfrog the problem.

**Figure 1** Coldplay performing at *Live8*, the charity concert in aid of the Make Poverty History campaign in 2005

## The development gap

Almost half of the families in the world survive on an income of less than US$2 (or £1.30) a day. More than 535 million workers live with their families in extreme poverty on less than US$1 a day. By comparison, the richest ten people in the world have more money than the combined wealth of the world's poorest 58 countries. This unit is, in part, about this gap between rich and poor. How do we measure it? Is the gap getting any smaller, and if not, why not?

The **development gap** between rich and poor countries often makes headline news. You may remember the 'Make Poverty History' campaign of 2005. The leaders of some of the world's richest nations, including the UK, discussed cancelling the **debt** owed to them by some of the world's poorest countries. At the same time, celebrity campaigners such as Chris Martin of Coldplay, Bono of U2 and Bob Geldof kept the story in the news by organising a series of concerts.

### The debt crisis

For many African countries, debt has been a huge hindrance to development over the last twenty or more years. Many took out loans in the 1970s and 1980s largely from the World Bank, which is funded by wealthier countries. At that time the value of oil and other **exports** was rising, and poor countries thought that they would be able to repay their debts as their economies grew. However, in the early 1980s, the price of oil crashed. Ever since, these countries have been struggling to pay back the original loans and the interest on their debt. Critics say this money would be better invested in health, education, water and sanitation projects, which would dramatically improve **quality of life**. For example, Niger has been repaying an average of US$36 million of its debts each year (in the period 2001 to 2005), whereas it can afford to spend only US$27 million each year on healthcare.

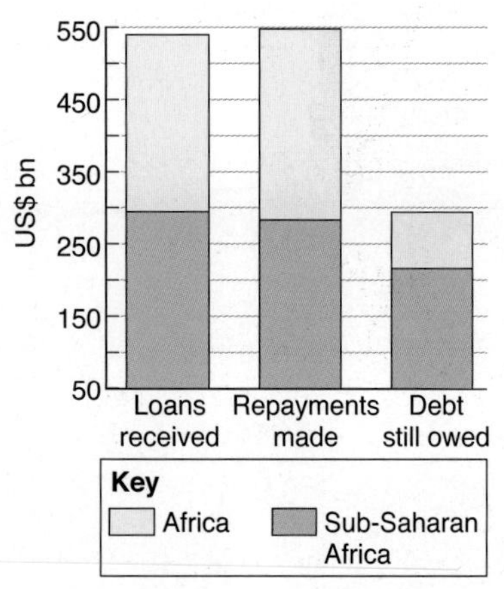


**Figure 2** Africa's debts, 1970 to 2002. **sub-Saharan Africa** is the large region south of the Sahara

**Figure 3** How do you see the world?

## The Brandt Line

Public awareness of the development gap is not new. It was first brought into the news headlines in the Brandt Report in 1980. This report, by Willy Brandt, a German politician, drew a line on the map that separated the richer countries from the poorer ones. This map was developed to separate the **More Economically Developed Countries (MEDCs)** from the **Less Economically Developed Countries (LEDCs)**. As you can see on Figure 4, the MEDCs are situated mainly in the northern hemisphere. The LEDCs are mainly in the tropics and southern hemisphere. The line loops around Australia and New Zealand to include them in the richer half of the map. This famous map draws attention to the gap between the richer North and the poorer South and is still in use today. But is it still relevant and accurate?

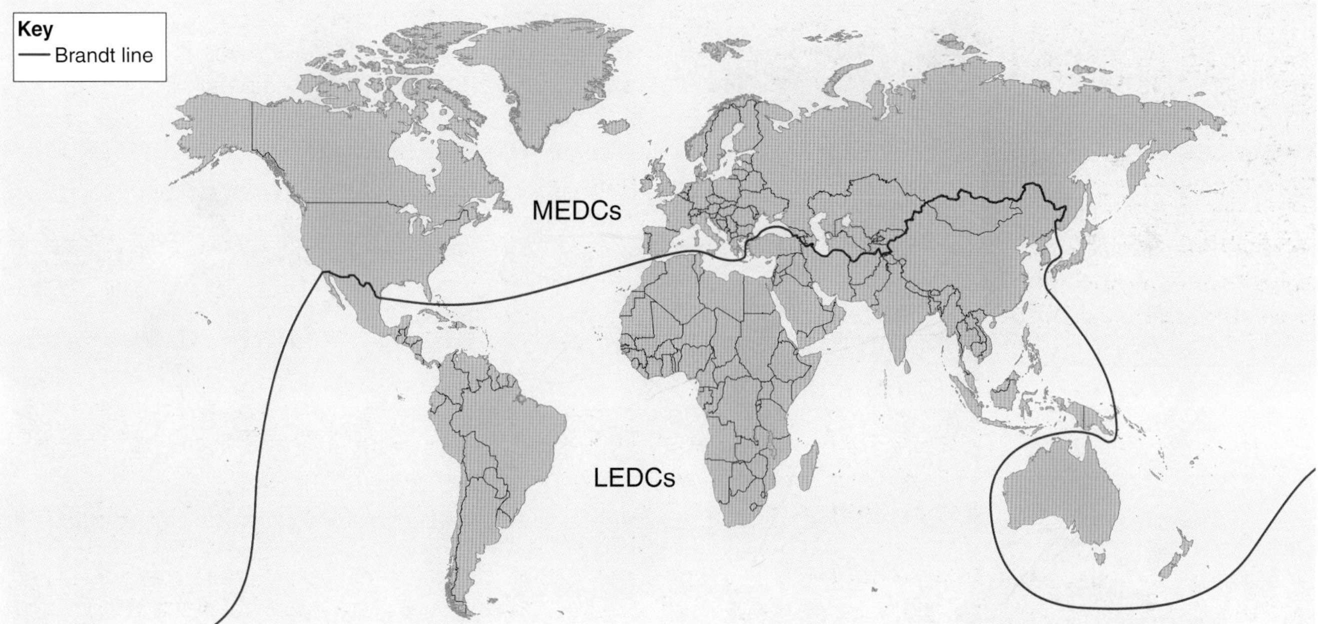


**Figure 4** The Brandt Line separates MEDCs from LEDCs

### Activity

**1** Study Figure 2.
- **a)** How much money have African countries:
  - i) received in loans
  - ii) repaid in debts?
- **b)** Explain why money is still owed. Do you think this is fair?

**2** Explain how cancelling LEDCs' debt would lead to improved quality of life.

**3** Discuss the cartoon, Figure 3.
- **a)** Describe each character: how they are dressed and what they are doing?
- **b)** Who do the two figures represent?
- **c)** Explain the actions of the larger one.

**4** Use Figures 1, 2 and 3 to create a newspaper headline and the first paragraph of a news article about world poverty.

**5** Discuss the concept of globalisation introduced on page 191.
- **a)** Working with a partner, make a list of any products, brand names, companies, films and music that you associate with each of the following places:
  - i) USA
  - ii) Australia
  - iii) Japan
  - iv) India
  - v) Africa.
- **b)** Now combine your list with that of two of your classmates. Discuss your lists. Do you think that globalisation is driven equally by MEDCs and LEDCs?

**6** Use Figure 2 and any other information from this chapter to justify the view that Africa's debt should be cancelled.

# Chapter 2
# Patterns of employment

**KEY QUESTIONS**

- What are the different ways of classifying and recording employment?
- How do patterns of employment vary from one place to another?
- How are patterns of employment changing, and how might technology affect employment in the future?

## How do we classify and record employment?

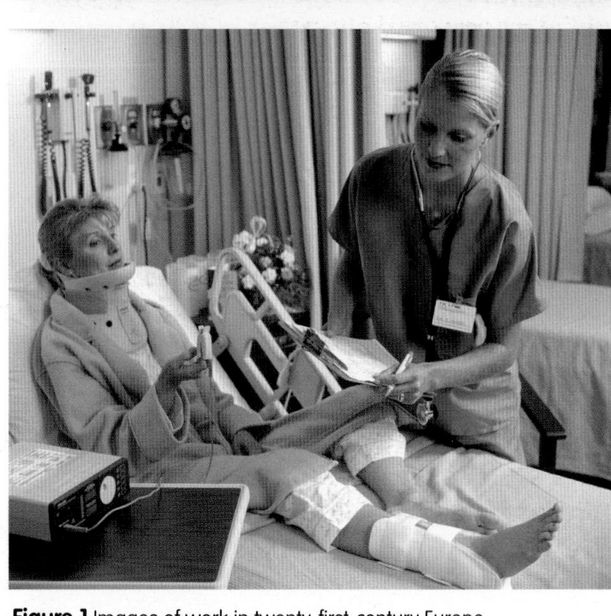

**Figure 1** Images of work in twenty-first-century Europe

## Primary, secondary and tertiary sectors

The usual way to classify employment is to sort all economic activities into one of three sectors of the economy. The three sectors are:

- **Primary sector**. This sector of the economy produces raw materials such as a food crop, timber or mineral. Occupations in fishing, farming, forestry and mining are all examples of primary economic activities.
- **Secondary sector**. The secondary sector is involved in processing and manufacturing. Food processing, the textile and clothing industry and the manufacture of microchips are all examples of secondary occupations.
- **Tertiary sector**. This sector provides services to other industries or to individual consumers like you and me. Employment in a school, shop, office or hospital are all examples of tertiary occupations.

The number of people working in the primary, secondary and tertiary sectors of the economy is known as the **employment structure** of that region or country. The primary sector is the world's largest employer. On a global scale, 43 per cent of the world's 3 billion workers have occupations in agriculture. However, the employment structure varies greatly from one region to another. In Europe less than five per cent of people are employed in primary economic activities, and in the UK this figure is less than two per cent.

## Public and private sectors of the economy

Employment can be recorded as being in either the **public sector** or **private sector**.

- People working in the **public sector** are employed by the national, regional or local government. A wide range of jobs which provide a service is available including doctors, nurses, teachers, planners, social workers, soldiers, refuse collectors.
- People working in the **private sector** are either **self-employed** or they work for a larger company or organisation that is not owned by the government. The private sector provides a wide range of jobs on the land (such as farming and forestry), in construction (design, engineering and building), in **manufacturing** and in services (offices, shops, and leisure and tourism).

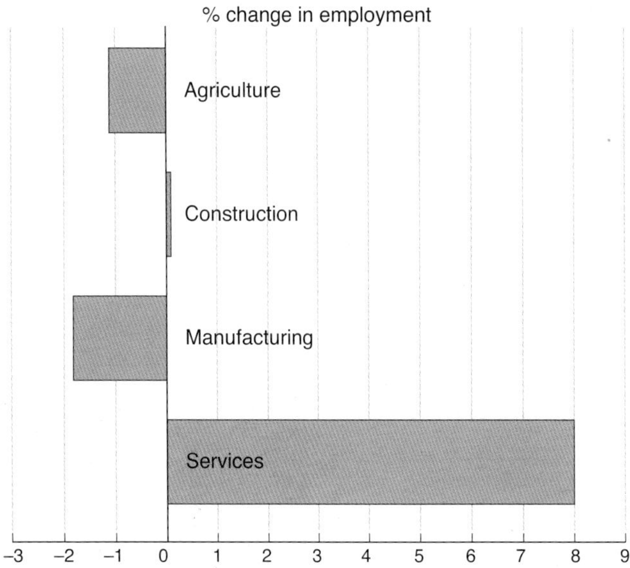


**Figure 2** Change in employment (millions of jobs) within the 25 countries of the European Union, 2000 to 2004

| | Manufacturing jobs lost or gained |
|---|---|
| Spain | Gained 500,000 |
| Italy | Gained 400,000 |
| France | Gained 146,000 |
| Germany | Gained 116,000 |
| UK | Lost 580,000 |

**Figure 3** Change in the number of manufacturing jobs, 1997 to 2002

### Activity

**1** Study the jobs shown in Figure 1.
  **a)** Sort these jobs into the primary, secondary or tertiary sectors.
  **b)** Sort each of the jobs into the private or public sectors.

**2** Study Figure 2.
  **a)** How many jobs were created in services?
  **b)** How many were lost in farming and manufacturing?

**3** **a)** Choose a suitable style of graph to represent the data in Figure 3.
  **b)** How have manufacturing jobs in the UK changed compared with:
    i) Spain
    ii) Germany?

## How does employment structure vary from one country to another?

Employment structure varies considerably from one country to another. In the poorest LEDCs, such as Mali, most jobs are in the primary sector and are **labour intensive**. This means that work is still done by hand rather than using labour-saving machines. Wealthier LEDCs such as Malaysia have smaller primary sectors and much larger secondary sectors. MEDCs have even fewer people employed in the primary sector.

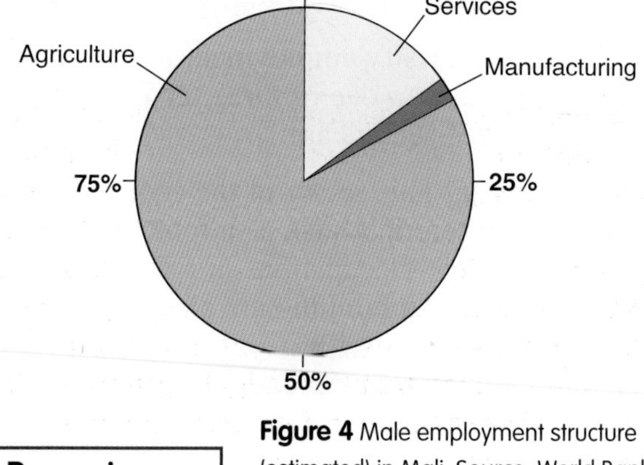


**Figure 4** Male employment structure (estimated) in Mali. Source: World Bank

| | UK | | Malaysia | | Romania | |
|---|---|---|---|---|---|---|
| **Male employment** | **1980** | **2000** | **1980** | **2000** | **1980** | **2000** |
| Agriculture | 3 | 2 | 34 | 21 | 22 | 40 |
| Manufacturing | 48 | 36 | 26 | 34 | 52 | 31 |
| Services | 49 | 62 | 40 | 45 | 26 | 29 |
| **Female employment** | **1980** | **2000** | **1980** | **2000** | **1980** | **2000** |
| Agriculture | 1 | 1 | 44 | 14 | 39 | 46 |
| Manufacturing | 23 | 12 | 20 | 29 | 34 | 21 |
| Services | 76 | 87 | 36 | 57 | 27 | 33 |

**Figure 5** Changing employment structure (figures show percentage employed in each sector). Source of data: World Bank

**www./genderstats.worldbank.org** is a useful interactive database provided by the World Bank. It holds data recorded by gender (male and female) for employment, education and health issues in a database searchable by country.

### Activity

**4** Study Figure 4. What percentage of Mali's population works in each sector of the economy?

**5 a)** Use Figure 5 to draw pie charts of male employment (in 2000) for each country.
**b)** Compare male employment in the UK (MEDC) with Mali (a poor LEDC).
**c)** Compare male employment in Mali with Malaysia (a wealthier LEDC).

**6 a)** Describe how the pattern of employment in the UK has changed.
**b)** Suggest reasons for these changes.

**7 a)** Describe how employment structure in Romania (a European country) is different from the UK.
**b)** What does this suggest about the spread of mechanisation in Romania compared with the UK?

**8 a)** Working with a partner, suggest a list of jobs that you think might be associated with each of the following industries:
i) fashion
ii) the film industry
iii) travel and tourism.
**b)** Now imagine you could go back in time to 1990, a time before most people had mobile phones, powerful graphics on their computers, or access to the internet. Suggest how some of the jobs you have identified would have been different without this modern technology.

**9** Use Figure 5.
**a)** Choose a suitable graphical technique to illustrate all the data.
**b)** Describe the main similarities and differences you see between:
i) how employment has changed between 1980 and 2000
ii) patterns of employment in MEDCs and LEDCs
iii) male and female employment.

## How is technology changing the way we work?

The world of work is changing fast. The government believes that as many as seven out of ten children who are starting primary school today will eventually work in jobs that haven't been invented yet! Find that hard to believe? Just consider some of the jobs that we take for granted today. For example, when you surf the web you are viewing pages designed by web designers: a job that didn't exist in the 1980s. Figure 7 shows another example of how technology is changing the workplace.

**Figure 7** A computer-generated image (CGI) from *King Kong*. An example of one of thousands of new jobs created by computing

Technological change is having a massive impact on all sectors of the economy. **Mechanisation**, which is the increased use of machines to replace human labour, has been a major cause of job losses on many European farms and factories. At the same time, new computer and communication technology is creating new jobs in some service industries. For example, the growth of some of the world's fastest-growing businesses is connected directly to growth in the internet. Google™, the search engine, and eBay, the online auction site, have grown rapidly since the mid-1990s as a direct result of the increased internet access of consumers like you and me.

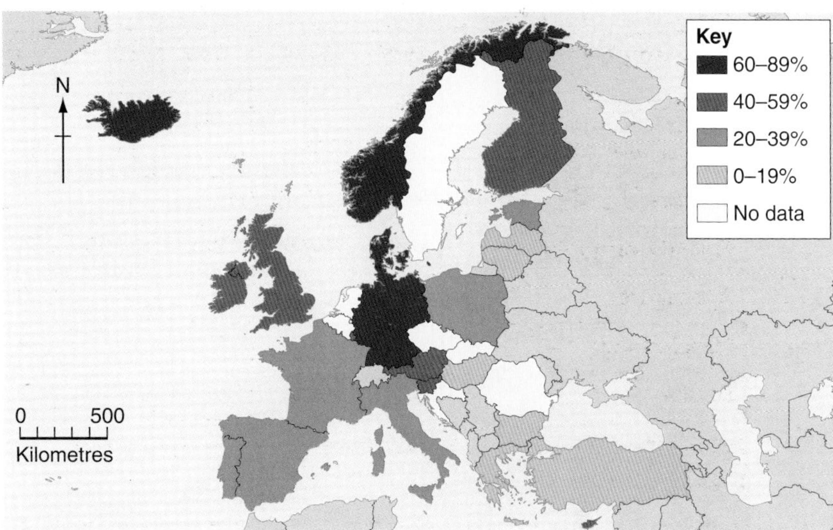


**Figure 8** Percentage of the population of Europe with internet access (2004). Source: Eurostat

| | Medium firms (50–249 employees) | | Large firms (over 250 employees) | |
|---|---|---|---|---|
| | 2003 | 2004 | 2003 | 2004 |
| EU average | 11 | 18 | 20 | 27 |
| Belgium | 26 | 25 | 41 | 35 |
| Germany | 12 | 25 | 17 | 30 |
| Greece | 13 | 10 | 18 | 12 |
| Spain | 4 | 6 | 13 | 14 |
| Ireland | 21 | 24 | 30 | 37 |
| Netherlands | 22 | 22 | 31 | 35 |
| Portugal | 5 | 9 | 15 | 20 |
| United Kingdom | 30 | 36 | 43 | 46 |

**Figure 6** Internet sales for selected EU countries. Numbers refer to the percentage of businesses that have some of their sales online. Source: Eurostat

### Activity

**10** Study Figure 6.

**a)** What type of company benefits most from internet sales: medium or large firms?

**b)** What is the impact of this trend on jobs in shops, in warehouses and for delivery companies?

**11** Look at Figure 8.

**a)** Describe the distribution (see page 143) of internet access in Europe.

**b)** Suggest reasons for the pattern that you see.

**12** Use Figures 6 and 8 to predict in which parts of Europe internet sales are likely to grow most in the future. Explain your decision.

West Midlands, UK

## Investigating the changing employment structure of the West Midlands

**Figure 9** An image of work in the mid-twentieth century. C.W. Brown painted scenes of coal mines and iron works in North Staffordshire. This one is dated 1947

From the 1950s through to the 1980s, the West Midlands was regarded as the home of UK manufacturing. However, since then, the West Midlands has seen a massive decline in the number of manufacturing jobs. At the same time, the number of people working in jobs which provide a service, such as the health service, retailing, banking, and leisure and tourism, have increased. This shift in employment is known as **de-industrialisation**.

The most obvious effect of this change is in the industrial landscape: just compare the images of North Staffordshire in Figures 9 and 10. The so-called 'heavy industries' of steel making, engineering and mining, which employed tens of thousands of (mainly) men have declined. In many places they have been replaced by out-of-town retail parks and leisure industries. The decline of manufacturing since 1980 has been due to the high costs of both labour and production in the UK. Companies have moved to other regions of the world where costs are lower.

**Figure 10** An image of work in the twenty-first century. This retail park occupies the same space as C.W. Brown's painting (Figure 9)

### Activity

**13 a)** State whether the industries shown in Figures 9 and 10 belong to the primary, secondary or tertiary sectors.

**b)** What does this tell you about how jobs changed between 1958 and 2006 in North Staffordshire?

**14** Study Figures 9 and 10. Compare the two images using these headings:
**Landscape** **Pollution** **Job opportunities.**

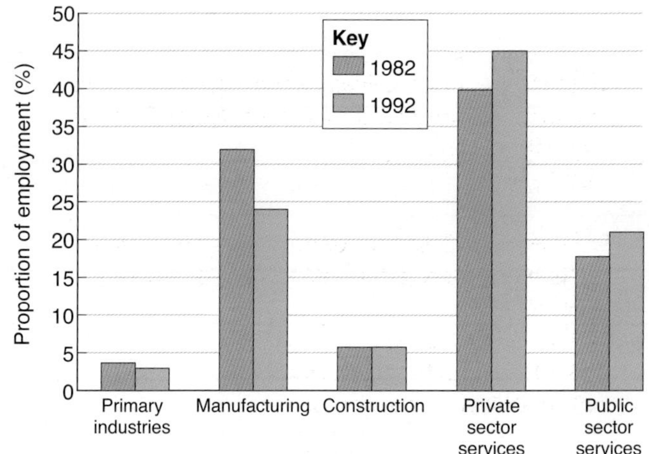


**Figure 11** Change in employment structure in the West Midlands by sector, 1982 to 1992

## What is the knowledge economy?

A recent development in the way we record employment is to identify jobs in the **knowledge economy**. These jobs require high levels of education or training. This sector of the economy includes:

- Manufacturing jobs:
  a) **High-tech industries** such as defence systems and medical equipment.
  b) Medium/high-tech jobs such as electronics.
- **Knowledge Intensive Service (KIS)** industries such as finance and education.

In 2004, 50.3 per cent of all workers in the UK worked in the knowledge sector of the economy. The West Midlands had fewer workers in the knowledge sector of the economy than most other regions of the UK. Figure 13 compares employment in the knowledge sector in Staffordshire, in the North of the region, with the rest of the West Midlands and the UK.

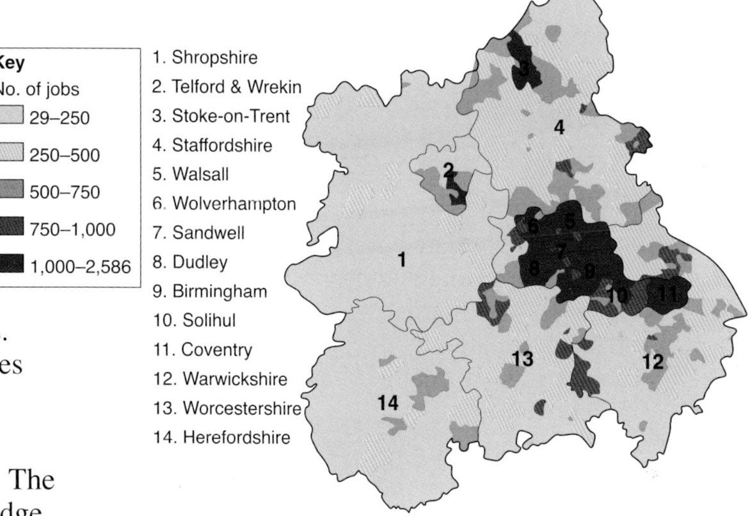


**Figure 13** Residents working in manufacturing jobs

| | | Staffs | West Midlands | UK |
|---|---|---|---|---|
| Jobs in high tech and medium technology manufacturing | as a % of all jobs | 6.6 | 6.4 | 4.4 |
| | % gain or loss | -39.0 | -32.5 | -25.0 |
| Jobs in Knowledge Intensive Services (KIS) | as a % of all jobs | 39.0 | 42.3 | 45.9 |
| | % gain or loss | 18.8 | 18.2 | 19.0 |

**Figure 12** Percentage of jobs in the knowledge economy in Staffordshire

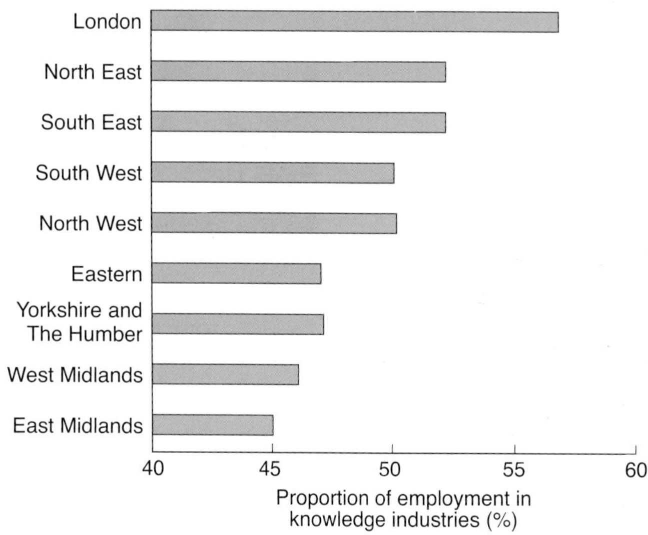


**Figure 14** Proportion of employment in the knowledge economy, 2003

### Activity

**15** Use Figure 11 to calculate the total percentage of workers employed in service sector jobs in:
**a)** 1982
**b)** 1992.

**16** Use Figure 11 to compare the way in which jobs have changed in each of the following sectors:
**a)** manufacturing
**b)** private sector services
**c)** public sector services.

**17** Use Figure 13 to describe the distribution (see page 143) of manufacturing jobs in the West Midlands region.

**18** Give two reasons why the employment structure in the West Midlands is changing. Use Figure 12 to help you give part of your explanation.

**19 a)** Choose a suitable graphical technique to show the data in Figure 12.
**b)** Use Figure 14 to compare Staffordshire with the rest of the UK in terms of:
i) percentage of jobs in the knowledge sector
ii) gains and losses in the knowledge sector.

Mali

Figure 15 Work in Mali: collecting water

## Widening our definition of work: a case study of formal and informal occupations in Mali

So far we have concentrated on the **formal occupations** of the public and private sector. These are jobs that receive a regular wage and which are recognised and regulated by the state. In the poorest LEDCs such as Mali formal work is scarce, so as many as 50 per cent of people are occupied in the **informal sector** of the economy. This sector includes many types of irregular jobs as well as types of work such as household chores and childcare. Figure 18 summarises the differences between the formal and informal sectors of the economy.

Figure 16 Work in Mali: scaring birds from the millet crop on a smallholding

Figure 17 Work in Mali: musicians

| | Informal economy | | Formal economy |
|---|---|---|---|
| | **Reproduction and subsistence** | **Petty commodity production** | |
| Examples of occupations | Daily household chores like:<br>• fetching water<br>• collecting firewood<br>• childcare<br>• preparing meals.<br>Subsistence means that a farmer with a small parcel of land produces only enough food to feed the family with no surplus to sell for cash. | Work in this sector involves the production of low-value goods or services. Examples in Mali include:<br>1. Growing cotton to sell to foreign buyers<br>2. Selling surplus fruit or vegetables on a street market,<br>3. Recycling scrap metal into a useful object such as a hoe or plough. | Since there are very few jobs in manufacturing, most formal economy jobs in Mali are in a service industry such as:<br>• a shop<br>• school<br>• hospital or health clinic<br>• a Non-Government Organisation (NGO) providing aid or advice.<br>These occupations may be either full time or part time. |
| Earnings | No earnings | Low earnings and irregular payments | Regular wage |
| Rights | No contract. No holidays or sickness benefit. No rules to protect your health and safety at work. | | Most formal occupations benefit from a contract, entitlement to holidays and sick pay, etc. |
| Responsibilities | It is unusual for workers to pay tax. | | Workers pay tax. |

Figure 18 The formal and informal sectors of the economy in Mali

**Figure 19** Work in Mali: a blacksmith recycling scrap metal

## Waste recycling: an example of informal work

Bamako is the capital of Mali. It has a population of at least 1.2 million and has grown quickly in recent years. The number of formal jobs available in the city has not grown as quickly as the city has, so many people find it hard to get a job with a regular salary. Consequently, many people work in the informal sector of the economy.

Typical informal jobs include working on street markets, running bars and recycling waste. Some workers collect waste, sort it and wash it. Others recycle it into useful tools and these are sold on market stalls. Organic waste is composted and sold to farmers on the outskirts of the city.

The city authorities recognise the value of the informal sector. The collection and disposal of solid waste had become a problem but has been solved by the informal sector.

There is a large market area in Bamako. All sorts of scrap metal is collected from all over the city and brought here where it is sorted and sold to specialist dealers. Everything from car parts to railways is brought here.

Some of the smaller scrap is sold simply as scrap, but a lot of it goes directly for recycling. There are workshops everywhere in this area, all making different items out of recycled metal: trunks, wheelbarrows, braziers and farming implements are just a few of the things they make.

The recycling market has been here for more than 20 years. Recycling began in the rural areas but now it has become more commercial.

Ploughs and hoes, as well as other farming implements, are made from scrap metal. Through this recycling market a car from Europe, say a Renault or a Peugeot, could end up being used to make ploughs for a poor rural farmer in the smallest, most distant village in Mali. When a car is imported it is used for as long as possible and when it can no longer be driven it's dismantled and every last piece of it is used to make something else.

**Daouda Ballo, Bamako Market**

**Figure 20** Extract from the Coolplanet section of Oxfam's website

## Activity

**20** Study the photographs on these two pages.

**a)** Describe whether the work shown belongs to the primary, secondary or tertiary sector of the economy.

**b)** Study Figure 18 and use it to describe whether the work in each photo belongs to the informal or formal sector. You could use a table like the one to the right for your answer.

| Figure | Formal or informal? | If informal, is this an example of reproduction, subsistence or petty commodity production? | Reason |
|---|---|---|---|
| 15 | | | |
| 16 | | | |
| 17 | | | |
| 19 | | | |

**21** Use Figure 20 to explain the benefits of the informal sector.

**22** Produce a chart which summarises the main differences between the formal and informal sectors.

### What are the costs and benefits of informal work for people and government?

Workers in the **formal sector** usually have a contract, which gives them some rights. They earn a regular wage which means they can save and plan ahead. Regular wage earners find it easier to borrow money and pay rent for housing. This sector is regulated by the state, so most employees will pay some tax. The government can then use this money to improve quality of life by investing in health and education.

But many people in Mali work in the informal sector of the economy. Earnings in this sector are low and irregular. This means that informal workers find it very hard to save, borrow money, or pay rent. That's why many people in African cities live in shanty towns (or **informal settlements**). Furthermore, the informal sector is not regulated by the state, so the government does not earn any tax from it. In this respect the informal sector can be seen as a problem for LEDCs like Mali, one of the world's ten poorest countries which need to invest heavily in better health and education.

However, governments of poor countries like Mali would find it hard to create enough formal-sector jobs for the number of children leaving education each year (see Figure 21). During the 1990s, the informal sector created 90 per cent of all new jobs in African countries. If people didn't take up informal work they would be unemployed.

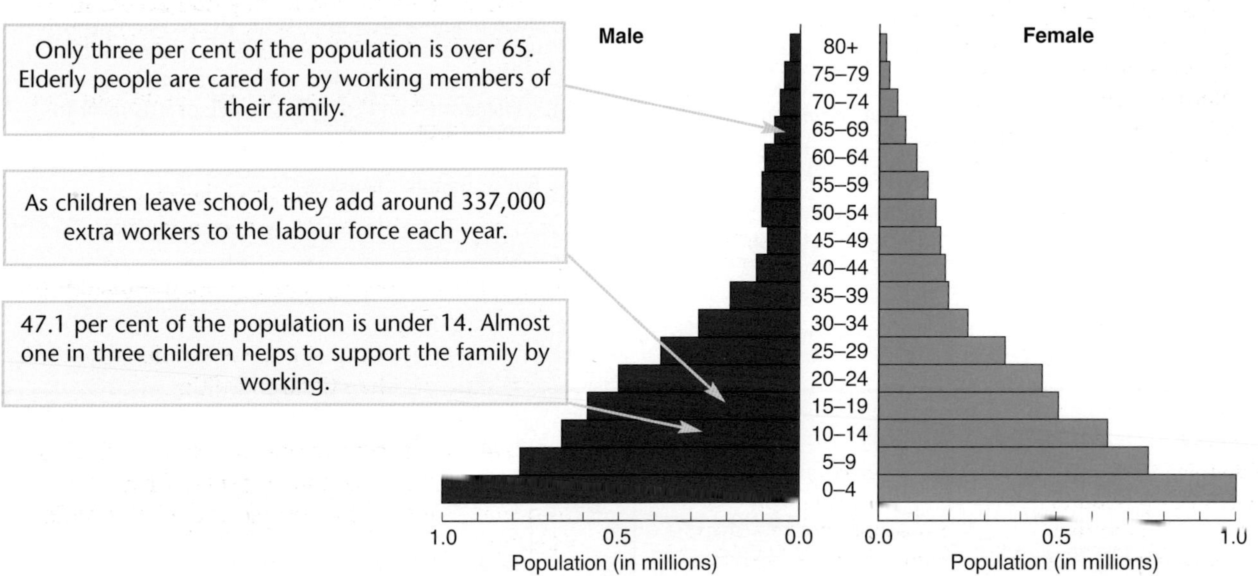


**Figure 21** Population pyramid for Mali

## Activity

**23** Study Figure 21.

**a)** Compare the percentage of under 15s to the percentage of over 65s.

**b)** Explain how this population structure creates both benefits and challenges for the government of Mali.

**Figure 22** African women spend a lot of time doing work that does not contribute directly to family or state income

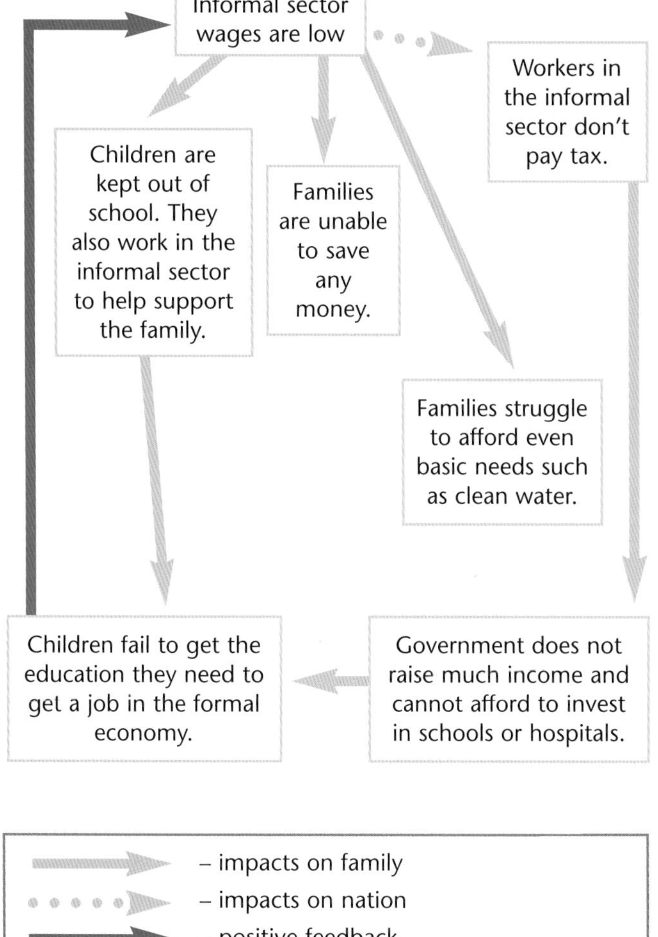


**Figure 23** The informal sector and the national economy

Long working days are the norm for women in the **Sahel.** Women work up to a total of 16 hours per day in the growing season, of which about half is spent on agricultural work. Time allocation studies from Burkina Faso and Mali show women working one to three hours a day more than men. In rural areas, the lack of basic services such as reliable water supplies, health centres, stores (shops) and transport adds considerably to the time women must also spend on household chores. Shortage of time constrains women's attendance at activities to benefit them, the time and attention they can pay to productive activities, and visits to health facilities.

**Figure 24** Extract from a World Bank report

## Activity

**24** Study Figures 22 and 24.

**a)** Give three reasons why women in Sahel countries such as Mali have such long working days.

**b)** Suggest a number of ways in which the lives of rural African women and children would be improved if they had access to a clean and safe water supply close to their home.

**c)** Suggest how women in Mali might use four extra hours a day.

**25** Study Figure 23. Explain carefully how a large informal sector in the economy may prevent:

**a)** the LEDC from developing greater wealth in its economy

**b)** the development of improved education, training and healthcare facilities.

**26** Using all of the information on pages 200–203, summarise the costs and benefits of the informal economy by completing a large table like this:

| | **Costs** | **Benefits** |
|---|---|---|
| For the government of Mali | | |
| For individuals working in the informal sector | | |

## Going Further

### The African brain drain: investigating an ethical issue

In the period 2000 to 2005, a total of between 10,000 and 15,000 newly trained nurses joined the UK National Health Service (NHS) each year from medical schools in LEDCs. The World Health Organization (WHO) estimates that at least twelve per cent of the doctors trained in India now live and work in the UK. This is good for the NHS, which had great difficulty in this period recruiting enough staff from the UK. However, it's not so good for the health service in African and other LEDC countries which are losing staff in a massive **brain drain**.

The World Bank estimates that as many as 70,000 of Africa's most highly qualified workers emigrate each year. This may be costing Africa US$4 billion a year. Another estimate suggests that only one-third of medical graduates remain in Ghana each year: the rest leave the country to find better-paid work abroad.

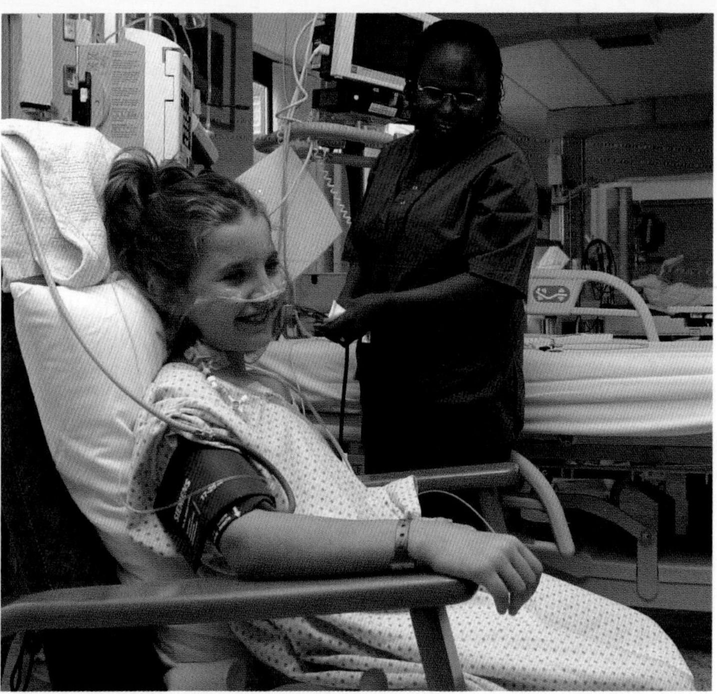

**Figure 25** The NHS estimates that 43 per cent of nurses and 31 per cent of doctors starting work in the NHS were trained outside the UK (2005 figures)

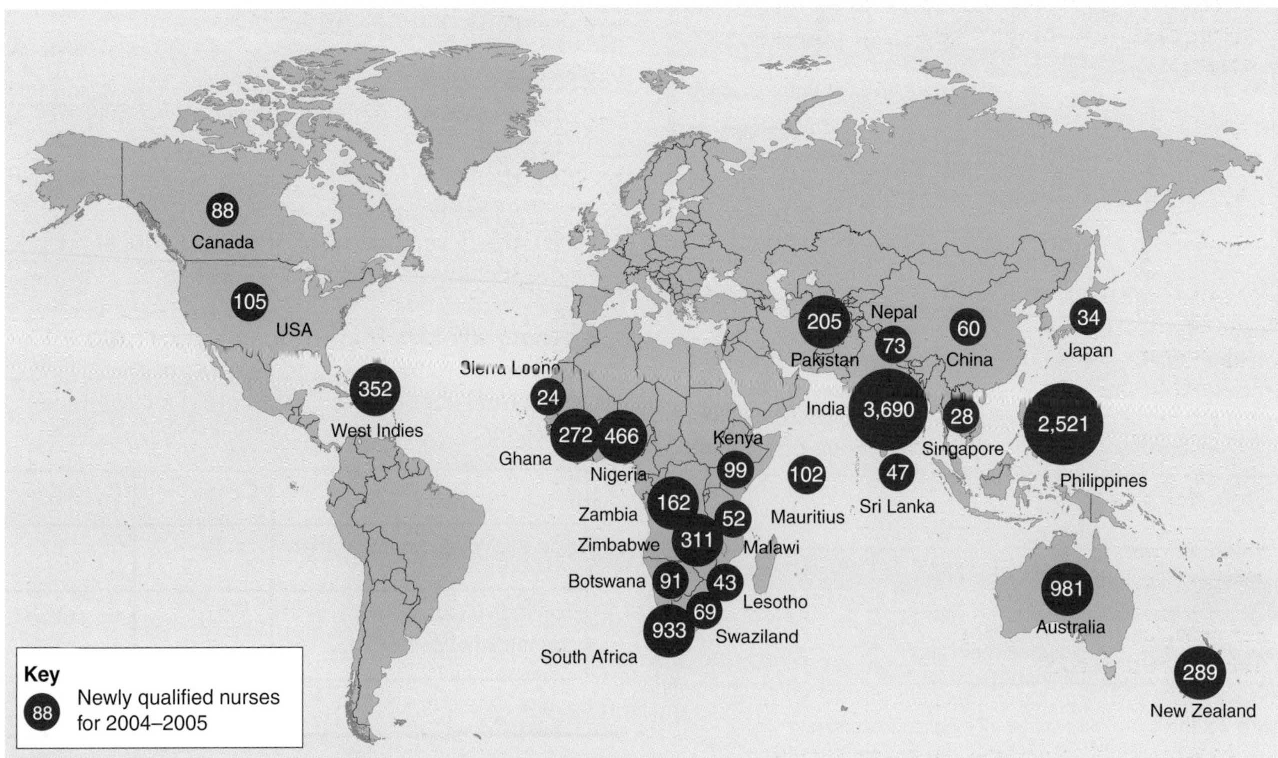


**Figure 26** New admissions to the 2004–2005 nursing register who qualified overseas

The costs and benefits of the brain drain from LEDC health services:

- Staff are able to earn many times more than they would do working in hospitals in their home country.
- Staff benefit from training in the latest techniques and treatments.
- Knowledge of new medical treatments and techniques can benefit the health service in the LEDC if staff eventually return.
- The NHS would have a massive shortage of doctors and nurses if they did not recruit from abroad.
- Waiting times are reduced and patients get faster treatment because staffing levels are kept high.
- Hospitals in Africa are desperately short of trained staff. Morale is low among staff who continue to work long hours for low pay.
- The brain drain means that money spent in an LEDC on university-level education is not converted into a skilled worker who pays tax and who therefore helps to pay for the education of others.

**27** Use Figure 26. Describe the distribution (see page 143) of countries which supplied more than 100 nurses to the NHS. How many of these countries were LEDCs?

**28 a)** Choose suitable graphical techniques to display the data in Figures 27 and 28.

**b)** Describe the patterns and trends shown by your graphs.

**29** Study the bullet-pointed list of costs and benefits above.

**a)** Sort the bullet points into a table using these headings:

| | Costs | Benefits |
|---|---|---|
| For the British NHS | | |
| For the health service in Africa | | |
| For individuals who emigrate from Africa to the UK | | |

**b)** Write a 200-word article in which you either strongly support or strongly oppose the migration of health workers from Africa.

| Origin of doctors | Number | Percentage who practise in the UK |
|---|---|---|
| South Asia | 24,362 | 11.5 |
| Europe | 15,855 | 7.5 |
| Sub-Saharan Africa | 8,959 | 4.2 |
| Middle East / North Africa | 4,708 | 2.2 |
| Other Asia | 2,332 | 1.1 |
| Oceania | 3,408 | 1.6 |
| Latin America and Caribbean | 1,080 | 0.5 |
| North America | 318 | 0.2 |

▲ **Figure 27** Doctors registered to practise in the UK by region of training

| Financial year | Number of admissions |
|---|---|
| 1998/1999 | 3,621 |
| 1999/2000 | 5,945 |
| 2000/2001 | 8,403 |
| 2001/2002 | 15,064 |
| 2002/2003 | 12,730 |
| 2003/2004 | 14,122 |
| 2004/2005 | 11,477 |

▲ **Figure 28** New admissions to the nursing register from abroad, 1998 to 2005

# Chapter 3
# How do we measure development?

**KEY QUESTIONS**

- What do we mean by 'development'?
- How can we measure global patterns of social and economic development?
- How useful is the Brandt Line, which divides the world into Less and More Economically Developed Countries?

## What do we mean by 'development'?

One common view of development is that it can be measured economically: that increasing wealth or decreasing levels of poverty are indicators of development. We will start by considering whether or not this is helpful.

**Development is...**

- reducing levels of poverty
- increasing levels of wealth
- reducing the gap between the richest and poorest members of society
- creating equal status for men and women
- creating justice, freedom of speech and political participation for everyone
- ensuring that everyone is safe from conflict and terrorism
- ensuring that everyone fulfils their basic needs: food, water and shelter
- ensuring that all children have good standards of education.

**Figure 1** Different ways of seeing development

**Figure 2** Development is…

**Figure 3** Development is…

### Activity

**1** Study Figure 1. Work in pairs to discuss this list.

**a)** What are the advantages and disadvantages of each of these statements as a definition of development?

**b)** Choose the five statements which you think give the best definition of development. Join with another pair and justify your choice.

**c)** Working in a team of four, produce a joint statement that defines development. Each member of the team must contribute and agree with the statement.

**2** Working on your own, explain which aspects of human development are illustrated by Figures 2 and 3. Write a caption for each Figure.

## Using national wealth as a measure of development

The wealth of a country is usually measured by its Gross National Product (GNP) per person. The GNP per person of a country is calculated by:

***Step 1*** Add up the total value of goods and services produced by people living in that country and by people abroad who are still citizens of that country.

***Step 2*** Divide this figure by the total number of citizens of that country.

This gives a figure which can be thought of as the average annual income for a citizen of that country. Helpfully, the World Bank and United Nations (UN) now refer to GNP as **Gross National Income (GNI) per person**. So for example, the average annual income (GNI or GNP) in Mali, Africa, is US$350 (or about US$1 a day). Remember, this is an average, so some people earn more than this and others earn less. In fact, 73 per cent of Mali's population earns less than US$1 a day.

Figure 4 shows the 1980 Brandt Line which divides countries into one of two categories: More Economically Developed Countries (MEDCs) to the North and Less Economically Developed Countries (LEDCs) to the South. It is also coloured to show GNP. The World Bank divides the countries of the world into four categories defined by GNP. It describes these as high income, upper middle income, lower middle income and low income countries. For the details of this classification check the details shown in the key to Figure 4.

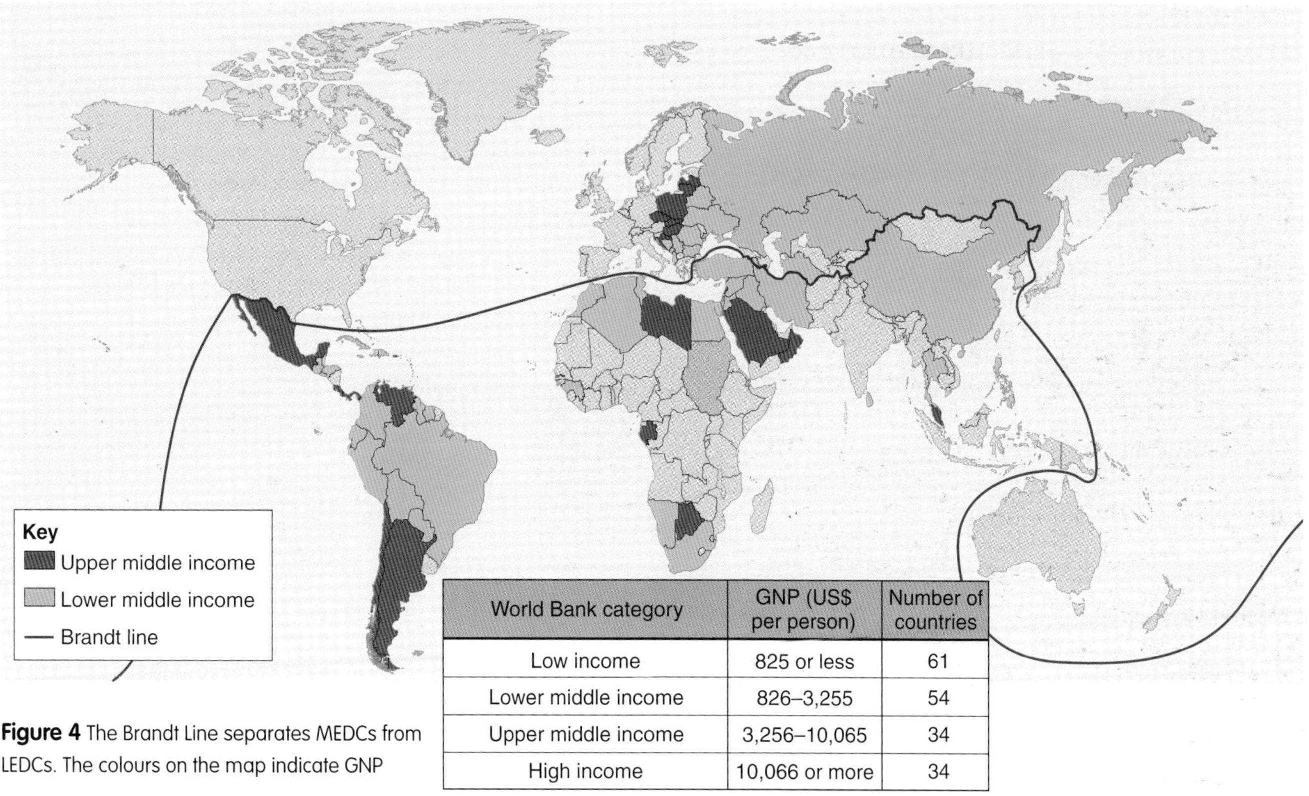


| World Bank category | GNP (US$ per person) | Number of countries |
|---|---|---|
| Low income | 825 or less | 61 |
| Lower middle income | 826–3,255 | 54 |
| Upper middle income | 3,256–10,065 | 34 |
| High income | 10,066 or more | 34 |

**Figure 4** The Brandt Line separates MEDCs from LEDCs. The colours on the map indicate GNP

### Activity

**3** Study Figure 4.

**a)** Describe the distribution (see page 143) of:

i) lower middle income countries

ii) upper middle income countries.

**b)** Identify countries which have:

i) an upper middle income but which are South of the Brandt Line

ii) a lower middle income but which are North of the Brandt Line.

**4** Which do you find most helpful: the two categories of the Brandt Line or the four categories defined by the World Bank?

**a)** Suggest the advantages and disadvantages of each system.

**b)** Do you think there is an argument to re-draw the Brandt Line? If so, where should it go?

## Using education data as an indication of development

Education data is often used to describe a country's level of development. Two commonly used indicators are:

- **adult literacy** – the percentage of the adult population who can read and write; male and female literacy rates are often shown as separate data
- **primary enrolment** – the percentage of children of primary school age who regularly attend primary school; again, enrolment for boys and for girls are often shown as separate data.

### Why use education data?

In MEDCs most children attend school and most adults can read and write. Most EU countries have 100 per cent primary enrolment and 100 per cent adult literacy. However, primary school is not available to all children in many LEDCs. A poor family cannot necessarily afford to send all of its children to school. Children are expected to help support the family by:

- looking after younger brothers and sisters
- doing chores around the house or farm
- doing an informal job and earning some money.

It is estimated that 110 million children of primary school age did not attend school in 2002. Of these, about 65 million (well over half) were girls. Young girls are more likely to be expected to support the family than boys.

| | 1990 | | 2004 | |
|---|---|---|---|---|
| | Male | Female | Male | Female |
| Sub-Saharan Africa | 60 | 40 | 69 | 53 |
| Middle East and North Africa | 66 | 39 | 74 | 52 |
| South Asia | 59 | 34 | 66 | 42 |
| East Asia and Pacific | 88 | 72 | 93 | 81 |
| Latin America and Caribbean | 87 | 83 | 90 | 88 |
| Russia and the countries of Eastern Europe | 98 | 94 | 98 | 95 |

**Figure 5** Improvements in adult literacy rate from 1990 to 2004 (%)

### Investigating gender inequality

Figure 5 shows that in many LEDCs adult literacy is higher in men than in women. This difference between men and women is an example of **gender inequality** and it has serious consequences. The child of an uneducated mother is twice more likely to die before the age of one than a child whose mother had a full education. The advantages of female education are summarised in Figure 7.

**www.unicef.org** is the website of the United Nations Children's Fund, a superb source of development statistics. The site has downloadable spreadsheets of data on wealth, health and education indicators.

### Activity

**5** Study Figure 5.

**a)** Copy and complete the following statement:
**The lowest adult literacy rate in 2004 was in .... In this region female literacy improved from ... per cent in 1990 to ... per cent in 2004. Male literacy improved from ... per cent to ... per cent over the same period.**

**b)** Choose a style of graph to show the improvements made by any one region in the table.

**6** Explain why some poor parents do not send all of their children to primary school.

**7** Explain why adult literacy is not useful for describing differences between the EU countries.

**8** Use Figure 7 and the model answer to extend the explanation of each of the following statements.
**An educated mother...**

- **spots the early signs of ill health in her child so...**
- **understands the importance of a balanced diet so...**
- **recognises the importance of a full education for her daughter so...**

**9** Use Figure 5 to identify those regions which:

**a)** have made the greatest developments in education

**b)** face the greatest challenges of gender inequality.

EXAMTECHNIQUE

## Extending your explanations: The 'So what?' question

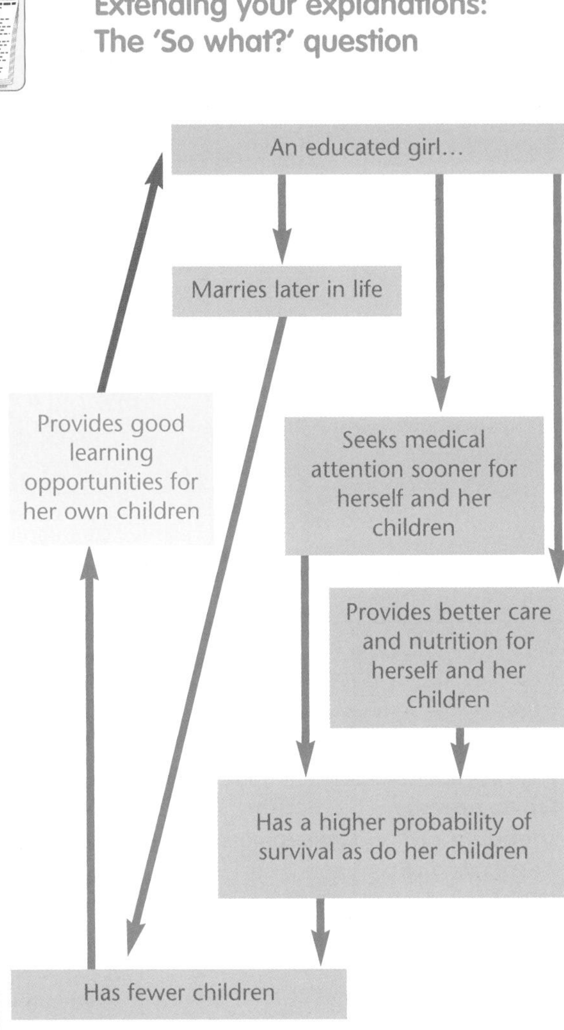


**Figure 7** The advantages of better education for girls

**Figure 6** School girls taking part in a youth radio programme in Botswana

'Explain' is a common command word in the GCSE Geography examination. Geographical explanations are seldom straightforward and the examiner is looking for evidence that you understand the complexity of the issue. So, to get a good mark you need to ask yourself the 'So what?' question. The model question and answer below show how this works.

### Question

Study Figure 7. Explain how an educated girl can improve the standard of living of her family in later life.

### Answer

An educated girl will want a good job and a career. (**So what?**) So she will marry later and have fewer children. (**So what?**) This means that she will not need to rely on her children to help support the family income. (**So what?**) So her children will complete their own education and will also have a better chance of a well-paid job when they finish secondary school or college.

## Activity

**10** Make a copy of Figure 8. Use what you have learned to create extra labels for parts 3 and 4 of the diagram.

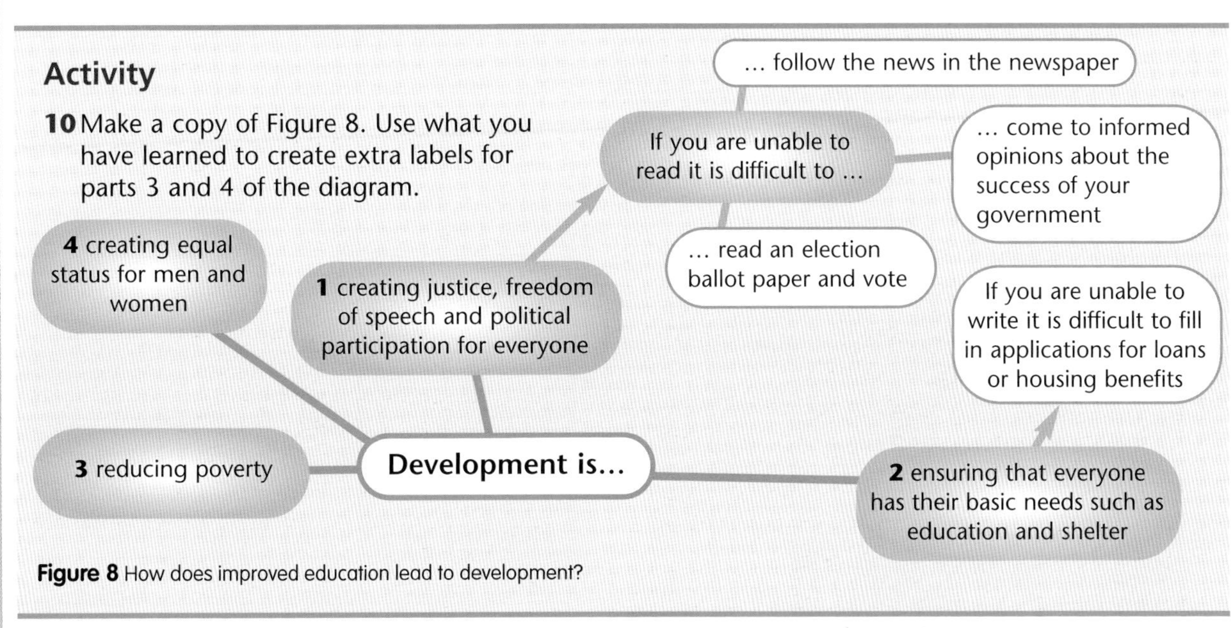


**Figure 8** How does improved education lead to development?

## Using health data as an indication of development

Health data is also often used to describe a country's level of development. Two commonly used indicators are:

- **infant mortality rate (IMR)** – the number of children who die before the age of one for every 1000 that are born. This figure varies widely, from 284 in Sierra Leone to only three in Sweden.
- average **life expectancy** – the average age to which people can expect to live.

| | Under-5 mortality rate | | Infant mortality rate (under 1) | |
|---|---|---|---|---|
| | **1960** | **2003** | **1960** | **2003** |
| Sub-Saharan Africa | 278 | 175 | 165 | 104 |
| Middle East and North Africa | 249 | 56 | 157 | 45 |
| South Asia | 244 | 92 | 148 | 67 |
| East Asia and Pacific | 208 | 40 | 137 | 31 |
| Latin America and Caribbean | 153 | 32 | 102 | 27 |
| Russia and the countries of eastern Europe | 112 | 41 | 83 | 34 |

**Figure 9** Improving healthcare has cut infant mortality

### Activity

**11** Study Figure 9.

**a)** Copy the following statement:

**The lowest infant mortality rate (IMR) in 2003 was in .... In this region IMR improved from ... per 1,000 in 1960 to ... per 1,000 in 2003. The highest IMR in 2003 is in the region of ....**

**b)** Choose a style of graph to show the improvements made by any one region in the table.

**12** Make a copy of Figure 11. Working with a partner, suggest how you could complete the blank spaces in the table.

### Why use health data?

A number of factors contribute to improved life expectancy and lower IMR. Increased government spending on healthcare, clean water and **sanitation** (sewage disposal) will all have an impact on health data. That's why this data is a useful indication of development. Around 17 million people die every year from infectious diseases such as HIV/AIDS, malaria and tuberculosis. Of these, 90 per cent are people living in LEDCs and many of these are children. Many of these deaths are preventable: improving the quality of water and providing mosquito nets would be very low-cost measures to achieve this.

| | **High life expectancy and low IMR might indicate that...** | **Low life expectancy and high IMR might indicate that...** |
|---|---|---|
| **Government spending on hospitals and clinics** | a wealthy government is able to prioritise health spending | |
| **Government spending on preventive medicine (e.g. immunisation)** | | lack of training facilities might result in too few medical staff |
| **Diet** | | |
| **Access to safe drinking water** | most people have access to clean water in their homes | |
| **State of sanitation** | | many people live in shanty housing with no proper sewage system |
| **Standards of personal and social education in schools** | | |

**Figure 10** What health data may be telling us about a country's development

## Changes to average life expectancy

Between 1960 and 2003, life expectancy increased in most countries of the world. Some of the biggest improvements were in LEDCs. For example, average life expectancy in South Asia leapt from 48 to 63 years. However, due to HIV/AIDS average life expectancy has decreased in 21 countries since 1960. All but one of these countries is in Africa. In Zimbabwe, the average life expectancy has fallen by a staggering 22 years from 55 to 33.

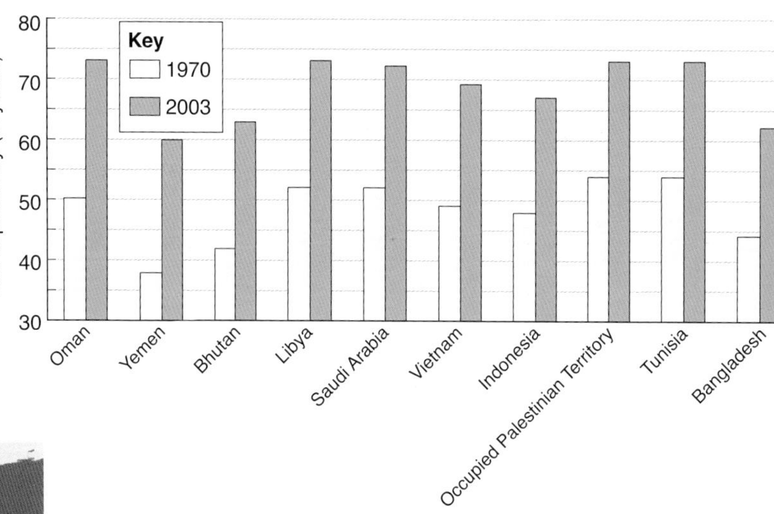


**Figure 13** Life expectancy in the ten most improved countries

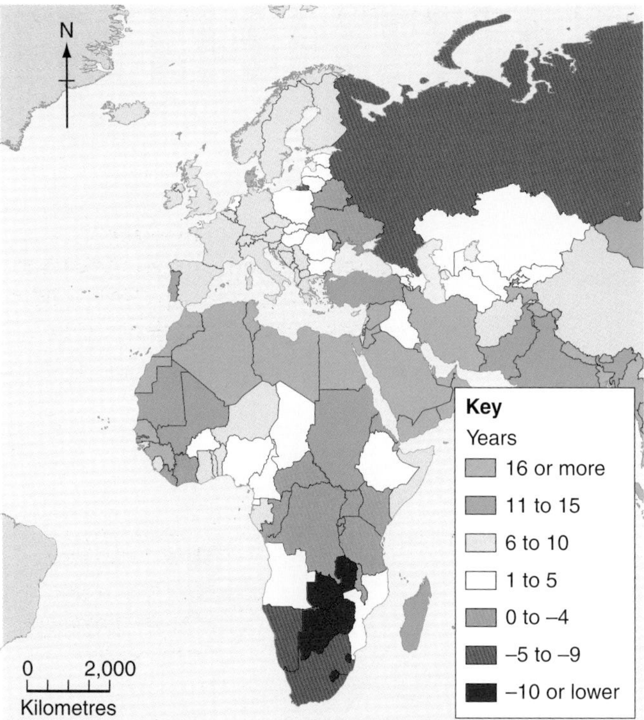


**Figure 11** Increase and decrease in life expectancy, 1960 to 2003

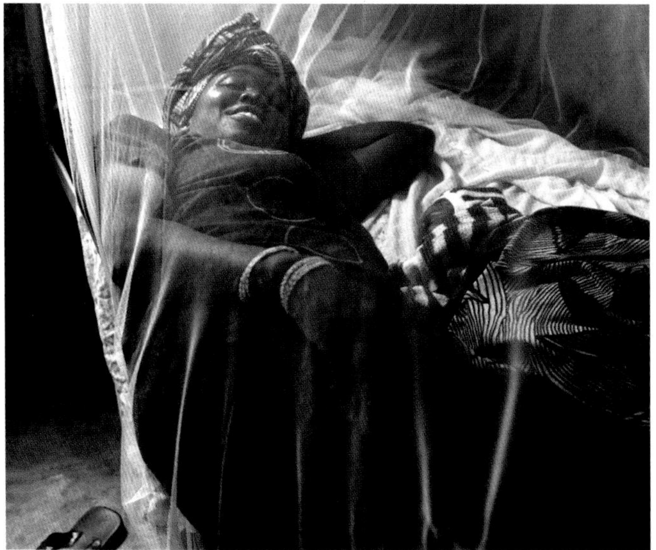

**Figure 12** Deaths due to malaria can be prevented cheaply by the use of mosquito netting

### Activity

**13** Study Figure 13. Which country:
- **a)** had the highest life expectancy in 1970
- **b)** had the highest life expectancy in 2003
- **c)** made the most progress between 1970 and 2003?

**14** Use Figure 14.
- **a)** By how much has life expectancy increased in:
  - i) Iceland
  - ii) the UK
  - iii) Mali
  - iv) Ghana.
- **b)** Describe the distribution (see page 143) of countries which have:
  - i) the most improved average life expectancy
  - ii) the greatest decrease in average life expectancy.

**15**
- **a)** Explain why people in wealthy MEDCs do not always have healthy diets.
- **b)** Explain what effect these diets might have on health data.

**16**
- **a)** Do some research into the main causes of death in MEDCs and LEDCs.
- **b)** Choose one major cause of death that is easily preventable in LEDCs and explain how this issue could be solved.

**17** Suggest why life expectancy has increased in some countries more than others.

## Going Further

### HIV/AIDS and its links to poverty

The main reason for the decline in life expectancy in Africa is the spread of HIV/AIDS. More than 20 million Africans have died from AIDS. At the end of 2004 a further 25 million Africans (including 3 million children) were infected with HIV. Not only is this causing a dramatic decrease in life expectancy, it is also the cause of a sharp rise in poverty. Figures 14 and 15 show how HIV/AIDS is linked to a vicious **cycle of poverty** because AIDS most commonly infects people of working age. Deaths among the workforce not only cause distress for families, they also reduce the earning power of the family.

However, it is possible to break out of the AIDS/poverty cycle. In Uganda, for example, HIV infection rates have fallen because the government introduced a programme of training for healthcare workers, as well as education and counselling for the public. On the other hand, HIV infection rates have risen sharply in Botswana and Zimbabwe where governments have failed to respond quickly with effective measures.

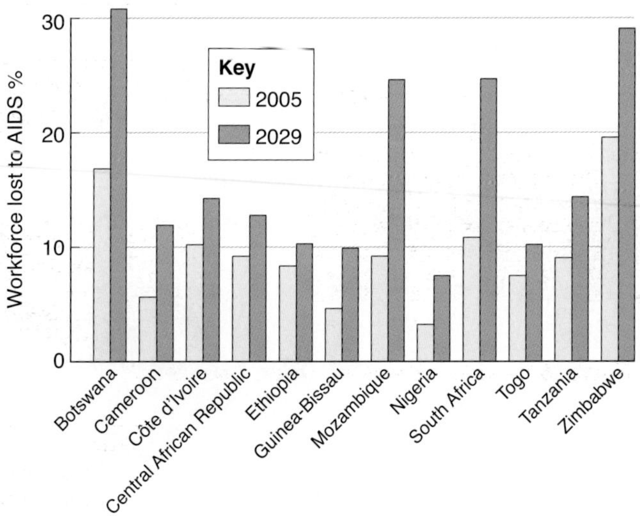


**Figure 14** Workforce lost to AIDS in 2005and estimated for 2029

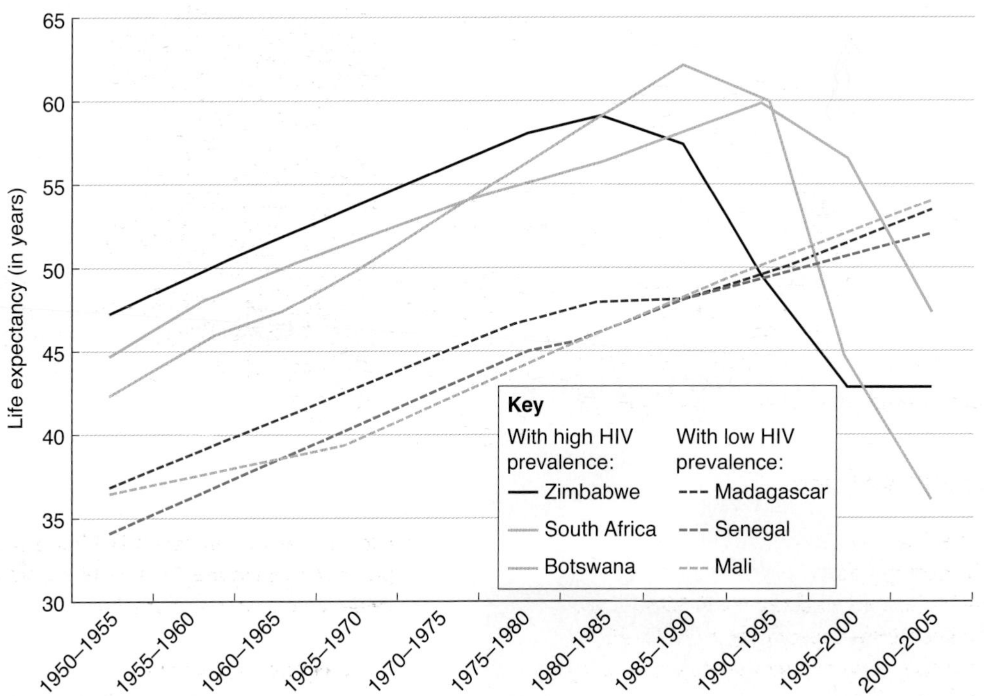


**Figure 15** HIV is reducing life expectancy in African countries

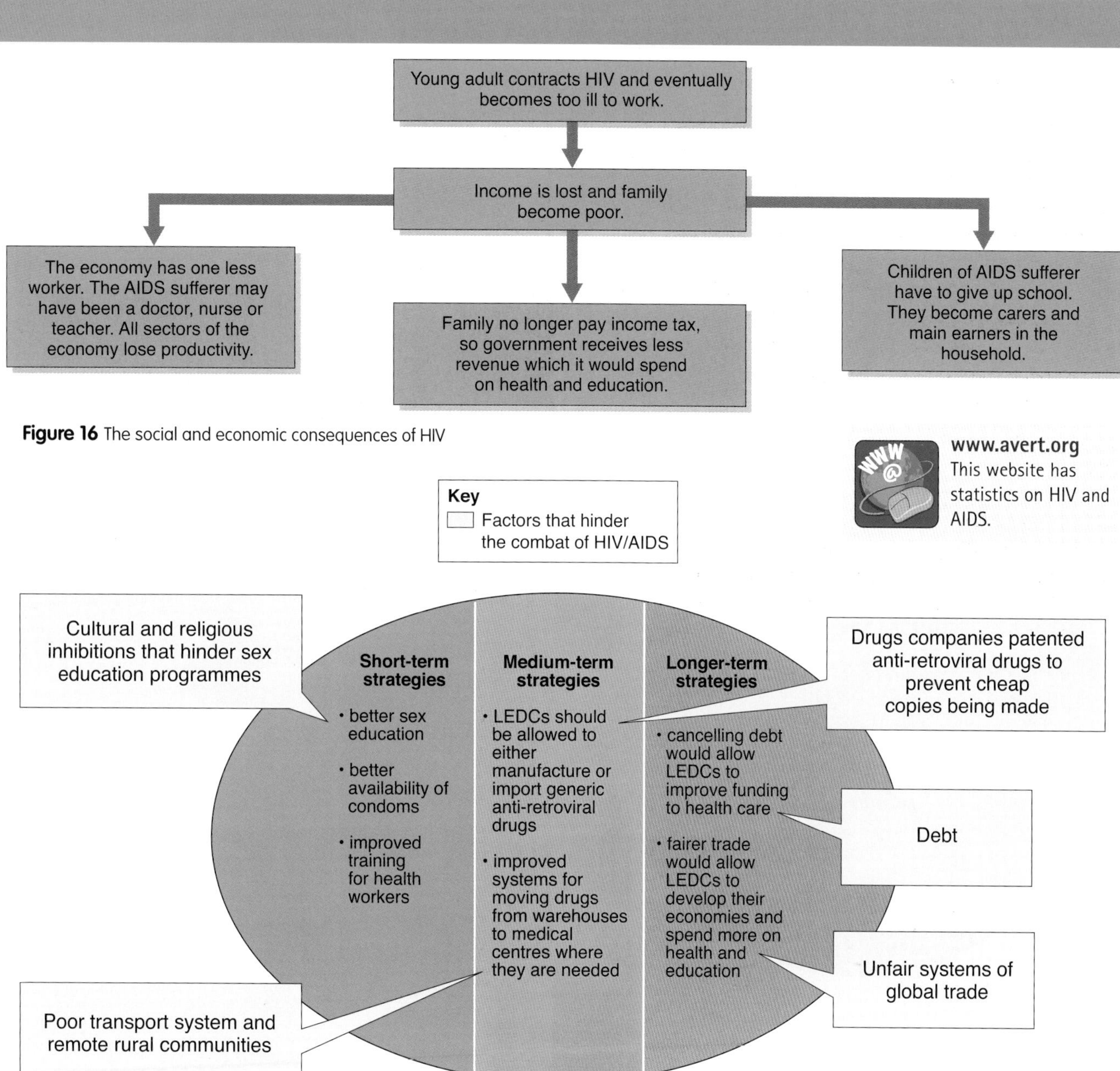


**Figure 16** The social and economic consequences of HIV

**www.avert.org**
This website has statistics on HIV and AIDS.

**Figure 17** Tackling HIV/AIDS in Africa

**18** Study Figure 15.

**a)** Which country had:

i) the highest life expectancy in 1980–1985

ii) the lowest life expectancy in 2000–2005.

**b)** Describe the trend of average life expectancy in Zimbabwe:

i) until 1980–1985

ii) after 1980–1985.

**c)** Compare what has happened to life expectancy in South Africa with that of Mali.

**19** Explain the links between HIV/AIDS and poverty. Use Figures 14 and 16 to provide evidence for your explanation.

**20** Using Figure 17, explain:

**a)** how various factors might prevent a government from introducing strategies to combat AIDS

**b)** how the international community could help combat AIDS in Africa.

# Chapter 4
# Trade

**KEY QUESTIONS**

- How does the international pattern of trade operate?
- What are the advantages and disadvantages of international trade?
- How could the global system of trade be made fairer for all countries?

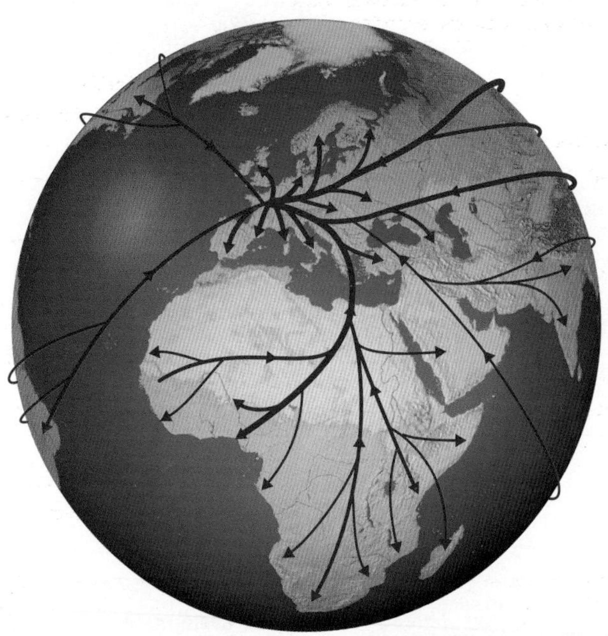

**Figure 1** International trade consists of a complex movement of goods and services

**Figure 2** Martin Luther King, the black American civil rights campaigner

## Investigating international patterns of trade

Figure 1 summarises the complex movement of goods and services that creates the international pattern of trade. Shop in the local supermarket, and you can buy a chocolate bar made from cocoa beans grown in Ghana, tomatoes grown in Spain or Holland, or a pair of trainers made in Vietnam.

Goods produced in one country and then sold abroad are exports. The goods which a country buys from abroad are **imports**. Countries also buy and sell services. In this chapter, we will focus on Ghana and Mali as case studies. Ghana's main exports are gold, cocoa and timber. These are all **primary commodities** – raw materials which have not been processed. Ghana's imports include oil (another primary commodity) plus machinery, tools, vehicles and medical equipment – all **manufactured goods**. Ghana also earns money from abroad by attracting foreign tourists; we say that this is another way in which Ghana earns **foreign exchange**.

## Why do we need trade?

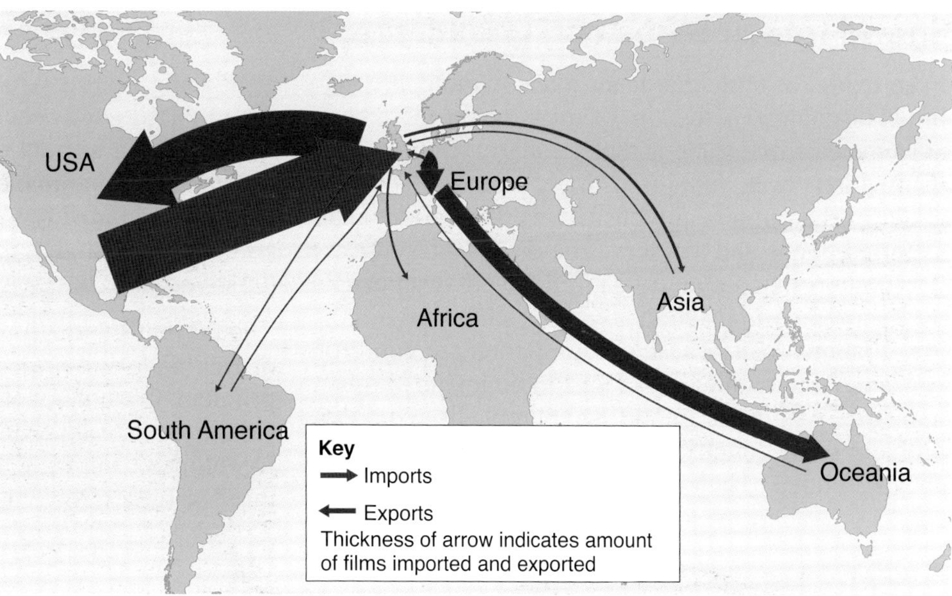


**Figure 3** Imports and exports of the UK film industry, 2004 (£million) between the UK and the rest of the world

Trade is essential because few countries in the world have enough raw materials, factories and service industries to be self-sufficient. Even wealthy countries rely on trade. Japan, for example, has no oil, gas and few other natural resources. It therefore relies on importing these primary commodities. Trade has many other advantages:

- The sale of exported goods and services creates wealth (foreign exchange) and jobs for the exporting country.
- Imported goods can be processed (for example, cocoa beans are turned into chocolate bars), creating jobs in the importing country.
- The complex pattern of trade strengthens the ties between different countries, a process known as **interdependence**.
- The fact that countries co-operate with each other is good for political stability and mutual understanding. Trade can create friendship between countries.
- The flow of people (for example, tourists or workers) and ideas (for example, music or film) between countries helps to create a better understanding of other cultures.

| USA and US co-production | 178 |
|---|---|
| Europe | 71 |
| India | 55 |
| Rest of the world | 54 |
| Total films | 358 |

**Figure 4** Country of origin of non-UK films released in the UK in 2004

### Activity

**1** Study Figure 2. Working with a partner:
  **a)** make a list of breakfast items
  **b)** suggest which countries might export these items to the UK.

**2** Use pages 214 and 215 and the glossary to write your own definitions of:
- interdependence
- foreign exchange
- primary commodities.

**3** Study Figures 3 and 4.
  **a)** To which regions does the UK export a greater value of film than it imports?
  **b)** What is the approximate value of the UK's film exports and imports to and from the USA?

**4** Suggest two different advantages of the trade in film between the UK and the rest of the world.

**5** Using the internet, research the main exporters of breakfast items such as coffee, tea and fresh orange juice.

**6** Explain why the UK might have one set of reasons for wanting to improve trade with the USA and different reasons for trading with Iran or the Palestinians in the Gaza Strip.

## Should trade be free and uncontrolled?

**Free trade**, or trade that takes place without any limits or control, is the aim of many countries. The advantage of free trade is that a country can export as many goods as it wants to its trade partners. This is good for the farmers and businesses who produce the exported goods and services. The disadvantage of free trade is that a country can find itself swamped by cheap imports made in countries which have lower labour costs. These cheap imports are good for consumers, but could cause jobs to be lost in similar industries within the importing country. To avoid this problem some countries protect themselves from cheap products. They can do this in one of three ways:

- Placing **quotas** which restrict the amount of these imported goods each year.
- Placing an **import duty** or tax on the imports to make them more expensive.
- Paying a **subsidy** to its own farmers and businesses so that their goods can be sold at a lower price to consumers.

The current international pattern of trade is a mixture of free trade and protected trade. This causes problems for both More Economically Developed Countries (MEDCs) and Less Economically Developed Countries (LEDCs). Figure 5 summarises three of these problems.

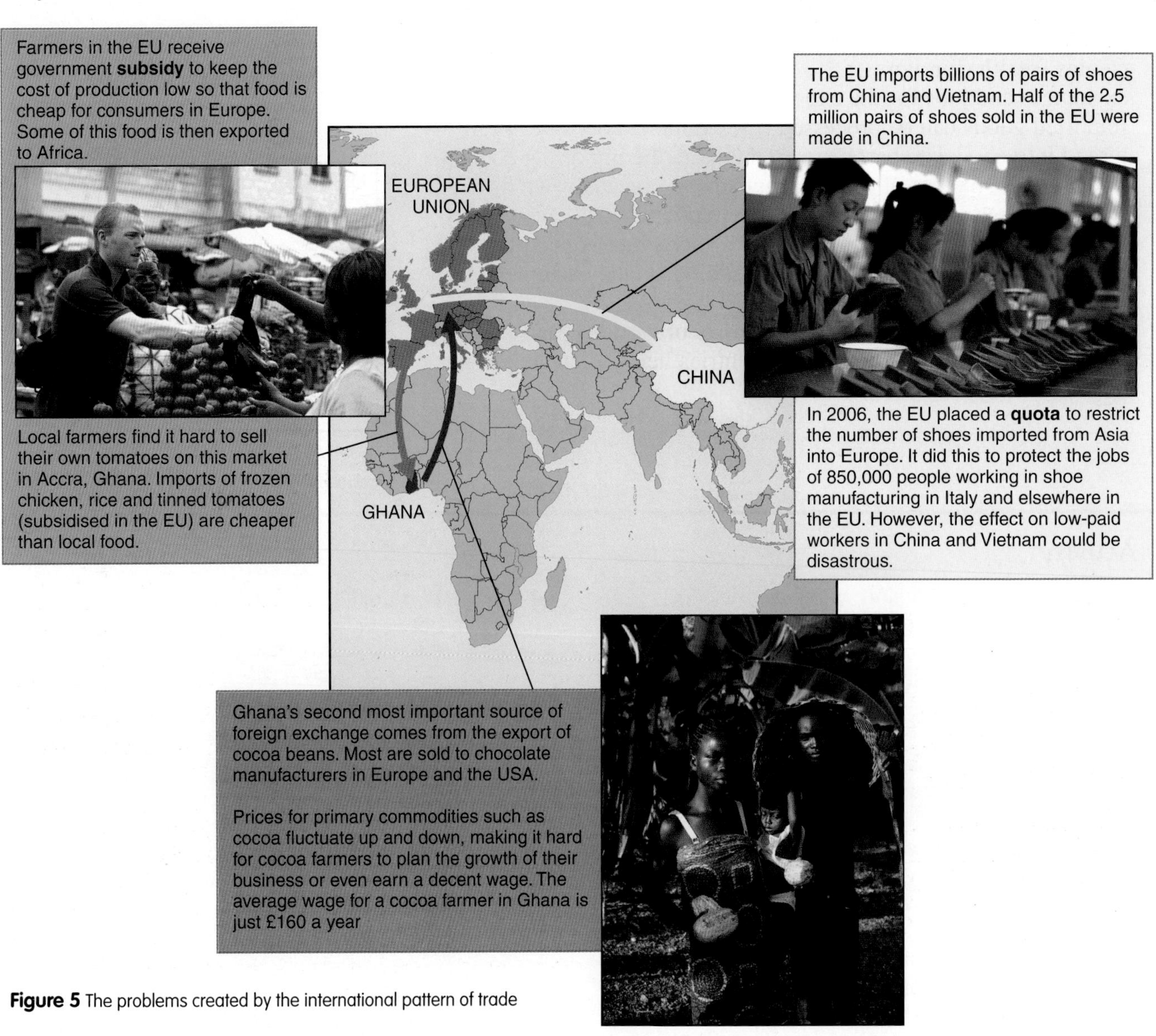


**Figure 5** The problems created by the international pattern of trade

## Trade blocs

Trade is made easier where partnerships have been agreed between countries. These trading partnerships are known as trade blocs. The European Union (EU) is one example of several **trade blocs** that exist around the world. Figure 6 shows two more. Each country within each bloc already has a free trade agreement with other countries in the bloc, or is working towards a free trade agreement. For example, China already has free trade agreements with some members of the Asia-Pacific Economic Co-operation (APEC) and is working towards similar partnerships with the other LEDC members of the group by 2010. However, it has no free trade partnership with the UK or with the EU. That is why the EU is able to impose the quota on imports of Chinese shoes described in Figure 5.

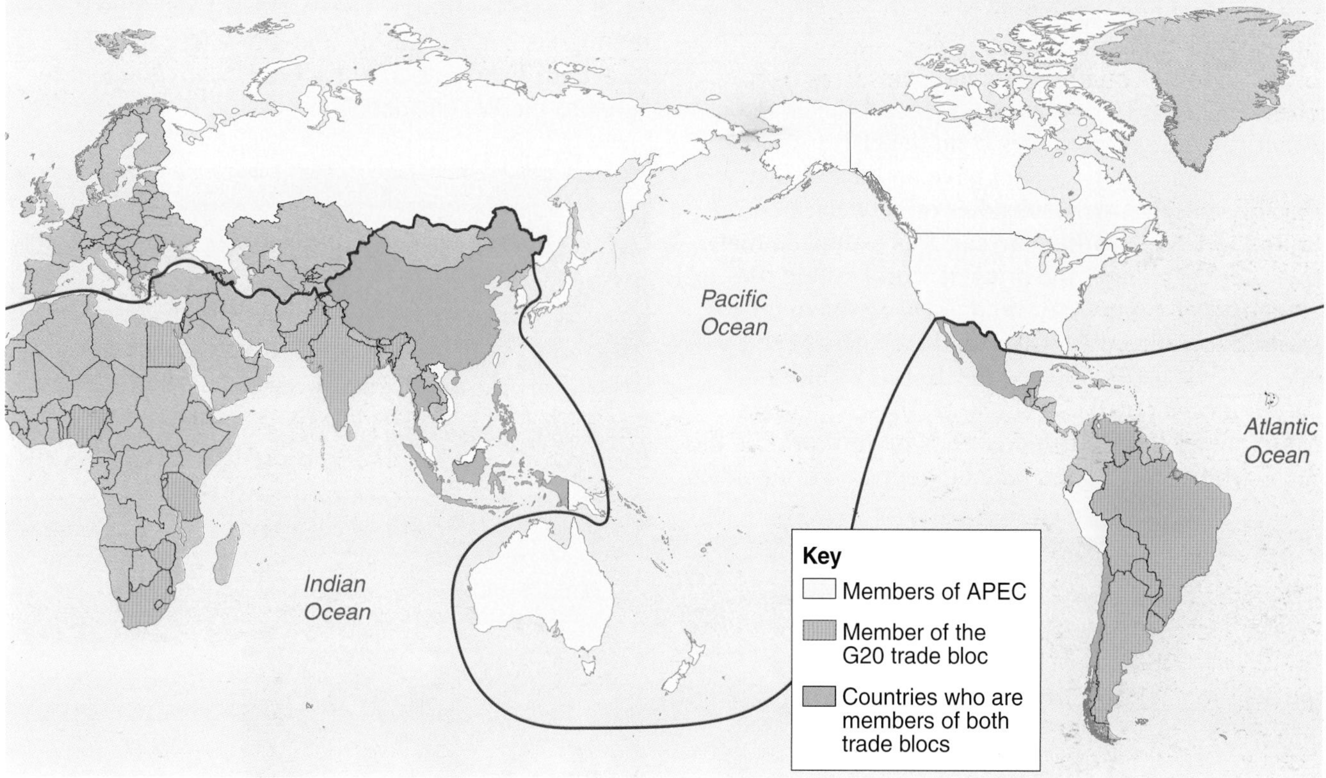


**Figure 6** Trade blocs: APEC and G20

### Activity

**7** Use the evidence in Figure 5 to explain the advantage of quotas and subsidies for:
**a)** consumers in Europe
**b)** farmers and businesses in Europe.

**8** Explain the likely effect of:
**a)** the EU shoe quota for workers in Vietnam
**b)** the import of cheap food for farmers in Ghana.

**9** Use Figure 6.
**a)** Describe the distribution of APEC countries.
**b)** Compare the distribution of APEC countries with that of G20 countries.

**10** Explain the advantage of free trade for the LEDC countries in the G20 trade bloc.

## A case study of subsidies and trade: Mali, cotton and poverty

The USA is the world's largest producer of cotton, producing 40 per cent of all cotton on the world market. Most farms are large and highly mechanised. It costs about 92 pence to produce one kilo of American cotton. This is 3.5 times higher than the production cost in West Africa: farmers in Burkina Faso can produce cotton for 26 pence a kilo. This is because African farmers use labour intensive methods of production, and the cost of their labour is very low.

The US Government wanted to protect the 25,000 American cotton producers from the effects that cheap cotton imports would have on their industry. For this reason it paid subsidies of between US$2.7 billion to US$3.4 billion a year. It is estimated that this subsidy reduces the price of world cotton by about 25 per cent. Other producers also have to sell their cotton cheaply, or they find they cannot sell it at all. This has badly affected the 10 to 11 million cotton farmers of West Africa. Of these countries Mali, one of the poorest countries in the world, is the main producer. Farmers here do not receive subsidies from their government and have to sell their cotton for little more than it cost to produce.

In 2004, Brazil protested to the World Trade Organization (WTO) about the US cotton subsidy. If the USA removed its subsidy it is estimated that the farmers of West Africa would earn an extra US$190 million a year and Brazil's farmers could earn an extra US$600 million. The WTO ordered the USA to remove its cotton subsidy and allow free trade. It took until February 2006 for the US government to agree to the WTO's decision.

**Figure 7** Cotton farms in the USA are large and highly mechanised

**Figure 8** Cotton is Mali's biggest export. Most is grown by small-scale farmers who earn less than US$2 a day

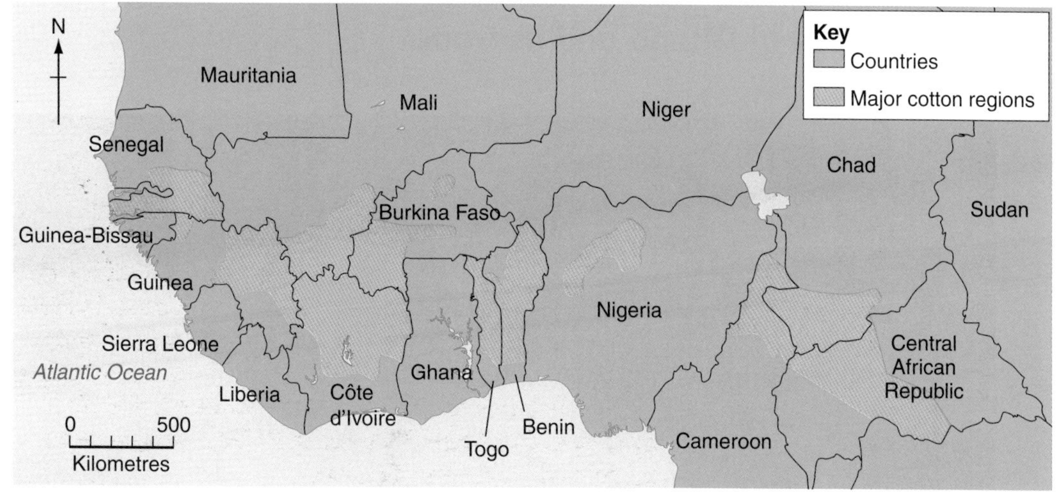


**Figure 9** The cotton growing region of West Africa

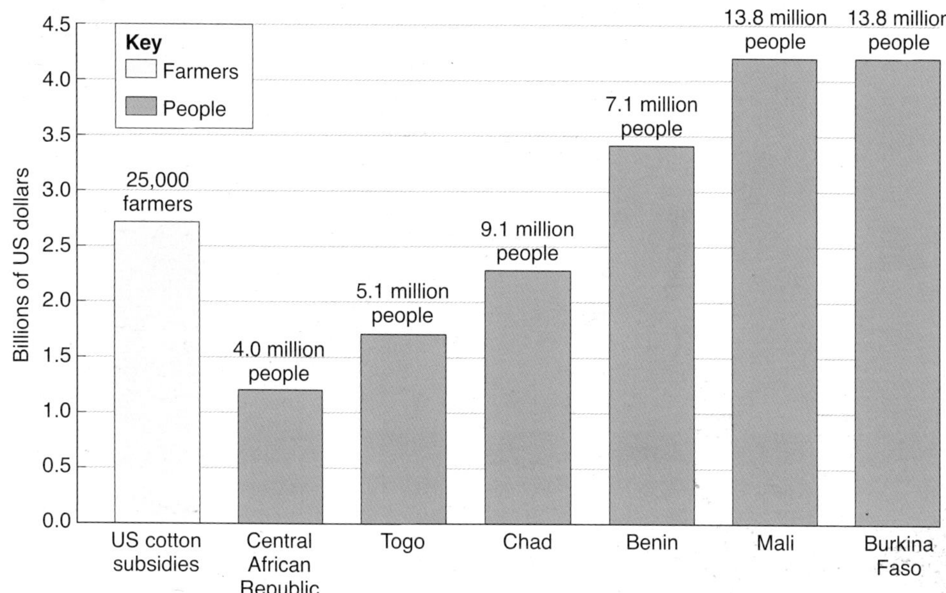


**Figure 10** The amount paid in US cotton subsidies is similar to the entire national income of several countries in sub-Saharan Africa

## Activity

**11** Describe the distribution (see page 143) of the cotton-growing areas in West Africa.

**12** Make notes about this case study. Include:

**a)** a sketch map of Mali to show the location of the cotton-growing area

**b)** a definition of farm subsidies and an explanation of why they were given to US cotton farmers

**c)** the effects that the US cotton subsidies had on African exports and wage levels for farmers.

**13** Produce a presentation (a poster, a talk, or a digital presentation) that explains why farmers in Brazil and Mali thought that the cotton subsidies were unfair.

**14** Study Figure 10.

**a)** Compare the amount of the US cotton subsidy to the national wealth of Mali.

**b)** Explain why it is important to know how many people live in each African country compared with the number of US cotton farmers.

## A case study of Ghana and its trade

**Figure 11** Joyce Oppong Kyekyeku and her daughter Doris breed chickens for a living but they are competing against cheaper imported chickens from Europe. The Ghanaian Government imposed tariffs on the imports but was forced to drop them by the International Monetary Fund

Like all countries, Ghana needs to trade successfully in order to create wealth and jobs. However, Ghana faces a number of problems with the international pattern of trade.

Ghana is not a member of any of the major trade blocs. For this reason it cannot rely on free trade with other countries. One of its main exports is cocoa beans. This product has a relatively small tariff when it enters the EU: buyers pay only three per cent tax. However, the EU tariff on imports of processed cocoa products is higher. For example, buyers of cocoa butter pay a 7.7 per cent import tax. This tariff is in place to protect the chocolate manufacturers in the EU from cheap imports of cocoa products. It also makes it hard for manufacturers in Ghana to sell their cocoa products in Europe.

Another problem that Ghana experiences with trade is that food imported from the EU is sold so cheaply that it undercuts the cost of locally grown food. Imports of rice, chicken and tinned tomatoes are particularly cheap because the EU has subsidised the farmers who produce these goods. Any that cannot be sold in Europe are then sold cheaply in Africa: a practice known as **dumping**. Ghana tried to place import tariffs on these items but was forced to drop them as a condition of its loan from the World Bank.

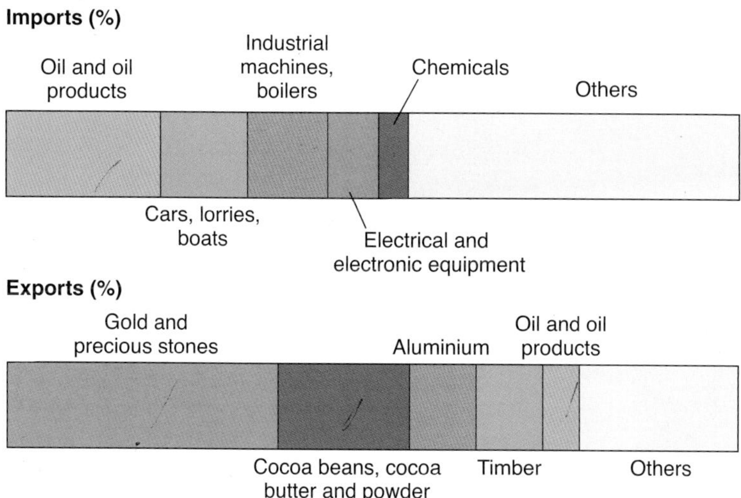


**Figure 12** Ghana's main imports and exports

**Figure 14** Michael Stipe of the band REM has milk dumped on him to draw attention to the Make Trade Fair campaign. EU milk subsidies mean that European cows 'earn' US$2 a day, which is more than the daily income of a Ghanaian farmer

**Figure 13** The Make Trade Fair logo was launched by Oxfam in 2002. Oxfam is a **Non-Governmental Organisation (NGO)** which is drawing attention to the dumping of subsidised products in LEDCs

**www.maketradefair.com**
This is the homepage of the Make Trade Fair campaign. You'll find explanations of why the current pattern of international trade is unfair for LEDCs.

## Activity

**15** Use Figure 12 to complete the following description of Ghana's pattern of trade:

**Ghana's largest export is ... at 37 per cent, followed by cocoa beans which make up ... per cent of Ghana's exports. Oil is the largest single import which makes up ... per cent of all imports.**

**16** Which of Ghana's imports/exports are:

**a)** primary commodities

**b)** manufactured or processed goods.

**17** Explain why Ghana would benefit from joining a trade bloc such as the G20.

**18** Suggest how Ghana could benefit from the Make Trade Fair campaign.

**19** Design a poster or leaflet featuring information about Ghana and headed 'Make Trade Fair for Ghana'.

## Ghana's cocoa farms

Almost 90 per cent of all of Ghana's cocoa is grown on smallholdings: tiny farms that are smaller than 3 hectares. About 2.5 million smallholders in Ghana grow cocoa as their main crop. Most of the cocoa is sold for export; only about five per cent of Ghana's cocoa crop is processed into chocolate in Ghana.

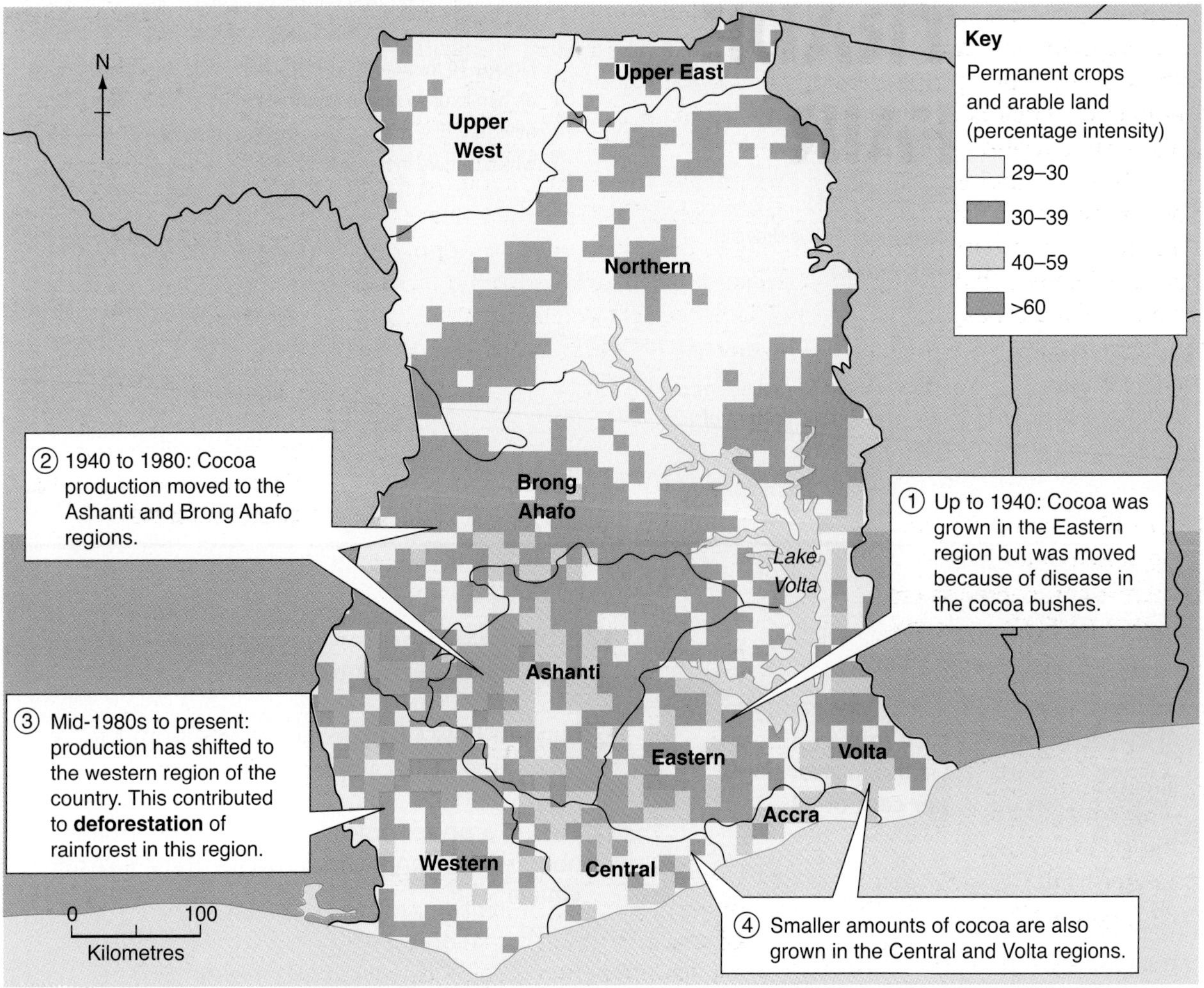

**Figure 15** A cocoa farmer lays out cocoa beans on giant tables made of rush matting to dry in the intense Ghanaian sun. After six days they will have developed a full flavour

N

Upper East
Upper West
Northern
Brong Ahafo
Lake Volta
Ashanti
Eastern
Volta
Accra
Western
Central

Key
Permanent crops and arable land (percentage intensity)
29–30
30–39
40–59
>60

① Up to 1940: Cocoa was grown in the Eastern region but was moved because of disease in the cocoa bushes.

② 1940 to 1980: Cocoa production moved to the Ashanti and Brong Ahafo regions.

③ Mid-1980s to present: production has shifted to the western region of the country. This contributed to **deforestation** of rainforest in this region.

④ Smaller amounts of cocoa are also grown in the Central and Volta regions.

0 100
Kilometres

**Figure 16** Where cocoa is grown in Ghana

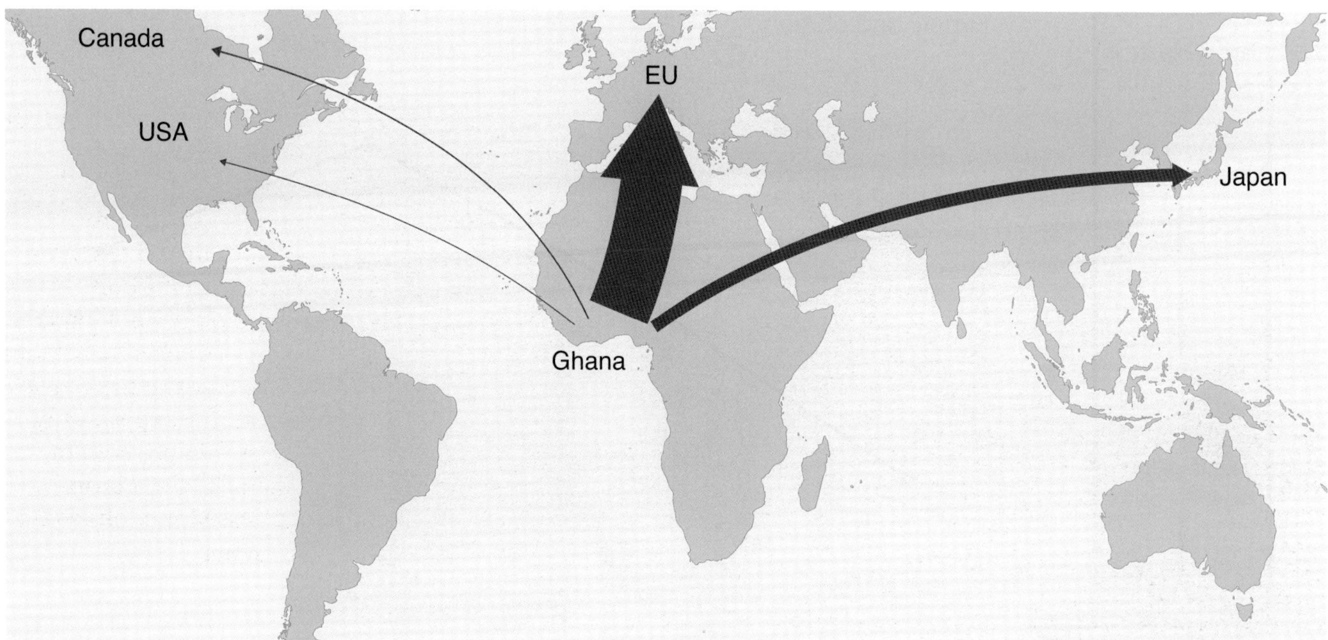


**Figure 17** Exports of cocoa from Ghana, 2003 to 2004

## Ghana and the cocoa trade

One major problem for cocoa growers is that the price they get for their crop is so low. The average income for a cocoa farmer is only about £160 a year. This is because of the way in which primary commodities such as cocoa beans are traded on the world market. Traders in Europe buy cocoa beans on the London Stock Exchange. They shop around and buy the beans from whichever supplier is cheapest. It's a buyer's market. If Ghana's farmers are asking too much for their beans, the buyers will shop around and buy from Côte d'Ivoire or whoever is cheapest. The price can go up or down from day to day, depending on supply and demand. Figure 18 shows that the EU buyers can purchase cocoa from a number of suppliers, but Ghana relies heavily on the EU for selling its cocoa. This fluctuating price makes it very difficult for farmers in Ghana to earn a fair wage for all of their work.

| Import partner | Thousand tonnes of cocoa beans |
|---|---|
| Côte d'Ivoire | 658 |
| Ghana | 466 |
| Cameroon | 119 |
| Nigeria | 116 |
| Indonesia | 9 |

**Figure 18** Imports of cocoa into the EU, 2003 to 2004

### Activity

**20** Use Figure 17 to complete the following statement:

**All of Ghana's cocoa exports are sold in LEDCs / MEDCs. … is the largest buyer of Ghana's cocoa.**

**21** Use Figure 18.

**a)** Choose a suitable technique to illustrate the data.

**b)** How much cocoa is imported to the EU from Ghana compared with the other trading partners?

**22** Study Figure 16.

**a)** List the four regions of Ghana which have most permanent crop land.

**b)** Which regions have least permanent crop land?

**23** Draw a simple sketch map of Ghana to show the main cocoa-growing area today.

**24** Use an atlas (or the internet) to research patterns of rainfall in Ghana. Use this information to explain the pattern of permanent crop land in Figure 16.

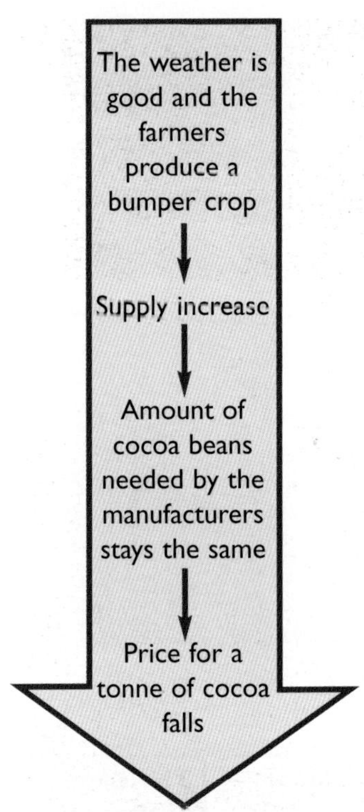


Figure 19 Supply and demand

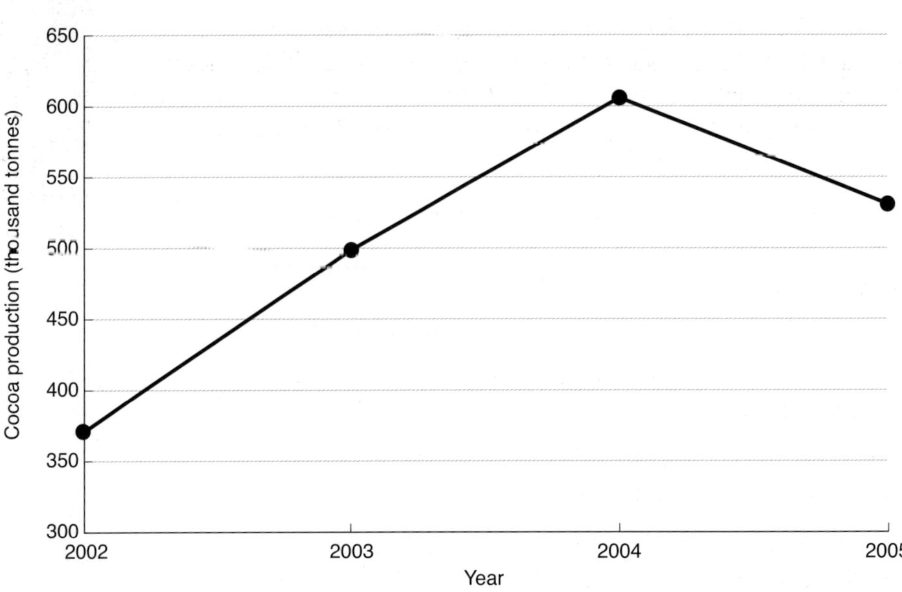


**Figure 20** The amount of cocoa produced in Ghana fluctuates from year to year

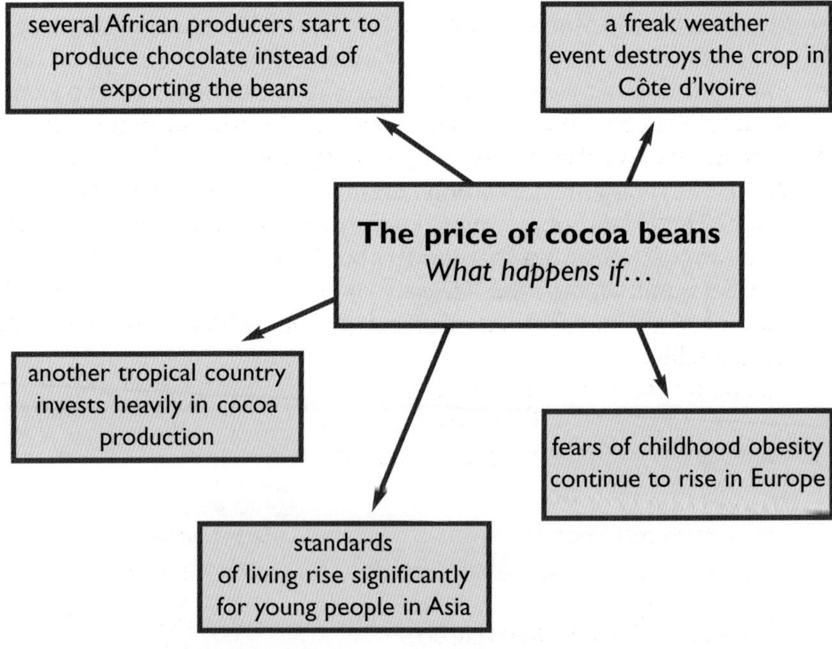


**Figure 21** A futures wheel for cocoa

## Activity

**25** Study Figure 19. Make a similar flow chart which starts with the following statement:
*A disease in many cocoa plantations means that the harvest is poor.*

**26** Look at Figure 20.

**a)** Describe the trends in cocoa production in Ghana over this three-year period.

**b)** Using your understanding of supply and demand, predict in which years the price of cocoa would have been highest and lowest.

**27** Look at Figure 21. Suggest what will happen to the price of cocoa beans on the world market for each of these future scenarios.

**www.icco.org**
contains facts about cocoa production and the cocoa trade.

### The Kuapa Kokoo co-operative of cocoa farmers

Figure 22 The FAIRTRADE Mark

The concept of fair trade has been around for more than 30 years. The Fairtrade Foundation was established in 1992 as an independent certification body that licenses the FAIRTRADE Mark to products that meet international standards which are set by Fairtrade Labelling Organisations International (FLO).

The FAIRTRADE Mark guarantees a better deal for farmers and workers in developing countries so that they can enjoy a better standard of living.

- The farmer receives a payment that is agreed and stable.
- The farmer also receives an additional payment called a **Social Premium**.
- One of the many aims is to develop a long-term trading partnership with the producers.

Figure 23 The Premium is used by the producers for community projects such as this village well

Kuapa Kokoo is a co-operative of cocoa farmers in Ghana. The co-operative sells part of its cocoa bean crop to Divine Chocolate Ltd. in the UK who make Fairtrade chocolate products such as Divine and Dubble. The main benefits of this arrangement are:

- Farmers receive an extra US$150 per tonne for their cocoa which is about ten per cent more than the usual price on the world market.
- The co-operative also receives a Social Premium that is then used to fund community projects such as the well in Figure 23.
- Farmers receive training to help them deal with problems such as pests or diseases which affect the cocoa crop, for example black pod.
- Members of the co-operative can borrow small amounts of money from a **micro-credit** bank which is known as the Kuapa Kokoo Credit Union.
- The farmers have elected a trusted member of the village to weigh and record their cocoa beans. This makes trading more official and people more accountable.
- Kuapa Kokoo are shareholders in Divine Chocolate Ltd. Profits from the sale of chocolate bars are invested in projects in Ghana.

**www.kuapakokoogh.com** is a website describing the co-operative.

## Activity

**28** Make some notes to show how Fairtrade has helped:

**a)** cocoa famers who belong to Kuapa Kokoo

**b)** the wider community.

**29** Use Figure 16 (on page 222) to make a sketch map of Ghana. Label it using Figure 24 to show how different regions have benefited from Fairtrade.

| Project | Number of projects in different regions | | | | | Total |
|---|---|---|---|---|---|---|
| | Western | Central | Eastern | Brong Ahafo | Ashanti | |
| Boreholes/ hand dry well | 121 | 11 | 6 | 9 | 27 | 174 |
| Women's project IGA | 1 | 0 | 0 | 0 | 0 | 1 |
| School/ education | 0 | 1 | 1 | 0 | 2 | 4 |
| Corn Mills | 10 | 4 | 3 | 2 | 8 | 27 |
| Construction of latrines | 0 | 0 | 0 | 0 | 2 | 2 |
| Bridge | 0 | 0 | 0 | 0 | 1 | 1 |
| **Total** | **132** | **16** | **10** | **11** | **40** | **209** |

Figure 24 How Kuapa Kokoo used the Social Premium, 1993 to 2002

Unit 4

# Chapter 5
# Patterns of international aid

**KEY QUESTIONS**

- What is the international pattern of aid?
- What different types of aid are available?
- Is aid successful in creating development?

## Investigating different kinds of aid

Why give aid? Who gives it and what is it for? We will seek to answer these questions before examining a case study of aid projects in Mali and Niger.

### Emergency aid

The tsunami of 26 December 2004 was the biggest natural disaster in living memory. The massive series of waves, generated by an earthquake, killed approximately 250,000 people in thirteen different countries and left hundreds of thousands of people homeless. Aid was needed urgently to protect the lives of the survivors from the spread of disease. This was an example of **emergency aid** relief. The immediate aid that was needed included:

- distributing food and clean water to those affected by the disaster
- giving medical attention to those who had been injured
- providing temporary shelter for those who had lost their homes
- monitoring the distribution of the aid to make sure that all those who needed it, including the women and children, had their fair share.

**Activity**

1 Describe the distribution (see page 143) of countries which received emergency aid after the tsunami.

2 Explain the aims of the emergency aid:
  a) in the days immediately after the disaster
  b) six months later.

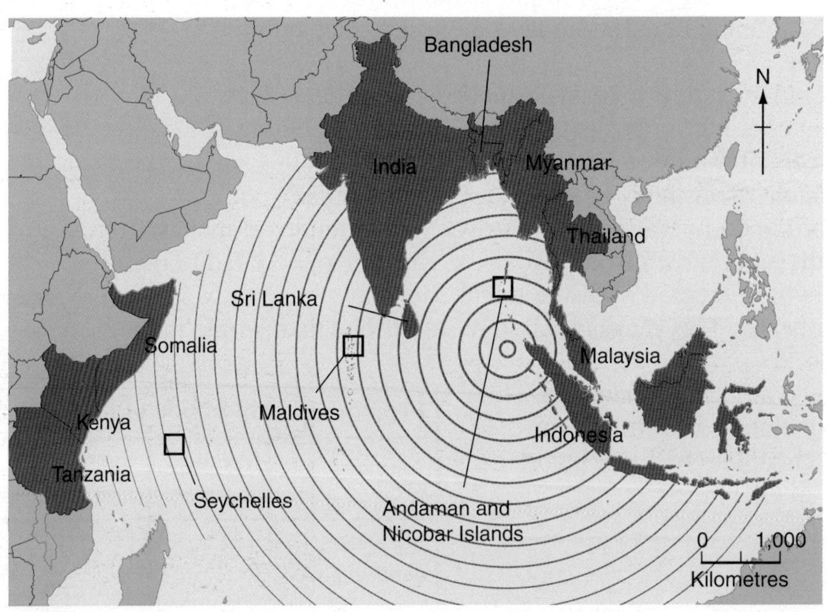


**Figure 1** The countries which required emergency aid after the tsunami of 26 December 2004

### Medium- and longer-term projects

Six months later, more than 500,000 people in Sri Lanka alone were still living in 'tent cities'. The focus of the aid had moved on to medium- and longer-term projects, which included:

- building permanent housing to replace the houses destroyed in the tsunami
- getting people back to work so that they could help themselves rather than relying on aid. This included training projects to teach people new skills
- repairing boats and nets so that fishing communities could get back to work.

No timber is needed in the roof so the building does not require local trees to be cut.

Holes in the concrete roof are filled with waste material such as broken tiles. This saves concrete and costs 77 per cent of a concrete slab roof.

The brick walls are built using a 'rat trap bond'. This wall is just as strong as a solid wall but it uses 20 per cent less bricks. This wall costs about 74 per cent of a traditional wall.

The flat roof space can be used for storage or drying fish and fishing nets. This provides extra space for low income families who cannot afford a house with a yard or garden area.

The air that is trapped in the wall acts as insulation helping to keep the house cool in the day.

**Figure 2** The benefits of the replacement housing in southern Sri Lanka built to a design by Practical Action

## Long-term development aid projects

Images of the tsunami disaster filled the newspapers and television screens around the world, and created a very generous response from donors. However, emergency aid is only a small part of the aid given by both governments and Non-Governmental Organisations (NGOs) such as Oxfam, ActionAid or Christian Aid. Most aid is, in fact, planned over long periods of time to tackle poverty and improve quality of life. This is known as long-term, or **development aid**.

**http://practicalaction.org** is the website of Practical Action, formerly the Intermediate Technology Development Group. It has lots of case studies of how an appropriate and sustainable level of technology can be used to provide aid.

**Figure 3** How Christian Aid (an NGO) spent its money in the financial year 2004–2005

| **Expenditure 2004–2005**<br>Direct charitable expenditure | **£m** | **%** |
|---|---|---|
| Development programmes | 36.6 | 52 |
| Emergencies | 12.0 | 17 |
| Campaigning, education and advocacy | 8.6 | 12 |
| Management and administration | 0.9 | 1 |
| Total | 58.1 | 82 |
| Fundraising | 12.9 | 18 |
| **Grand total expenditure** | **£71.0m** | |

## Activity

**3** Study Figure 2. Explain the benefits of this design for:
- the aid organisations which funded the reconstruction
- people who were rehoused
- the local environment.

**4** Study Figure 3 and complete the following statement.

**Christian Aid is an NGO which stands for .... In 2004/05 they gave ... million to long-term development programmes, which is ... per cent of their budget.**

**5** Compare the amount of money spent by Christian Aid on emergency aid and on development programmes.

## Overseas Development Aid

The UK Government funds many long-term development projects abroad. This is called **Overseas Development Aid (ODA)**. The UK government gave £4.1 billion of ODA in the financial year 2004–2005. This is expected to rise to £6.5 billion by 2007–2008. Some of this is given directly to fund projects in Less Economically Developed Countries (LEDCs) such as Ghana.

This is known as **bi-lateral aid** because the aid passes directly from one country to a partner country. The rest of the UK's aid is pooled with money donated by the other governments of the European Union (EU). The EU then decides which projects to fund. This type of funding is known as **multi-lateral aid** because many donors are involved.

| | 1990 | 1995 | 2000 | 2002 | 2003 |
|---|---|---|---|---|---|
| Total ODA as a percentage of national income | 0.27 | 0.29 | 0.32 | 0.31 | 0.34 |
| Percentage of ODA that is given as part of a multi-lateral partnership | 44.1 | 46.4 | 39.8 | 28.8 | 38.5 |
| Percentage of ODA that is given as part of a bi-lateral partnership | 55.9 | 53.6 | 60.2 | 71.2 | 61.5 |

**Figure 4** The changing pattern of the UK Government's Overseas Development Aid (ODA)

## The food crisis in Mali and Niger, 2005

In 2004, the **subsistence** farmers of Mali and Niger were hit by a double problem: a particularly severe drought and a plague of locusts virtually destroyed their crops. By July 2005 the crisis came to the attention of the world's media. By then it was estimated that 3.3 million people (including 800,000 children) were at risk from a serious food shortage. UNICEF, which was already working in Niger because it has a programme of long-term development aid in the country, was struggling to cope with the scale of the problem and asked for extra help to give emergency aid.

**Figure 5** The food crisis in Niger

### Activity

6 Study Figure 4.

**a)** Choose a suitable technique to graph the change in ODA as a percentage of national income.

**b)** The United Nations has set all MEDC governments a target of giving 0.7 per cent of their wealth as ODA by 2015. Using the trend of the graph you have drawn, predict whether the UK will meet this target.

7 Study Figure 4. What has happened to the percentage of aid that is given as bi-lateral aid?

8 Can you suggest any advantages for the UK Government (or tax payer) of having more bi-lateral aid than multi-lateral aid projects?

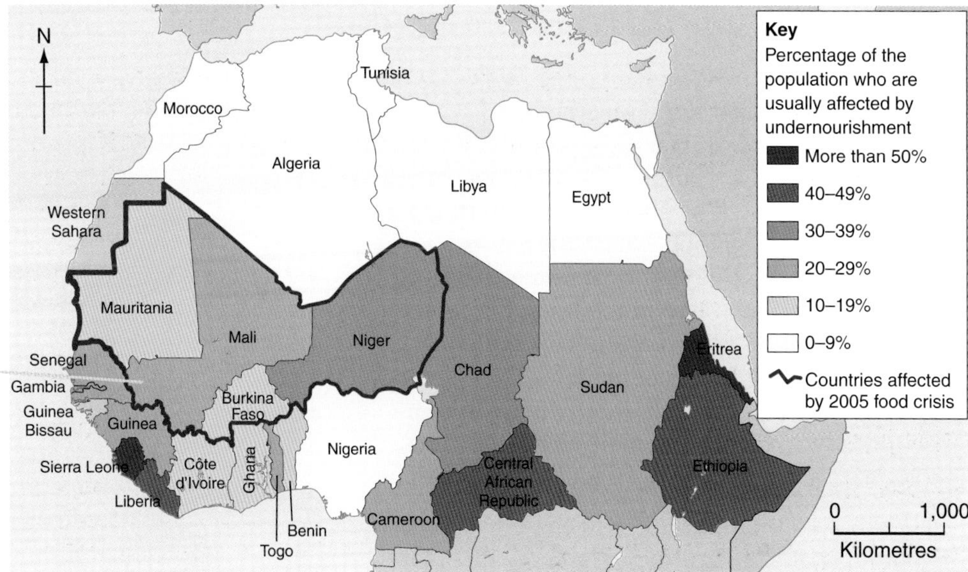

**Figure 6** Location of the 2005 food crisis in Africa and percentage of population in the region who are usually undernourished

Countries affected by the 2005 food crisis are circled here.

In light of this emergency, UNICEF Niger has routed an additional US$270,000 to treat 14,000 malnourished children for six months.

However, the children's agency urgently needs US$1.03 million to treat another 17,000 severely malnourished children with therapeutic food (a peanut butter based food called plumpynut and therapeutic milk) for six months, and make cereal accessible to another 163,000 people through the purchase of 641 tonnes to restock 65 cereal banks.

During the 2004 agricultural season, swarms of desert locusts consumed nearly 100 per cent of the crops in some areas. In addition, parts of the country received insufficient rainfall resulting in poor harvests and dry pasturelands, affecting both farmers and livestock breeders.

On a regular basis, UNICEF implements strategies to prevent malnutrition at the community level. Here are some examples:

- 245 cereal banks were opened in UNICEF's intervention zones to make staple grains (millet and sorghum) available. Before the harvest, when food supplies are low and hunger increases, cereal banks loan food to mothers. After harvest, the women repay their loans in cash or grain.
- UNICEF also supports 300 women's groups that promote exclusive breastfeeding and monitor children's growth in the villages. Women with malnourished children receive loans of goats to enrich their families' diets with milk and cheese.
- Twice a year, vitamin A supplements are provided to all children under the age of five. Supplementary feeding centres receive therapeutic food for severely malnourished children. This food is high in protein and fat.

**Figure 7** Extract from UNICEF website describing the reaction to the Niger food crisis in 2005

## Activity

**9** Use Figure 6 to describe the distribution (see page 143) of countries that have:

**a)** between 0 and nine per cent of the population who are undernourished

**b)** more than 30 per cent of the population who are undernourished.

**10** Suggest reasons why some countries in Africa are more vulnerable to food shortages than others.

**11** Read the web extract in Figure 7.

**a)** Give two reasons for the food crisis.

**b)** Use Figure 7 to give examples of both UNICEF's emergency aid and long-term aid programmes.

**12** Explain the difference between the aims of UNICEF's emergency aid and long-term strategies to prevent malnutrition.

## Long-term development aid projects in Niger and Mali

Oxfam is one of many Non-Governmental Organisations which provides long-term development aid to Niger and Mali. In one of their projects they are working with the Association for the Indigenous Development of the **Sahel** (ADESAH), a local NGO, to support primary schools for the children of **pastoral farmers** who live in the border area between western Niger and northern Mali. This nomadic community of cattle and goat herders is very poor. Many families do not feel they can afford to send their children to school, especially girls. The project supports 48 primary schools. Its successes include:

- In 2004, 4,053 pupils were enrolled in school, including 1,818 girls (44.85 per cent).
- Women are deeply involved in the management of the schools and participate physically and financially in the payment of children's school fees and in the canteen.
- The ratio of pupil to books has improved from one book for five pupils to two books for three pupils.

**www.oxfam.org.uk** **www.trickleup.org**
**www.wateraid.org.uk**
The NGOs whose websites are listed above have long-term aid projects in Mali and Niger.

### Activity

**13** Give three details which describe the group who benefit from Oxfam's project.

**14** Give two facts that can be used as measures of success of this project.

**15** Use what you learned in Chapter 3 (pages 208–209) to explain why Oxfam may have chosen to fund a project that gives aid to girls and women.

**16** Use the internet links to prepare a brief report on a long-term aid programme to either Mali or Niger. Include in your report:
- how different groups of people (for example, children, women, farmers) benefit from the aid
- facts you could use to evaluate the success of the project.

## Going Further

### The Millennium Development Goals

The United Nations (UN) has set development targets known as the **Millennium Development Goals (MDG)** which it aims to meet by 2015.

1 End extreme poverty and hunger:
- Halve the number of people living on less than a dollar a day.
- Halve the number who suffer from hunger.

2 Achieve universal primary education:
- Ensure that all boys and girls complete a full course of primary schooling.

3 Promote gender equality:
- Make it easier for girls as well as boys to access primary and secondary education.

4 Reduce child mortality:
- Reduce by two-thirds the number of children who die before their fifth birthday.

5 Improve health for mothers:
- Reduce by three-quarters the number of women who die in childbirth.

6 Combat AIDS, malaria and other diseases:
- Halt and begin to reverse the spread of these killer diseases.

7 Ensure environmental sustainability:
- Protect the environment, so that future generations can continue to benefit from it.
- Halve the number of people without access to clean water.
- Improve life for 100 million people who live in shanty towns by 2020.

8 Build global partnerships for development:
- Make improvements to aid.
- Boost freedom, justice and democracy.
- Make it easier for the poorest people to have access to medicines.
- Cancel some debts and reduce others.
- Make world trade fairer.

**Figure 8** Target 2015 UN Millennium Development Goals

## Going Further continued

| | Average income per person (GNP US$) | | |
|---|---|---|---|
| | Low income countries | High income countries | Ratio of high to low income |
| 1975 | 150 | 6,200 | 41 |
| 1985 | 270 | 11,810 | 44 |
| 1990 | 350 | 19,590 | 56 |
| 1995 | 430 | 24,930 | 58 |

**Figure 9** Is the gap between the richest countries and the poorest countries getting wider? In 1975 the average income in high income countries was US$6,200, which was 41 times greater than the average income in low income countries

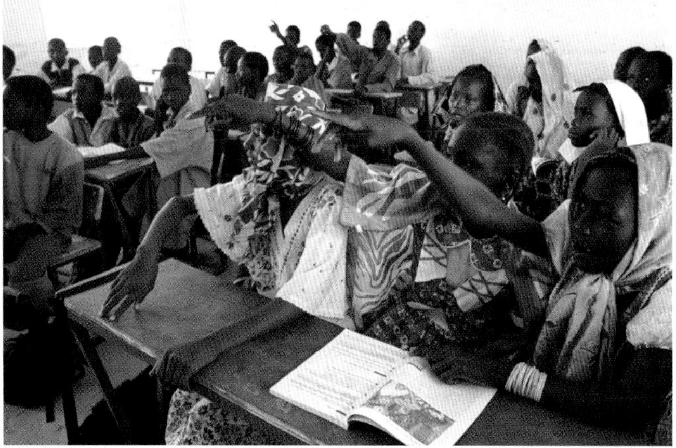

**Figure 10** Class in Taboye school, Mali, which has received support from Oxfam and the local NGO ADESAH. It's an MDG to ensure that all boys and girls in the world complete their primary education

| | Kg of cereals per person | | | | | | | | | | | |
|---|---|---|---|---|---|---|---|---|---|---|---|---|
| Year | 90–91 | 91–92 | 92–93 | 93–94 | 94–95 | 95–96 | 96–97 | 97–98 | 98–99 | 99–00 | 00–01 | 01–02 |
| Africa | 10.0 | 8.6 | 10.2 | 5.0 | 5.0 | 3.4 | 2.3 | 2.7 | 3.0 | 3.4 | 4.3 | 2.6 |
| Asia | 1.0 | 1.0 | 0.9 | 1.1 | 1.2 | 1.2 | 0.7 | 0.9 | 1.5 | 1.2 | 1.2 | 1.1 |
| Latin America and the Caribbean | 4.4 | 4.3 | 3.4 | 3.4 | 2.4 | 1.2 | 1.2 | 1.0 | 1.9 | 1.5 | 1.2 | 1.4 |

**Figure 11** Cereals given as aid to relieve food shortages (in kg of cereals per person)

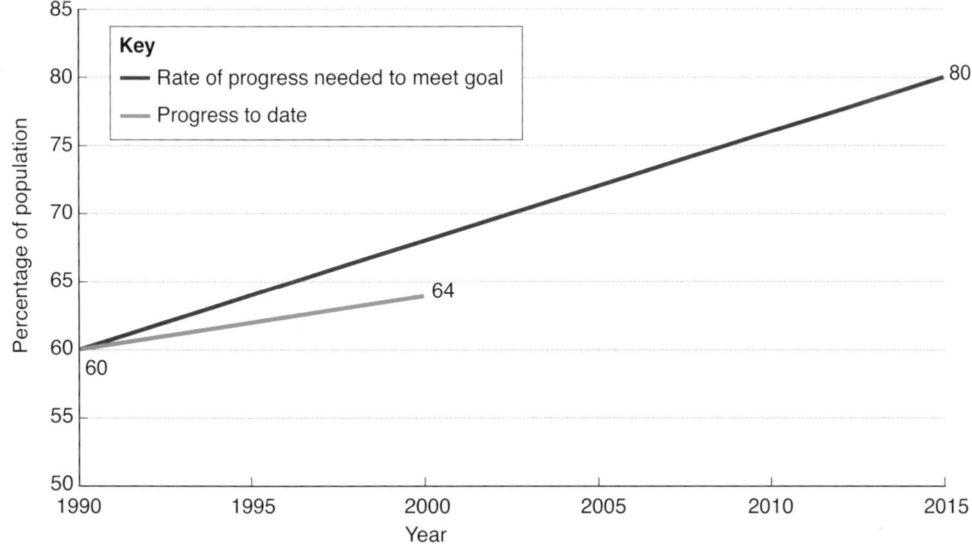


**Figure 12** Proportion of people in Africa with sustainable access to an improved water source

**17 a)** Use the ratios in Figure 9 to plot a graph that shows how many times richer people are in MEDCs compared with the lowest income LEDCs.

**b)** Describe the trend shown on your graph.

**18 a)** Choose a suitable graphical technique to represent the data in Figure 11.

**b)** Describe the trends shown by your graph.

**19** Study Figure 12. If the current trend continues, what percentage of Africans will have access to clean water by 2015?

**20** Taking evidence from this chapter, suggest whether you think the pattern of international aid is successful in improving quality of life.

# Chapter 6
# Economic activity in a global world

**KEY QUESTIONS**

- What factors influence the location of economic activity?
- How are large trans-national companies, such as Nokia, organised and how do they influence patterns of work and development in different parts of the world?
- What are the advantages and disadvantages of a globalised economy for regions in the UK or other countries?

## Investigating the role of trans-national companies in the global world of business

The world is increasingly interdependent: more and more places are being linked together by flows of money, ideas and goods. This process is known as globalisation. Key players in the process of globalisation have been **trans-national companies (TNCs)**.

Products such as soft drinks, fast food, mobile phones and clothing have global appeal and a global marketplace. The production and sale of these consumer goods is dominated by a relatively small number of manufacturers known as trans-national companies. For a company to be defined as a TNC it has to have branches in more than one country. The branches of a TNC include offices, factories and research and development (R&D) laboratories. Why do TNCs have branches located in different countries?

### Activity

1 Study Figure 2 and use it complete a table like the one below:

| Type of employment | Example | Place | MEDC or LEDC |
|---|---|---|---|
| Primary | 1 Drilling for oil<br>2 …… | | |
| Secondary | 1 Processing coltan<br>2 | China | LEDC |
| Tertiary | 1<br>2 | | |

2 Study Figures 1 and 2 and use them to complete the following description:

**Sixty-three per cent of Nokia's employees work in the continent of …. A total of … per cent of their employees work in China and other Asian and Pacific countries. Many of these work in … industries making items such as … and …. Most of Nokia's sales are in …. Second is China with other Asian and Pacific countries with a total of … per cent of sales.**

3 Work in pairs to structure a globalisation enquiry.

**a)** Choose one of these titles: 'World in your living room' or 'World in your wardrobe'.

**b)** Brainstorm all the different places you might find 'Made in…' information.

**c)** Design a data collection sheet that you could use to record results from your classmates.

**d)** Collect the data from at least five classmates and plot the data on a world outline map or make a large poster with photos you have collected from magazines or the internet.

4 Suggest why Nokia equips its phones with SIM cards and batteries made by a number of different manufacturers in Asia.

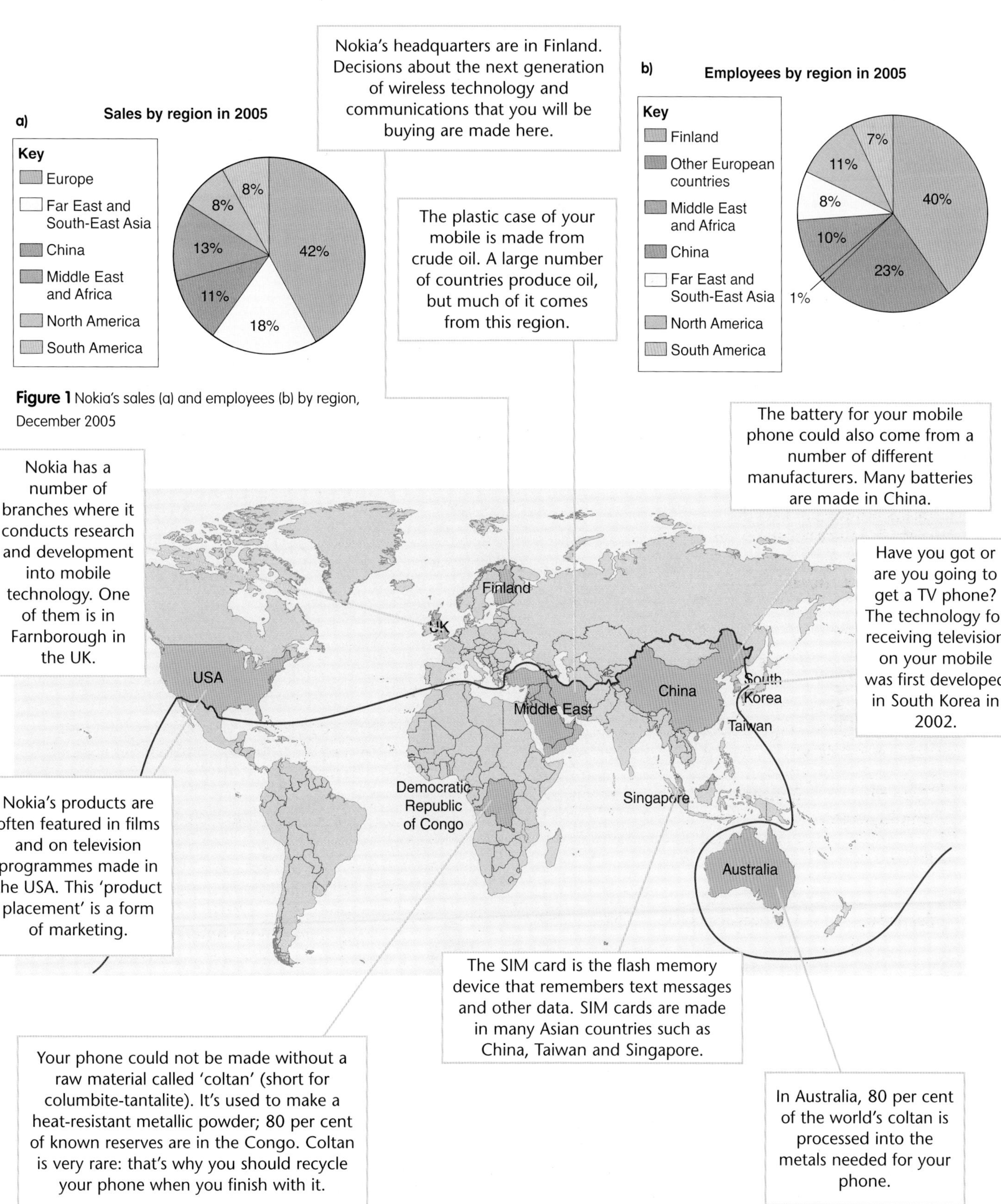


**Figure 1** Nokia's sales (a) and employees (b) by region, December 2005

**Figure 2** The world in your mobile phone

Nokia

## A case study of a trans-national company

Nokia is the world's largest manufacturer of mobile phones and other mobile devices. It also provides network and communication services to other businesses, improving communications. Nokia is a Finnish TNC. Its head office is in Helsinki, Finland, but it has offices and factories all around the globe. Nokia employs more than 58,000 people worldwide. Nokia has **plants** (offices, factories and laboratories) in many different countries:

- Research and development laboratories (R&D) in eleven countries.
- Factories in nine countries.
- Sales offices in more than 130 countries.

Why does Nokia have plants located in so many different countries?

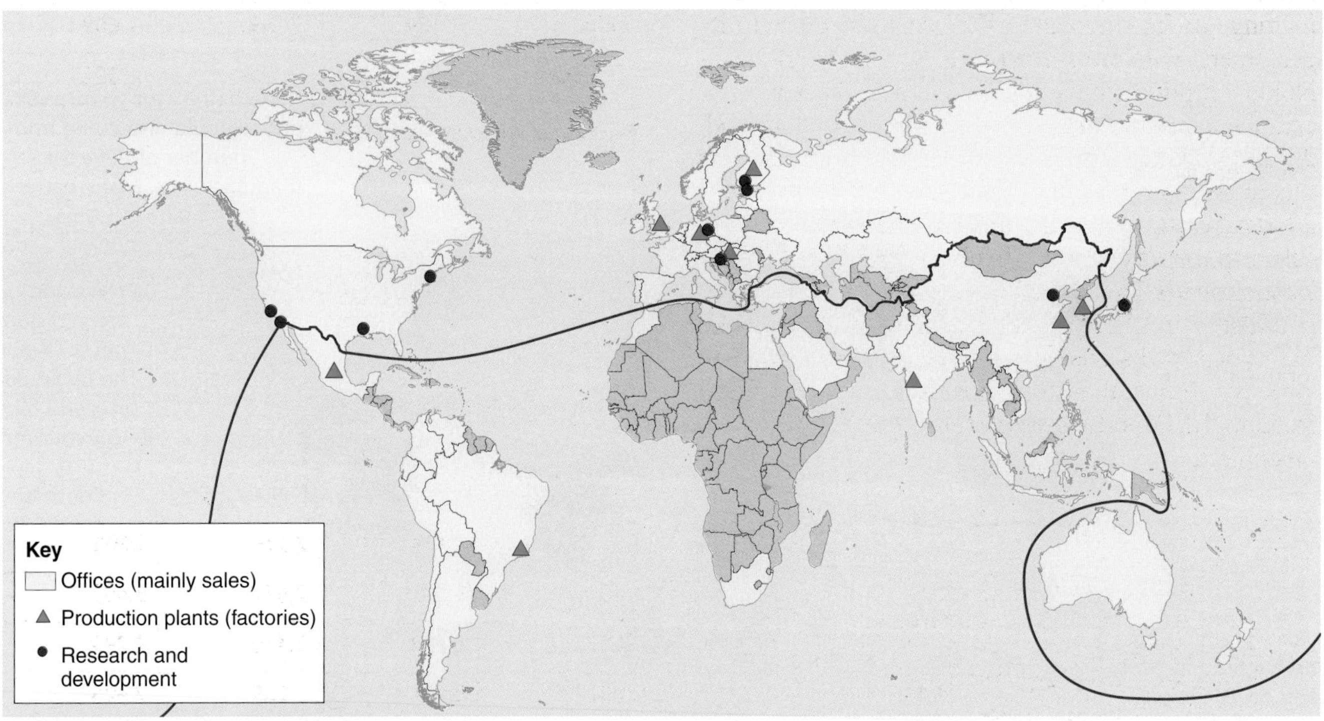


**Figure 3** The global distribution of Nokia's factories, laboratories and offices

### Activity

**5** Study Figure 3.

**a)** Describe the distribution (see page 143) of countries in which Nokia has production plants.

**b)** Describe the distribution of countries in which Nokia has R&D laboratories.

**Figure 4** Adverts for Nokia and Pepsi (another TNC) in Moscow, Russia

## Locating business to minimise costs

TNCs such as Nokia have branches in many countries because they want to reduce costs. With lower costs, their profits are higher. TNCs such as Nokia keep costs low by opening factories and offices in regions of the world that have:

- low labour costs
- cheap land or building costs
- low **business rates** (the tax paid by a company).

## Locating business to be close to the customer

Another reason why Nokia is constantly expanding its range of factories and offices is to be close to its customers, who are spread right across the globe. Nokia's products have massive appeal. Nokia estimates that the mobile phone market had around 2.2 billion people in 2005 and the company expects this to rise to 3 billion by 2008 and 3.5 billion by 2010. Growth in mobile phone ownership and subscription has been particularly strong in Less Economically Developed Countries (LEDCs). As consumers in LEDCs have become wealthier, Nokia has expanded its business into Asia, Africa and South America. It has, therefore, opened new sales offices in many LEDCs, located closer to these new customers.

| | 2003 | 2004 | 2005 |
|---|---|---|---|
| Finland | 22,274 | 23,069 | 23,485 |
| USA | 6,636 | 6,706 | 5,883 |
| China | 4,595 | 4,788 | 5,860 |
| Hungary | 2,571 | 3,778 | 4,186 |
| Germany | 3,486 | 3,522 | 3,610 |
| Brazil | 1,497 | 2,640 | 2,184 |
| UK | 1,947 | 1,903 | 1,956 |
| Mexico | 1,290 | 1,160 | 1,901 |
| India | 184 | 591 | 1,609 |
| Denmark | 1,270 | 1,296 | 1,362 |

**Figure 5** Nokia's employees, 2003 to 2005

### Activity

**6** Choose two countries, one from each of the following lists:
MEDCs: Germany, UK, USA
LEDCs: China, India
**a)** Choose a suitable technique to graph the data shown in Figures 5 and 6 for your chosen countries.
**b)** Describe the trend shown on each graph.

**7** Study Figures 5 and 6. Suggest two alternative reasons for:
**a)** the increased sales in LEDCs
**b)** the rising employment figures in LEDCs
**c)** the falling employment figures in some MEDCs.

**8** Study the distribution of Nokia's branches in Figure 3 (see page 234) again. If jobs in R&D are more specialised and highly paid than in other branches, suggest how this distribution:
**a)** benefits workers in MEDCs
**b)** disadvantages workers in LEDCs.

| | 2003 | 2004 | 2005 |
|---|---|---|---|
| China | 2,023 | 2,678 | 3,403 |
| USA | 4,488 | 3,430 | 2,743 |
| UK | 2,711 | 2,269 | 2,405 |
| India | 1,064 | 1,369 | 2,022 |
| Germany | 2,297 | 1,730 | 1,982 |
| Russia | 569 | 946 | 1,410 |
| Italy | 1,003 | 884 | 1,160 |
| Spain | 748 | 768 | 923 |
| Saudi Arabia | 547 | 750 | 897 |
| France | 867 | 604 | 870 |

**Figure 6** Nokia's sales, 2003 to 2005 (€ millions)

## The advantages and disadvantages of TNC investment

When a TNC such as Nokia opens a new factory or office it can have a positive impact on local people and the local economy. Some jobs are created by the firm itself: Nokia employs 2,000 people in the UK at three sites. This is a **direct benefit** of the investment made by Nokia in the UK. These new jobs may help to stimulate extra work for other local businesses. This extra work is an **indirect benefit** of the investment made by the TNC. These benefits to the local economy are known as a **positive multiplier**.

### Different jobs in different locations

Nokia employs a wide range of staff. Some are highly qualified or skilled, such as business managers or R&D staff. Other staff, such as some assembly workers or sales staff, do not require high-level qualifications or as much training. So, like many other TNCs, Nokia has chosen to locate the assembly of basic products in their range in LEDCs where wages are lower.

However, the more highly trained R&D staff tend to work in More Economically Developed Countries (MEDCs). Here, Nokia develops new products, such as hand-held devices capable of filming video, playing games and surfing the web. These devices use the latest technology and therefore need more highly trained staff to develop and produce them. These high-tech products are also aimed at wealthier consumers, usually in MEDCs, so it makes sense to make them in Europe.

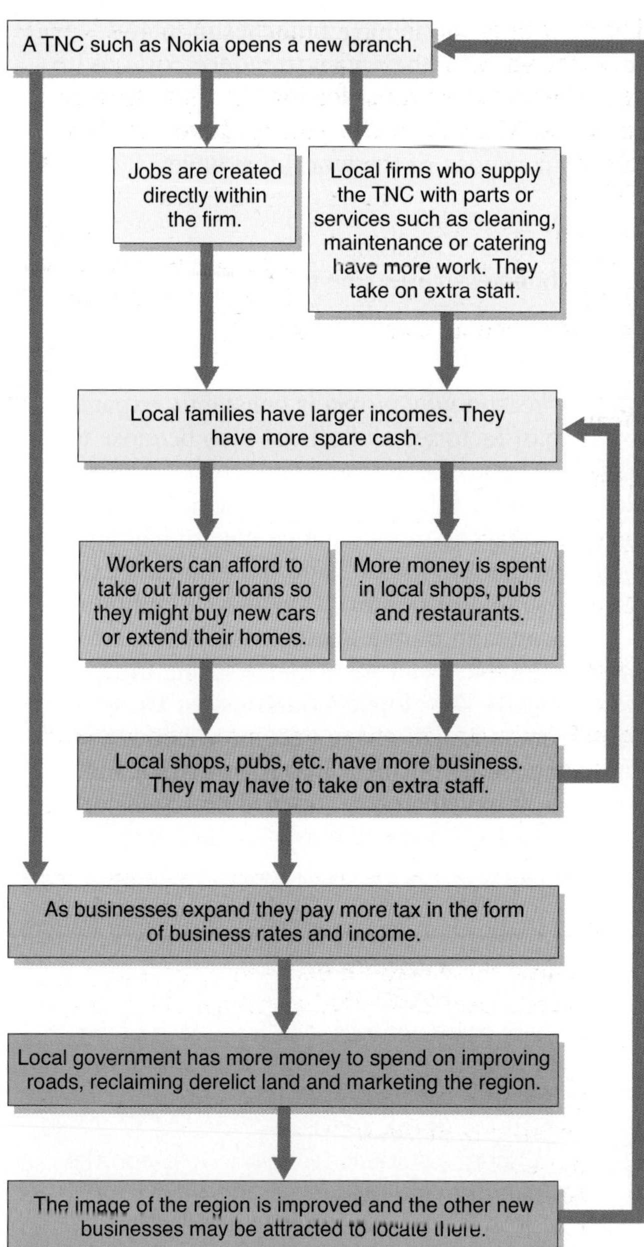


**Figure 7** The positive multiplier effect

**Figure 8** A Chinese worker tests mobile phones at a production plant in Ningbo, China

## The advantages of new technology for Africa

The growth of mobile technology and of TNCs such as Vodacom who provide mobile networks has helped improve communications in some African countries. Many African countries have very few telephone landlines, so rural areas are often cut off. Instead of investing in landlines, countries like Tanzania have used mobile technology to leapfrog the problem. In 2001, Africa became the first region in the world where there are more mobile phone users than people using landlines.

| Year | Subscribers (millions) |
|---|---|
| 1998 | 2 |
| 2002 | 28 |
| 2003 | 51 |
| 2004 | 82 |

**Figure 9** Number of mobile phone users in Africa Source: International Telecommunication Union (ITU), *The Economist*

**Figure 10** African communities benefit from the development of the mobile network. In this case, the mobile company Vodacom is funding a project called *Lovelife* in South Africa. *Lovelife* is an HIV education campaign which targets 16–25-year-olds

### Activity

**9** Explain the difference between direct and indirect benefits of TNC investment in a new factory or office.

**10** Summarise the benefits of the positive multiplier under these headings:
- **a)** Jobs
- **b)** Earnings
- **c)** Spending
- **d)** Image of the region.

**11** Draw a line graph of the data in Figure 9 and describe the shape of your graph.

**12** Explain why Nokia continues to expand in Africa.

**13** Summarise the benefits that Nokia gets from opening new branches in LEDC countries.

**14** Explain two benefits that African countries such as Tanzania get from the growth of mobile technology TNCs such as Nokia or Vodacom.

### Where is Nokia in the UK and why is it located here?

Nokia employs 2,000 people in the UK at three sites. These are all in the South of the UK, in regions known as the M4 corridor and M11 corridor. Figure 11 suggests why this region is so successful at attracting investment from TNCs.

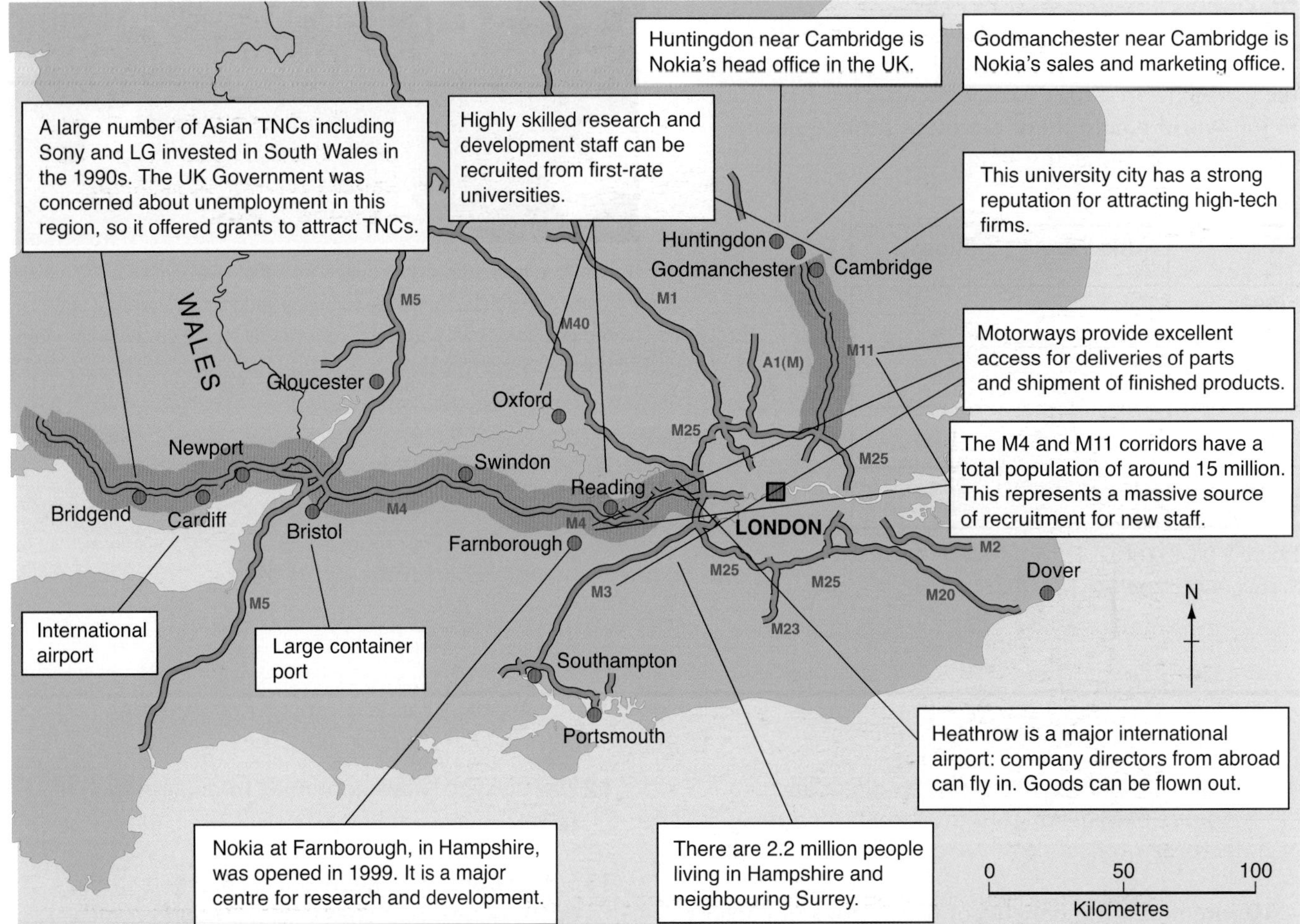


**Figure 11** The location of Nokia in the UK

| Type of business | Number | Foreign TNCs |
|---|---|---|
| Biomedical | 18 | 4 |
| Computers and telecommunications | 25 | 8 |
| Technical consultants | 7 | 2 |
| Energy | 1 | 0 |
| Environmental | 1 | 1 |
| Financial | 4 | 0 |
| Industrial technologies | 4 | 1 |
| Other | 13 | 4 |
| Total | 73 | 20 |

**Figure 12** Types of business, and number owned by foreign TNCs, on Cambridge Science Park

### Negative multipliers

It's difficult to know exactly how many jobs have been created in the UK by the investment of foreign TNCs. Figure 12 suggests that one in four businesses on the famous Cambridge Science Park are foreign TNCs. At the other end of the M4 corridor, South Wales experienced a boom in investment by foreign TNCs. By the mid 1990s, 60 Japanese firms employed 20,000 people in Wales. However since 2001, some of these firms, including Sony and LG, have cut jobs and closed factories in South Wales. TNCs tend to protect decision-making and research jobs, and these are usually located in the home nation, not abroad.

**EXAM**TECHNIQUE

## Using evidence from OS map extracts

Your exam will include an Ordnance Survey map extract similar to Figure 13. The examiners may ask you to use evidence from the OS map to answer a question. This means using place names and four-figure or six-figure references from the map to locate particular features. For example:

### Question

Use evidence from Figure 13 to describe the positive aspects of the local environment for Nokia's employees.

### Answer

Workers at the Nokia factory will:

- appreciate open views of a woodland area to the south-west of the factory in grid square 8355
- be able to play golf at the golf course at 851548.

**Figure 13** An Ordnance Survey extract of the Nokia site, Farnborough. Scale 1:50,000 Sheet 186. Nokia's research and development plant is in grid square 8355

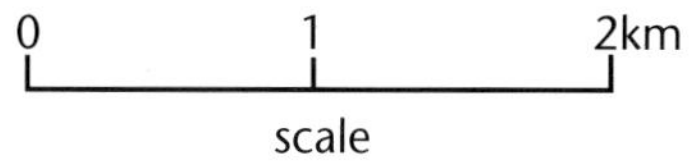


## Activity

**15** Study Figure 11.

**a)** Give five reasons why TNCs might be attracted to the M4 and M11 corridors.

**b)** Suggest why Nokia is located in Surrey and Cambridgeshire, rather than in South Wales.

**16 a)** Choose a suitable technique to graph the data in Figure 12.

**b)** Suggest why these types of business are located so close to Cambridge.

**17** Use evidence from Figure 13 to explain why Nokia may have located in grid square 8355 near to Farnborough.

**18** The closure of a workplace can have a deep impact on the local economy. This downward spiral of decline is known as a negative multiplier effect. Using Figure 7 on page 236 to give you ideas, draw a diagram to show the negative multiplier effect.

# Chapter 7
# The impact of work and development on the environment

**KEY QUESTIONS**

- How do different economic activities damage the environment?
- What conflicts exist between the environment and the needs for development and the creation of wealth?
- How can people conserve the environment and benefit from sustainable development?

China

## Investigating economic growth in China and its impact on the environment

Since the early 1990s China's economy has been growing rapidly. Chinese businesses and foreign trans-national companies (TNCs) have invested in new service industries and factories making everything from shoes to high-tech electronics. As China's economy has grown, the Gross National Income (GNI) or average income per person has also grown. Fewer people in China live in poverty and the **standard of living** for ordinary Chinese people is improving. By 2020, it is expected that the Chinese GNI per person will be similar to the GNI in the USA today. However, this development is causing a massive impact on the environment. It seems that this type of growth is **unsustainable**.

### Local impacts

The factories and power plants that have created China's economic success are also creating a pollution problem. The burning of fossil fuels releases nitrogen dioxide ($NO_2$) – a pollutant which combines with moisture in the air and results in **acid rain**. Nitrogen dioxide also causes breathing and other health problems. As the Chinese have become wealthier, car ownership has increased rapidly. Cars also emit nitrogen dioxide from their exhausts. The result is a thick smog of pollution which hangs over eastern China. This smog often reaches levels that are dangerous for human health in cities such as Beijing. Research by the European Space Agency shows that **emissions** of nitrogen dioxide in China increased by 50 per cent in the period from 1995 to 2005. Chinese official figures admit that 400,000 Chinese people die every year from diseases caused by air pollution. The World Bank says that sixteen of the twenty most polluted cities in the world are in China.

**Figure 1** Smog in Beijing reduces visibility and causes breathing problems and eye irritations

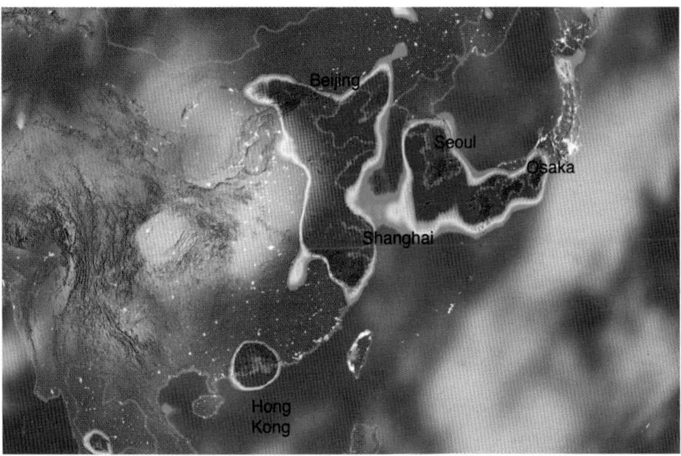


**Figure 2** A false-colour satellite image of East Asia showing levels of nitrogen dioxide pollution. The brightest red colours show the highest concentrations of $NO_2$. Yellows and greens show lower concentrations of $NO_2$

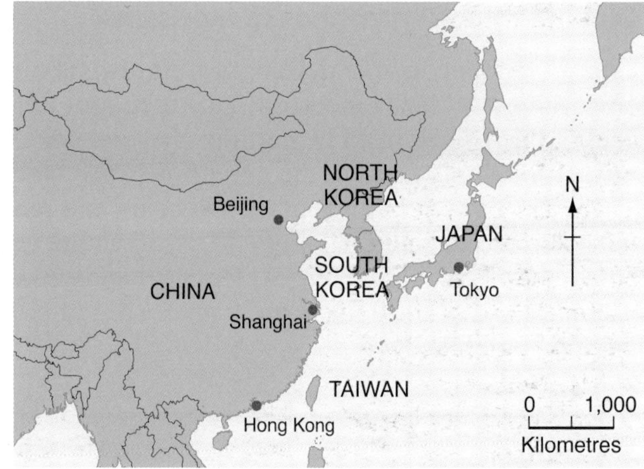


**Figure 3** China and east Asia

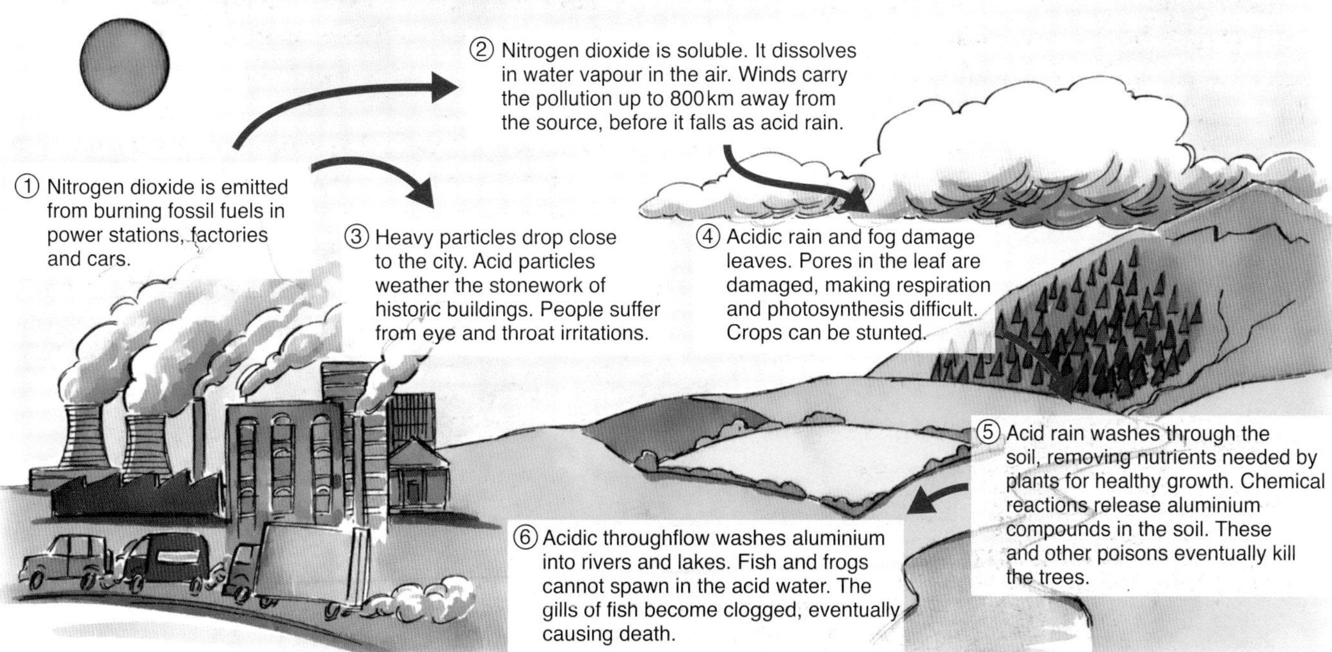


**Figure 4** How emissions of nitrogen dioxide lead to acid rain

## Activity

1. List three sources of nitrogen dioxide pollution.
2. Use Figures 2 and 3 to describe the distribution (see page 143) of the highest concentrations of nitrogen dioxide.
3. Use Figure 4 to help explain the pollution pattern on Figure 2.
4. List the effects of acid pollution under the headings:
   **a)** Human health
   **b)** The environment
   **c)** The economy.

## Global impacts: greenhouse emissions

China's rapid economic development is also having consequences for the global environment. China's industrial growth requires electrical power. About 80 per cent of this is generated by burning coal and coke. This method of electricity production emits more of the **greenhouse gas** carbon dioxide than any other. There are plans to build another 500 coal-fired power stations to keep pace with the growing demand for energy. Many of China's other growing industries also emit a lot of greenhouse gases. The steel and cement industries are two examples. Steel and cement are both needed to build China's rapidly growing cities.

| Year | Thousands of tonnes of carbon |
|---|---|
| 1950 | 129 |
| 1960 | 2,202 |
| 1970 | 2,022 |
| 1980 | 12,060 |
| 1985 | 20,665 |
| 1990 | 31,136 |
| 1995 | 67,843 |
| 2000 | 83,836 |

**Figure 5** Recent increases in emissions of carbon dioxide from China's manufacture of cement are due to massive growth of the construction industry

### Activity

**5 a)** Use Figure 5 to draw a line graph.
**b)** Describe the increase in emissions from cement making.
**c)** Use the trend of this graph to predict likely emissions from this source in 2010.

**6** Use Figure 6.
**a)** Compare the number of people in China who have no electricity with those in:
i) South Asia including India
ii) Africa south of the Sahara.
**b)** Explain how the development of these regions could lead to greater greenhouse gas emissions.

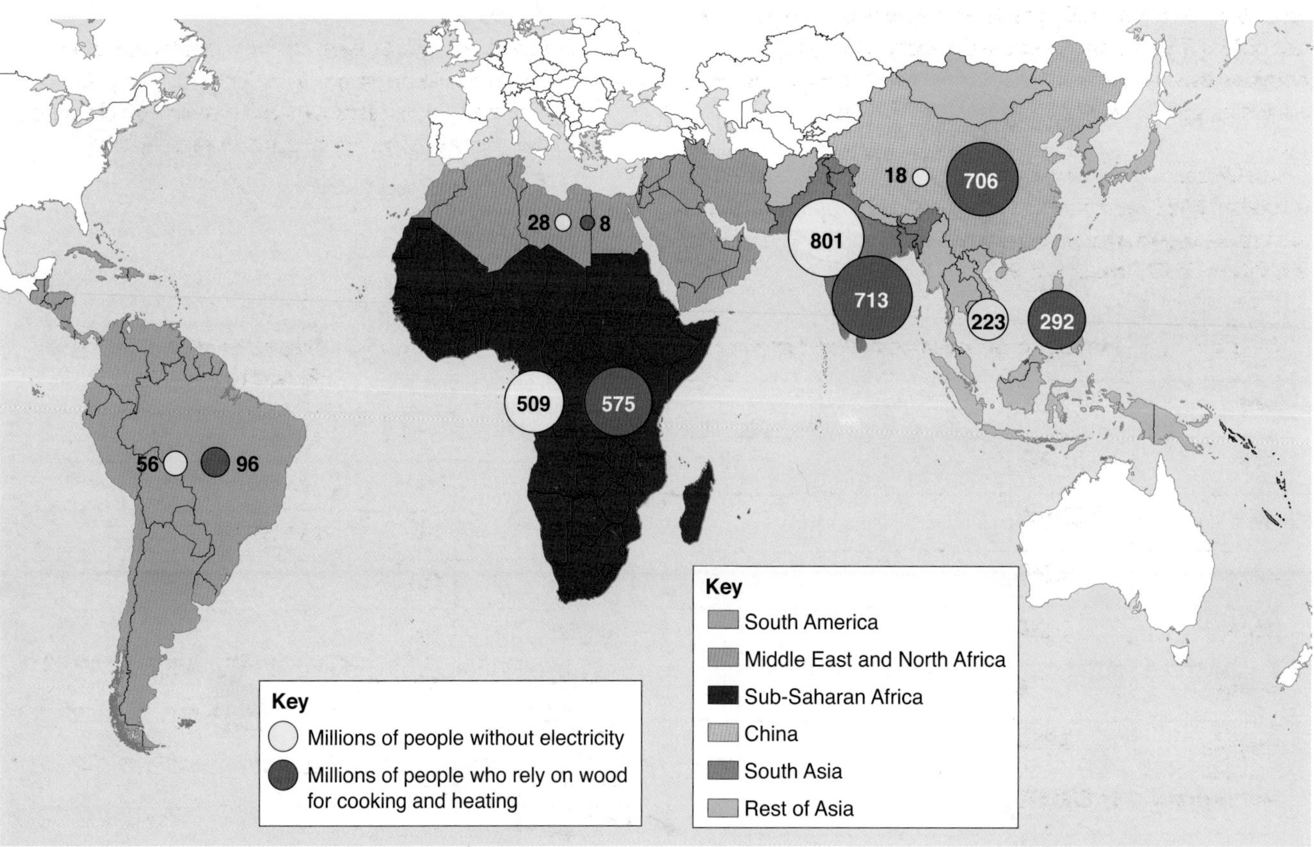


**Figure 6** Global energy poverty: the number of people without electricity

## Going Further

### Advanced web searches

It has never been easier to research topical geographical issues thanks to search engines such as Google. But how do you know if a website is a reliable source of information?

A search for 'global warming' will produce hundreds of thousands of results. But which ones are useful? Use the search engine's advanced search facility to search under particular domains. A domain is the abbreviated part of a web address that gives information about the type of website. For example, '.co' and '.com' are business websites whilst '.sch' indicates that the website was created by a school. The final part of the domain is an abbreviation for the country in which the website was created.

### Is the website reliable?

Knowing about domains will help you to identify what type of website it is, before you even click on the link. Most weblogs, newspapers and companies are '.com' (or '.co.uk' in the UK), so if you want their opinion this would be a useful place to look. Most pressure groups, such as Greenpeace, or Friends of the Earth are '.org'. These websites are usually full of facts and figures but they can be one-sided. If you want to know the facts rather than opinions then you should concentrate on '.edu' or '.ac.uk' addresses which belong to university websites.

A Google search for 'China greenhouse gas emissions' found a total of 1,180,000 possible web addresses. So an advanced search was conducted using the domain names. The results are shown in Figures 7 and 8.

**7** Which web domain would be most useful to find:
  **a)** newspaper reports
  **b)** university research
  **c)** a pressure group?

**8** **a)** Make a copy of Figure 8. Log on to a computer and continue this advanced search to complete the table.
  **b)** Graph the data.
  **c)** What does this graph tell us about the geographical origin of many websites? Consider the population, wealth and geographical location of each country to explain why some countries have produced more websites on this topic than others.

**9** Imagine you have to produce a short report on China's economy and its greenhouse gas emissions. You will need to find both facts and opinions.
  **a)** Use the internet to find one example from each of the following domains:
    i) .com
    ii) .org
    iii) .edu
  **b)** Assess how useful each of the websites you have found would be to you in writing your report. Prepare a short presentation in which you describe the strengths and weaknesses of each of the websites.

| Domain | Number of websites found in search |
|---|---|
| .org | 580,000 |
| .com | 1,030,000 |
| .edu | 122,400 |
| .co.uk | 6,240 |
| .ac.uk | 2,610 |
| .sch.uk | 6 |
| .org.uk | 3,990 |
| Any domain | 1,180,000 |

**Figure 7** A Google search for 'China greenhouse gas emissions' by domain

| Country | Domain | Number of websites found in search |
|---|---|---|
| China | .cn | 37,200 |
| USA | .us | 126,000 |
| UK | .uk | 134,000 |
| India | .in | |
| Russia | .ru | |
| Australia | .au | |
| New Zealand | .nz | |
| Brazil | .br | |
| Canada | .ca | |

**Figure 8** A Google search for 'China greenhouse gas emissions' by country domain

## Going Further

### Sustainable development

China's economic success has created huge wealth for some. It is also beginning to improve the standard of living and quality of life of many ordinary Chinese people. However, it is obvious that this development is also harming the environment. The current growth of China and many other countries, both More Economically Developed Countries (MEDCs) and Less Economically Developed Countries (LEDCs), is unsustainable. What China needs to do is find a way of improving the lives of people now without using up too many natural resources or polluting the environment so badly that future generations will have a lower quality of life. This would be **sustainable development**.

> 'Sustainable development is development which meets the needs of the present without compromising the ability of future generations to meet their own needs'.
>
> ***Our Common Future*, World Commission on Environmental Development (WCED) report 1987**

Development can be described as sustainable development if it:

- improves standards of living for people today
- uses natural resources at a rate which can be renewed. For example, trees are replanted when mature timber is felled
- businesses take responsibility for their impact on the environment. They reduce waste and pollution. They also pay the cost for cleaning up the environment if there is accidental damage such as an oil spill.

**Figure 9** 'Squeezing the Earth'

| Country | Number of Earths needed to sustain the whole world at that level of national consumption |
|---|---|
| USA | 5.3 |
| UK | 3.1 |
| France | 3.0 |
| Germany | 2.5 |
| Russia | 2.4 |
| Brazil | 1.2 |
| Mauritius | 1.0 |
| China | 0.8 |
| India | 0.4 |
| Malawi | 0.3 |

**Figure 10** The ecological footprint of selected countries: the number of Earths needed to support the whole world at current levels of consumption

**10** Work in pairs to discuss Figure 9. Which continents are shown being squeezed? Why was this half of the world shown? What or who does the hand represent?

**11** Study Figure 10.

**a)** Sort these countries into LEDCs and MEDCs.

**b)** Explain why one group of countries is using more of the world's resources than the other.

**c)** Explain what is likely to happen to the world's resources as LEDCs continue to develop.

**12 a)** Study Figure 11. Choose a suitable graphical technique to represent the data.

**b)** Compare the growth of the UK population to its growing ecological footprint.

**c)** What conclusions do you draw from this data about development (sustainable or unsustainable) in the UK?

**13 a)** Study Figure 12 and calculate your own ecological footprint.

**b)** Discuss and then list the factors which might increase or decrease your own ecological footprint.

**14** Explain why the unsustainable use of resources by some societies will result in poverty for others.

| Year | UK ecological footprint | UK population (millions) |
|---|---|---|
| 1961 | 1.0 | 52.8 |
| 1971 | 1.7 | 55.9 |
| 1981 | 2.0 | 56.4 |
| 1991 | 2.5 | 57.4 |
| 2006 | 3.1 | 60.0 |

**Figure 11** The UK's growing ecological footprint: number of planet Earths needed to support the UK's growing levels of consumption

**1 What do you eat?**

| | |
|---|---|
| Fresh food | 5 |
| Processed food | 10 |
| Ready meals | 15 |

**2 Where was last year's holiday?**

| | |
|---|---|
| UK | 10 |
| Europe | 20 |
| Rest of world | 150 |

**3 What kind of home do you live in?**

| | |
|---|---|
| Flat | 5 |
| Terraced house | 15 |
| Detached | 35 |

**4 How do you travel?**

| | |
|---|---|
| Walk or cycle | 3 |
| Public transport | 25 |
| Car | 50 |

**5 How often do you wash?**

| | |
|---|---|
| Bath every day | 20 |
| Shower every day | 4 |
| Shower every other day | 2 |

**How much did you score?**

**24–49**
Well done, your ecological footprint is close to the world average. Your lifestyle is sustainable. If everyone lived like you we could survive on the resources of just one planet Earth.

**50–99**
Your ecological footprint is similar to the European average. If everyone lived like you we would need the resources of between one and three planet Earths.

**100–199**
Your ecological footprint is larger than that of the average European. If everyone lived like you we would need four or more planet Earths.

**200+**
Your ecological footprint is similar to those living in the USA. If everyone lived like you we would need more than five planet Earths to sustain your quality of life.

**Figure 12** Calculate your own ecological footprint

China

## Investigating China and the timber trade

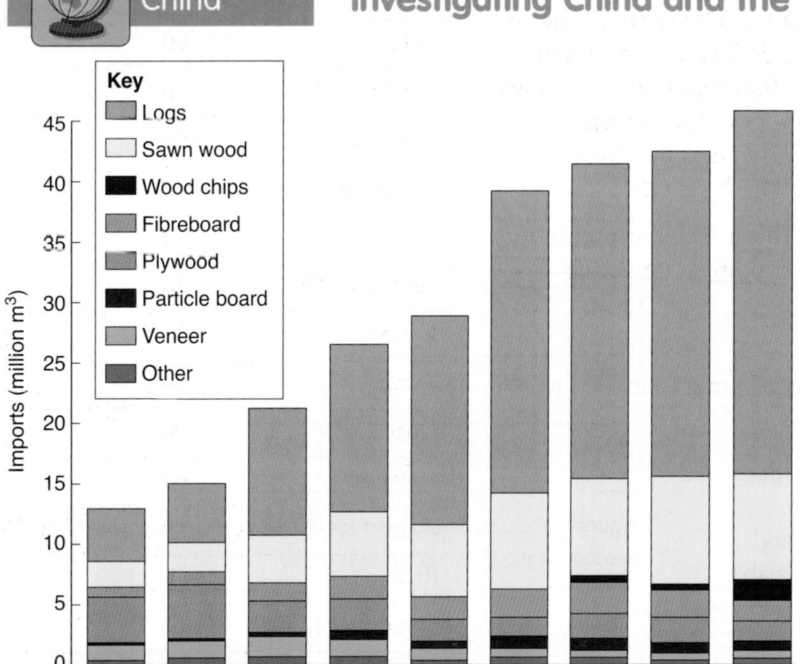


**Figure 13** Imports of timber products to China, 1997 to 2005

China's imports of timber and forest products have grown rapidly in recent years. Softwoods from the conifer forests of East Russia make up a large part of the imports. China also imports a lot of hardwoods from tropical rainforests. Some timber imports are used in China's furniture and paper industries. A lot is used in the rapidly growing plywood industry. Plywood is used in the building industry. Demand for plywood in China has shot up as Chinese cities have experienced a massive building boom.

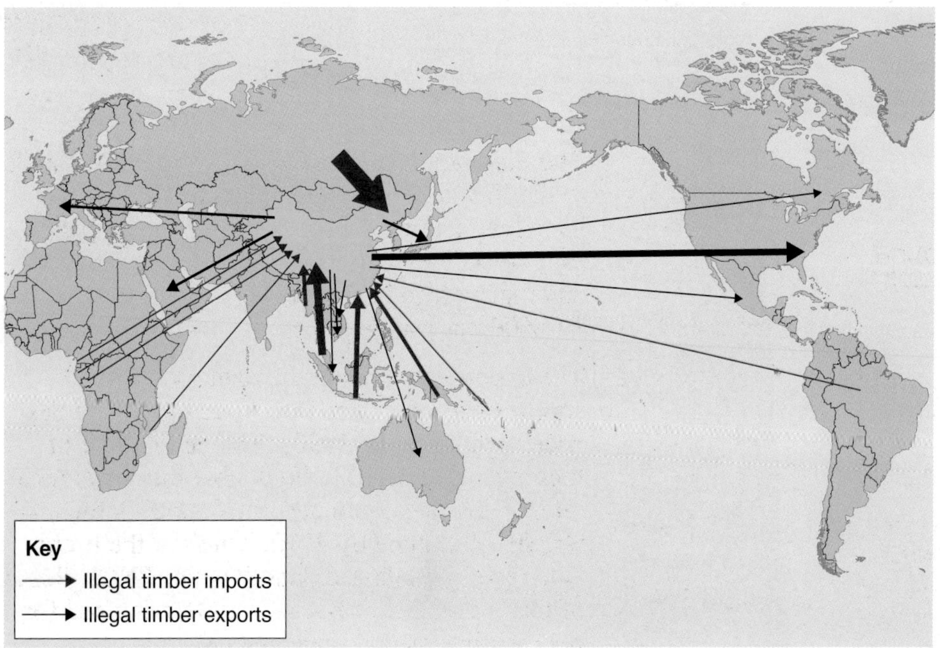


**Figure 14** Illegal imports and exports of wood-based products (2005) estimated by Global Timber, a UK-based NGO

### Activity

**15** Use Figure 13 to estimate the import of the following products in both 1997 and 2005:

**a)** Total timber imports

**b)** Logs

**c)** Sawn wood

**d)** Plywood.

**16** What does the decrease in the import of plywood tell you about China's own plywood industry?

**17** Use Figure 14.

**a)** From which region of the world does China import most timber illegally?

**b)** Use an atlas to name the three tropical countries from which China illegally imports most timber.

The growth of timber imports to China is causing serious concern to some Non-Governmental Organisations (NGOs). The timber trade is unsustainable at the current rate. It is causing deforestation in many countries where logging is much more rapid than replanting schemes. It is estimated that if logging continues at this rate, the natural rainforests of Indonesia will be all gone by 2015, and the massive conifer forests of Far East Russia will have gone by 2025.

Deforestation damages wildlife habitats and often leads to problems of soil erosion. In many cases the logging companies are acting illegally. Illegal logging practices include:

- cutting trees without permission
- cutting trees close to rivers where soil erosion can then lead to flooding
- ignoring the rights of local land owners
- paying bribes to local officials
- non-payment of taxes.

| | Percentage |
|---|---|
| Brazil | 80 |
| Burma | 90 |
| Cambodia | 100 |
| Cameroon | 50 |
| Congo | 90 |
| Equatorial Guinea | 90 |
| Gabon | 70 |
| Indonesia | 90 |
| Liberia | 100 |
| Malaysia | 60 |
| Papua New Guinea | 70 |
| Russia | 80 |
| Solomon Islands | 70 |

**Figure 15** Percentage of imports of timber to China in 2004 that are considered to be illegal according to the NGO Global Timber

### Activity

18 Use a world outline map to plot the countries named in Figure 15. Use a suitable technique to show the values in Figure 15 on your map.

## Solomon Islands Logging in the Solomon Islands

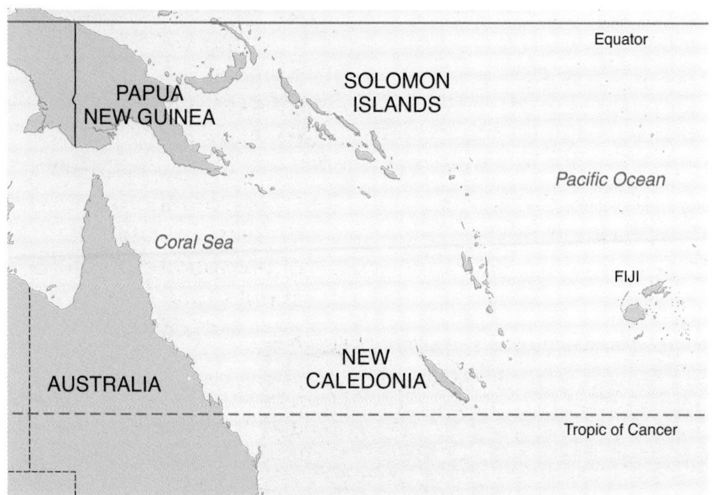


**Figure 16** Location of the Solomon Islands

The Solomon Islands are a large group of islands to the East of Papua New Guinea. The islands have few natural resources apart from tropical rainforest. The economy is in a very poor state and the average income is very low – GNI is just US$600 per person.

The export of timber is the country's main source of income. The rate of deforestation has been high since the 1990s. The annual rate of logging is estimated to be double the sustainable rate. If this rate continues, the country's forests will have all gone by 2020. Much of the timber is logged by Malaysian and Korean TNCs. Some of these TNCs have been severely criticised for poor environmental management.

### Activity

**19** Use Figure 16 to copy and complete the following:

**The Solomon Islands are located to the ... of Papua New Guinea. They are between the Tropic of ... and the Equator.**

## Why is the forest resource so important to local communities?

The second-largest island in the Solomons is Santa Isabel. The island is heavily forested and most communities are located around the coastline. The rainforest is an important resource for villagers. They use it to gather foodstuffs such as fruit, nuts and honey. They also collect leaves, berries and bark to make custom medicine (herbal remedies). For many communities the forest is also an important source of firewood, timber for houses and boat building, palms for roofing materials, and craft materials such as vines for ropes.

**Figure 17** A skid track to remove felled logs has been created on a slope that was marked on the plan as being far too steep. This has caused soil erosion

### Why is logging unsustainable?

The communities in the North of Santa Isabel sold logging rights to a Malaysian TNC. This meant that the land was still owned by the community, but the logging company paid the community for the right to log timber for a fixed period of time. They made various promises to protect the environment during logging. Figures 17 and 18 provide evidence that the TNC operating in Santa Isabel broke these promises. Their poor logging practices have resulted in severe soil erosion, silting up of rivers and flooding.

Commercial logging firms such as this TNC make more profit if they work quickly. They use bulldozers to reach the valuable trees. For every tree cut for its timber, it is estimated that 40 or more are destroyed by the heavy machinery. This process destroys trees that have fruit, nuts or medicinal value to the villagers. The villagers have received payments from the TNC, but this amounts to only about one per cent of the value of the timber.

### Could logging be sustainable?

Logging can provide a better income for local people and not cause long-term damage to the environment. This can be achieved if:

- only a few trees are felled; if only two trees per hectare are felled every ten years, a rainforest will naturally recover
- saplings are planted to replace cut trees
- local people fell the trees and process the timber on site using small portable tools.

**Figure 18** Waste timber from the logging process blocking the Kahigi river. The TNC agreed not to fell trees within 50 m of any major river or 25 m of any minor stream

The Isabel Sustainable Forestry Management Project is one small example. It was funded by aid (€450,000) given by the European Union in the mid 1990s. The scheme created skilled labour for local people. Trees are carefully felled to avoid damage to trees of fruit or medicinal value. The timber is then cut into planks in the forest using a portable saw mill. This means that large machines are not needed. It also means that local people add value to the timber so more profit is retained by the village. This method of processing the timber means that the community keeps about 40 per cent of the finished value of the timber. The project was successful in protecting 17,000 hectares of forest, but the amount of timber produced has been very small.

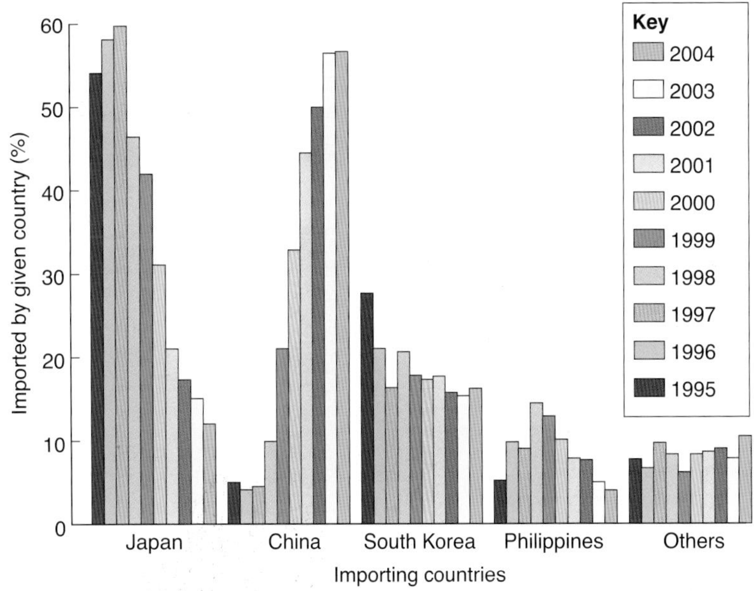


**Figure 19** The destination of timber exports from Papua New Guinea and the Solomon Islands

## Activity

**20** Explain why the forest is a valuable resource to the communities of the Solomon Islands.

**21** Study Figure 19.

**a)** Which country imported most timber in 2004?

**b)** Describe what has happened to exports to Japan compared with exports to China.

**22** Use the text on this page to complete a table like this:

| Effects on... | Unsustainable logging practices | Sustainable logging practices |
|---|---|---|
| Soils | | |
| Rivers | | |
| Fruit, nut and medicinal trees | | |

**23** Imagine you could visit the communities affected by commercial logging in Santa Isabel. Discuss what they might tell you about the impact of the TNC on their lives.

**24** Explain how the Isabel Sustainable Forestry Management Project is able to:

**a)** improve standards of living today

**b)** ensure decent standards of living for future generations.

# Chapter 8 Problem-solving exercise

## Investigating sustainable development in the Galapagos Islands

**Your enquiry...**

- How developed is Ecuador? What standard of living do people have?
- What are the main economic activities in the Galapagos Islands?
- How do these economic activities affect the natural environment?
- Is this kind of economic development sustainable?

**Your decision...**

How can the Galapagos Islands manage its economic development in a way that is sustainable?

**Figure 1** The marine iguana of the Galapagos depend on a clean and healthy marine **ecosystem**

### Part A: introducing Ecuador and the Galapagos Islands

Ecuador is a Less Economically Developed Country (LEDC) in South America.

It relies on the export of a number of primary commodities, as can be seen in Figure 3. Ecuador also earns money from abroad by attracting an increasing number of foreign tourists. Roughly one in six of these tourists visits the Galapagos Islands.

Much of Ecuador's trade is with the USA and the European Union. It has also formed a trading partnership with a number of other LEDCs. This trading bloc involves Ecuador, Bolivia, Colombia, Peru and Venezuela. It is known as the Andean Community of Nations (CAN in Spanish). Each country within this trading bloc has a free trade arrangement with other countries in the bloc.

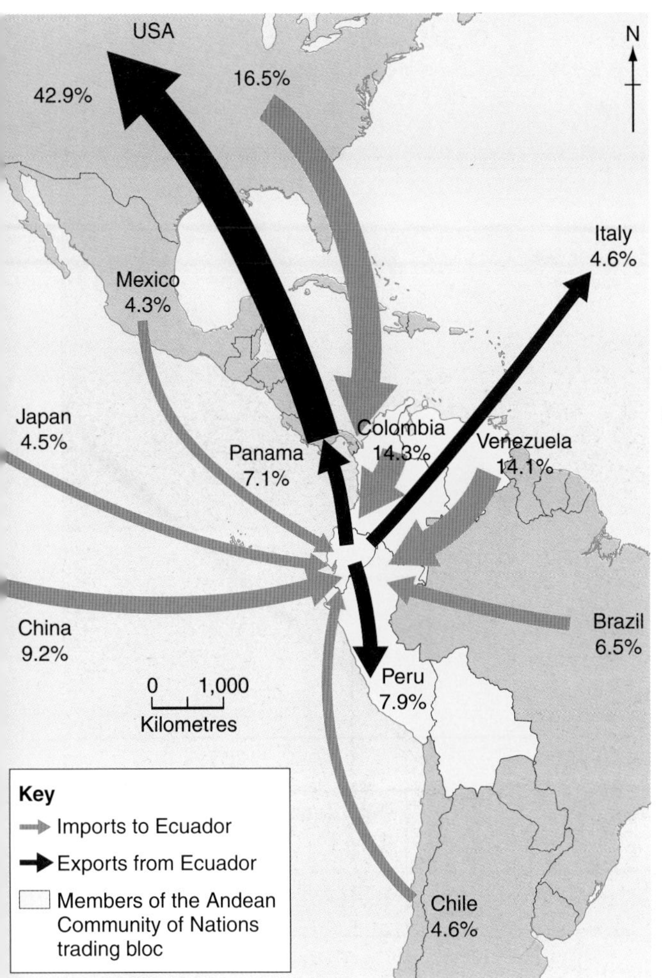


**Figure 2** Ecuador's main trading partners

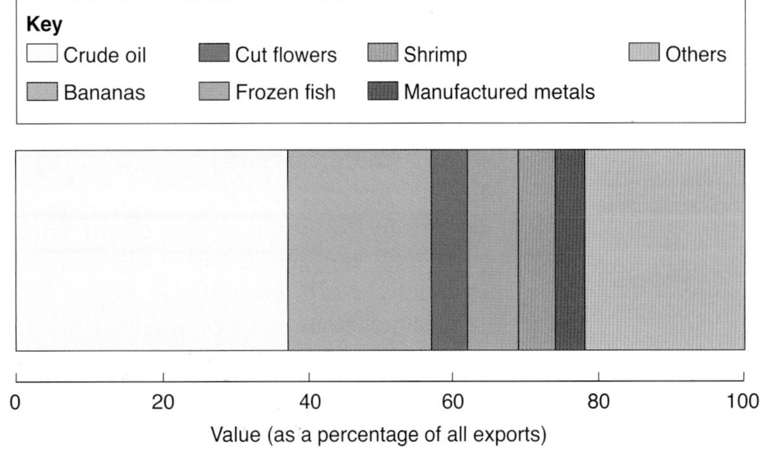


**Figure 3** Ecuador's exports

| Indicator | Ecuador | Average for South and Central America |
|---|---|---|
| Child (under 5) mortality (%) | 27 | 32 |
| Adult literacy (2000): male (%) | 93 | 90 |
| Adult literacy (2000): female (%) | 90 | 88 |
| Telephones per 100 population (2002) | 23 | 36 |
| Internet users per 100 population (2002) | 4 | 8 |
| GNI per capita (US$) (2003) | 1,790 | 3,311 |

**Figure 4** Development indicators for Ecuador

## Activity

**1** Use Figures 2 and 3 to complete the following statement:

**Ecuador's largest export and import partner is .... It also imports goods from ... and ... in Asia. Ecuador's largest export is .... Bananas are worth ... per cent of all exports from Ecuador.**

**2** Use Figure 3 to give three examples of Ecuador's primary commodity exports.

**3 a)** Describe the distribution (see page 143) of the Andean Community of Nations trading bloc.

**b)** Explain the advantages of being a member of a trading bloc.

**4 a)** Use Figure 4 to compare Ecuador's level of development with other South American countries.

**b)** Explain why it is important for the people of Ecuador that the country continues to develop its economy.

## The Galapagos Islands

The Galapagos Islands are a group of volcanic islands in the Pacific Ocean which belong to Ecuador. The Galapagos Islands are world famous for their wildlife: many plants and animals here occur nowhere else on Earth. Due to their unique environment, the Galapagos have international recognition and protection. The islands, and 133,000 km$^2$ of the marine environment that surrounds them, have UNESCO World Heritage Site status. It is also a Biosphere Reserve and whale sanctuary.

Economic activity in the islands depends largely on fishing and tourism. Both of these activities have the potential to harm the physical environment of the islands and the surrounding marine environment.

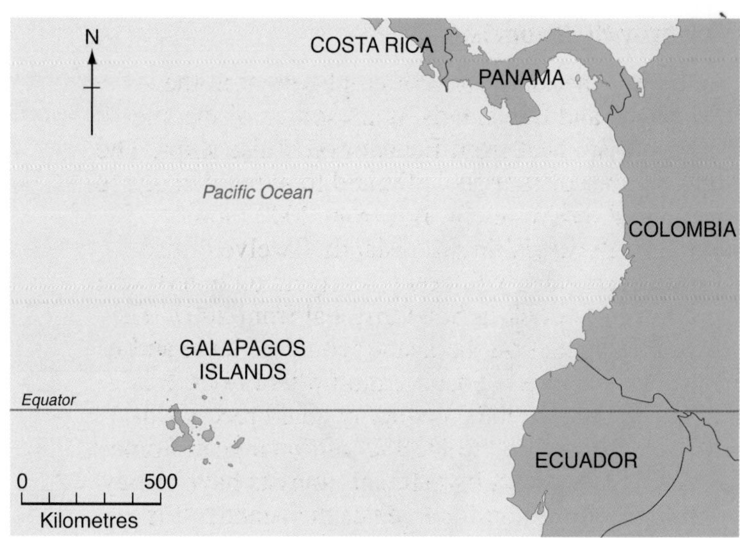


**Figure 5** The location of the Galapagos Islands

primary sector | secondary sector | tertiary sector

| Type of economic activity | 1982 | | 1990 | | 2001 | |
|---|---|---|---|---|---|---|
| | **Population 2,503** | **% 100** | **Population 4,759** | **% 100** | **Population 8,765** | **% 100** |
| Agriculture and fishing | 468 | 17.7 | 786 | 16.5 | 1,491 | 17.0 |
| Mining | 0 | 0.0 | 2 | 0.0 | 14 | 0.2 |
| **Total primary** | | **18.7** | | **16.5** | | **17.2** |
| Manufacturing | 109 | 4.4 | 200 | 4.2 | 503 | 5.7 |
| Electricity, gas and water | 11 | 0.4 | 28 | 0.6 | 43 | 0.5 |
| Construction (building) | 275 | 11.0 | 371 | 7.8 | 663 | 7.6 |
| **Total secondary** | | **15.8** | | **12.6** | | **13.8** |
| Retailing | 175 | 7.0 | 553 | 11.6 | 1,416 | 16.2 |
| Transport | 250 | 10.0 | 716 | 15.0 | 1,342 | 15.3 |
| Banking | 21 | 0.8 | 63 | 1.3 | 308 | 3.5 |
| Services (incl. tourism) | 1,073 | 42.9 | 1,916 | 40.3 | 2,243 | 25.6 |
| Other services | 17 | 0.7 | 100 | 2.1 | 688 | 7.8 |
| New businesses | 104 | 4.2 | 24 | 0.5 | 52 | 0.6 |
| **Total tertiary** | | **65.6** | | **70.8** | | **68.4** |

**Figure 6** Economic activity in the Galapagos Islands

## The growth of tourism

Tourism is the main form of employment in the Galapagos and the islands' main source of income. Most tourists visit from Ecuador on cruise ships. The total number of tourists is limited to avoid damage to the natural environment. But from 2007 more tourists will be visiting the islands. Twelve cruise ships a year, each with 500 passengers on board, will be allowed to dock in San Cristobal from 2007. The economic impact on the island would be huge and is expected to create a positive multiplier effect. It is estimated that the local economy could receive an extra US$20 million to US$30 million a year. Some of this will be direct investment: tourists have to pay a US$100 admission fee to enter the islands. It is argued that the islands desperately need the extra jobs that would be created by these extra visitors. There will be extra direct employment opportunities, such as tour guides. Other benefits will be indirect: for example, extra sales of fish to restaurants and to the cruise ship.

| Year | Tourist arrivals |
|---|---|
| 2000 | 68,865 |
| 2001 | 77,570 |
| 2002 | 82,226 |
| 2003 | 90,533 |
| 2004 | No data |
| 2005 | 122,000 |

**Figure 7** Tourist arrivals to the Galapagos. Source: Galapagos National Park

**Figure 8** Visiting tourists are a vital resource to the economy of the Galapagos

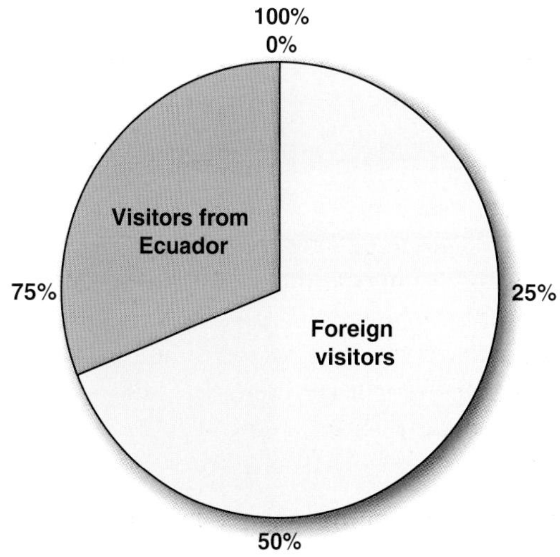


**Figure 9** The percentage of visitors to the Galapagos from abroad

### Activity

**5** Describe the location (see page 143) of the Galapagos Islands.

**6** Study Figure 6.
**a)** Draw a graph which shows how the total numbers of people employed in both agriculture and fishing and tourism have changed over time.
**b)** Describe the pattern of your graph.

**7 a)** Use Figure 7 to draw a suitable graph to show the increase in tourist arrivals to the Galapagos.
**b)** What percentage of tourists are foreign visitors?

**8** Define what is meant by direct and indirect economic benefits of investment.

**9** Explain how allowing extra tourists to visit the islands could create a positive multiplier effect.

## Part B: the conflict between fishermen and the travel and tourism industry

**Figure 10** The Galapagos albatross. A female lays about 25 eggs in its lifetime, but only two of these will hatch and survive. The Galapagos albatross therefore has a very low reproduction rate, which makes the natural rate of increase of its total population very slow

In 2004 fishermen from Ecuador began to demand the right to begin **longline fishing** (or longlining) in the waters around the Galapagos. Longline fishing uses a single line up to 130 km long, which is dragged behind the boat. The line contains thousands of hooks which are baited with scraps of fish and squid and are intended to catch large fish such as tuna and swordfish. However, they also catch and kill a large number of unwanted birds and animals, known as bycatch. The bycatch includes seabirds such as albatross, which swoop down on the baited hooks before they sink out of reach. They are then dragged under water and drowned. Conservation charities estimate that 300,000 seabirds are killed in this way each year around the world, as well as turtles, seals and cetaceans (whales and dolphins).

There have been violent clashes between fishermen and conservationists, who claim that the fishermen have already destroyed the local population of lobster and sea cucumber. Conservationists fear that longlining will kill seabirds, sharks, turtles and whales.

'If this situation doesn't change it will be catastrophic for the Galapagos,' says Xavier Bustamente, leader of Fundación Natura conservation group. The travel and tourism industry agrees with the conservationists on this issue. More than 100,000 tourists visit the islands every year. Tour operators believe that the special environment of the islands must remain unspoiled so that it continues to attract tourists. The International Galapagos Tour Operators Association warns that the fishing industry is worth only £6 million a year, whereas tourism to the islands earns £90 million.

**Figure 11** Huge numbers of birds, turtles and whales are caught as bycatch by longline fishing

This conflict has attracted attention at a much wider scale. Ecuador's Government would like to help the fishermen because the fishermen's union was very supportive at a time when the Government was weak. However, the Government is under pressure from the United Nations Educational, Scientific and Cultural Organisation (UNESCO) to conserve the Galapagos marine environment.

UNESCO sees the Galapagos as a very rare resource which must be protected from pollution, exploitation and **unsustainable development**. It protects the islands and their marine ecosystems as a World Heritage Site. This recognises the 'outstanding value to humanity' of these special ecosystems.

## Activity

**10** Give two reasons why longline fishing off Galapagos would endanger the local albatross population.

**11** The text describes four different groups of people. Each of these groups sees the resources of the Galapagos environment in a different way.

**a)** List the four different groups of people.

**b)** Which group/groups see the islands' ecosystems as a:

- financial resource that should be exploited
- vulnerable resource that needs protection
- rare resource that has scientific and cultural value
- resource that we should manage so that future generations will also benefit.

**c)** Choose two opposing groups and carefully explain their points of view.

**12** Explain why both increased fishing and increased tourism might be an unsustainable development for the Galapagos Islands.

**13** Imagine you have to explain the situation in the Galapagos to intelligent aliens. Explain why the Galapagos offers 'outstanding value to humanity' and why the islands' environment should be protected for moral, scientific and cultural reasons.

## Part C: time to decide. What is your plan for the sustainable development of the islands?

It's time to make your decision. How can the Galapagos Islands manage its economic development in a way that is sustainable?

**Human Impact**
Humans ... are an introduced and invasive species, and the islands have seen a dramatic growth in recent years. Settlers from mainland Ecuador have moved to the islands in search of a better life. This population pressure causes serious problems for conservation. With only three per cent of the islands set aside for human settlement, there is little room for people, and little for them to do except fish. Competition between local fishermen and the National Park and conservation workers has been heated and sometimes violent. Despite restrictions on new immigration, it continues.

**Figure 12** Extract from the International Galapagos Tour Operators Association website

| Year | Population* |
|---|---|
| 1950 | 1,346 |
| 1962 | 2,391 |
| 1974 | 4,037 |
| 1982 | 6,119 |
| 1990 | 9,785 |
| 2001 | 18,640 |
| 2015* | 40,000 |
| 2027* | 80,000 |

*Population figures for 2015 and 2027 are estimates

**Figure 13** Population growth in the Galapagos

### Activity

**14 a)** Use Figure 12 to explain how the settlers from Ecuador view the Galapagos as a resource.
**b)** Graph the data in Figure 13.
**c)** Explain how these two figures may indicate that development in the Galapagos is unsustainable.

**15** Create a sustainable development plan for the Galapagos.
**a)** Consider whether either fishing or tourism needs to be controlled.
**b)** Justify your plan.

**EXAMTECHNIQUE**

### Justifying your plan

In section C of paper 3/4 you will be asked to prepare a plan to show how you think a particular issue could best be tackled. You will be marked on how well you justify this plan: this means you have to explain why you think your plan is a good one.

**Tip 1**

Suggest how your plan might create benefits at different stages of its development.

- In the first few months I would .... The immediate benefits of my plan are .... This would be good because ....
- In the coming years I would.... In the long term the benefits of my plan would include .... This would be an advantage because ...

**Tip 2**

Suggest how your plan might have an impact on three key areas:

- The environment would benefit because ....
- The local economy would be strengthened by the creation of new jobs in ... and this would be a good thing because ....
- Local people would have improved facilities such as .... This would be beneficial because ....

# Glossary

## A

**Abrasion** – **Erosion**, or wearing away, of the landscape caused by friction. Abrasion occurs when rivers or waves carry sand or pebbles. The water uses these materials to do the work of erosion.

**Abstraction** – When people remove water from either a surface or **groundwater** store.

**Acid rain** – Unnaturally acidic rain caused by a high presence of certain pollutants (especially nitrogen dioxide and sulphur dioxide) in the atmosphere.

**Adult literacy** – The percentage of the adult population who can read and write.

**Affordable homes** – Houses that are either sold or rented at relatively low cost.

**Air pressure** – The force caused by molecules in the atmosphere pressing down on the Earth's surface.

**Alluvium** – Sediments deposited by a river. Alluvium may be fine grains, such as silt, or coarser sands and gravels.

**Annual temperature range** – The difference in temperature between the hottest and coldest times of the year.

**Anomaly** – An unexpected event or piece of data that does not follow the expected pattern or normal trend.

**Anticyclone** – A **high pressure** system in the atmosphere associated with dry, settled periods of weather.

**Aquifer** – A large **store** of underground water usually contained in **porous** rocks.

**Arch** – A landform sometimes found at the coast. Sea arches are formed by the **erosion** of weaknesses in a headland.

**Atmosphere** – The layer of gases surrounding the Earth. The atmosphere is one **store** in the **water cycle**.

**Attrition** – A type of **erosion** where rocks smash against each other making them smaller and more rounded.

## B

**Bar** – A coastal landform created by the **deposition** of sediment across the **mouth** of a river.

**Baseflow** – The normal flow rate of a river caused by **groundwater flow**.

**Bedding plane** – Lines of weakness between the layers of sedimentary rock.

**Bi-lateral aid** – Aid that is passed directly from one country to a partner country.

**Biodiversity** – The variety of living things.

**Biodiversity hot spot** – A region with a particularly great variety of organisms. Central America is one such hot spot.

**Biomes** – Very large **ecosystems** (for example, tropical rainforests or deserts).

**Brain drain** – The reduction in the number of highly qualified workers due to emigration.

**Bunds** – Small stone walls built along contour lines to retain soil moisture and prevent soil being washed away.

**Business rates** – A type of tax paid by a company.

## C

**Canopy** – The upper layer of a forest. The canopy receives most sunlight so contains many leaves, flowers and fruit.

**Carbon cycle** – The flow of carbon between various **stores**.

**Carbon sinks** – Places where carbon is stored over very long periods of time, for example, in fossil fuels.

**Catchment area** – The area from which a river collects its water. This is also called a **drainage basin**.

**Cave** – A natural cavity in rock. This landform is created by **weathering** and **erosion**.

**Channel braiding** – Where a river splits into two or more connected channels before joining up again.

**Channel precipitation** – Water falling directly into a river.

**Circular migration** – The flow and return of people between rural and **urban** areas. People leave the countryside when there are few farming jobs and return at busier times of the year.

**Climate** – Taking **weather** readings over long periods of time, and then working out averages, patterns and trends.

**Climate change** – A long-term change in the annual **weather** conditions. These changes can be natural or caused by human actions.

**Cloud forests** – Tropical forests located in mountains where they are permanently surrounded by cloud.

**Clustered** – Where geographical features are grouped together.

**Commute** – When people who live in rural areas travel every day to jobs in **urban** areas.

**Condensation** – The process in the **water cycle** where water changes state from gas to liquid.

**Confluence** – The point at which two rivers meet.

**Continentality** – The climatic condition of large land masses heating up and cooling down very quickly.

**Corrosion** – The wearing away of the landscape by chemical processes such as **solution**.

**Counter-urbanisation** – The movement of people and businesses from large cities to smaller towns and rural areas.

**Cut-off** – The point where river **erosion** closes the neck of a **meander** to leave an ox-bow lake.

**Cycle** – A repeating series of events, such as the **water cycle** or **carbon cycle**.

**Cycle of poverty** – A theory which suggests that children of poor families find it difficult to earn higher incomes.

**Cyclone** – A **low pressure** system in the atmosphere associated with unsettled **weather**, wind and rain.

## D

**Debt** – The money owed by a country.

**Deforestation** – The cutting down or burning of trees.

**De-industrialisation** – A shift in employment from **manufacturing** to jobs that provide a service.

**Delta** – A river landform found at the **mouth** of a river where **deposition** causes new land to be formed.

**Depopulation** – The loss of people due to migration and low birth rates. For example, many of the rural areas of Iceland are suffering from depopulation.

**Deposition** – The laying down of material in the landscape. Deposition occurs when the force that was carrying the **sediment** is reduced.

**Desertification** – When the **climate** of a dry region becomes even drier. Vegetation dies or is eaten by grazing animals and the soil becomes vulnerable to soil **erosion**.

**Development aid** – Help which is given to tackle poverty and improve **quality of life**. Development aid is given to long-term projects such as improving education or healthcare rather than to deal with an emergency such as a famine.

**Development gap** – The difference in wealth between rich and poor countries.

**Direct benefit** – An immediate advantage created by an improvement in the economy. For example, a direct benefit of a new company opening a factory in a region is new jobs.

**Discharge** – The amount of water flowing through a river channel or out of an **aquifer**. Discharge is measured in cubic metres per second (cumecs).

**Distributaries** – The channels which flow away from the main river channel in the **delta** of a river after the main river channel divides.

**Diversify** – When a much wider variety of new business opportunities and jobs is created in a region.

**Drainage basin** – The area from which a river collects its water. This is also called a **catchment area**.

**Drip flow** – Rainwater that falls onto vegetation and then drips from the leaves.

**Drought** – A long period of time with little **precipitation**.

**Dumping** – The practice of selling goods cheaply abroad if they cannot be sold at home. For example, tomatoes that cannot be sold in Europe are sold cheaply in Africa.

## E

**Economic migrant** – A migrant who moves in order to find work.

**Ecosystem** – A community of plants and animals and the environment in which they live. Ecosystems include both living parts (e.g. plants) and non-living parts (e.g. air and water).

**Ecotourism** – Small-scale tourist projects that create money for conservation as well as creating local jobs.

**Emergency aid** – Help that is given urgently after a natural disaster or a conflict to protect the lives of the survivors.

**Emergent** – The tallest trees in a forest that poke out above the **canopy**.

**Emissions** – Chemicals released into the atmosphere by industry, such as nitrogen dioxide.

**Employment structure** – The number of people working in the **primary**, **secondary** and **tertiary sectors** of the economy.

**Enhanced greenhouse effect** – A strengthening of the greenhouse effect caused by the release by humans of large concentrations of **greenhouse gases** into the atmosphere.

**Erosion** – The wearing away of the landscape. See **abrasion**, and **hydraulic action**.

**Estuary** – The tidal part of a river where it widens into the sea.

**Evaporation** – Where water changes state from liquid into vapour.

**Evapotranspiration** – The combined loss of water from vegetation from both evaporation and transpiration.

**Event-led regeneration** – Improvements to an urban area or region triggered by a massive event such as the Olympics.

**Exports** – The sale of products from one country to another.

## F

**FAIRTRADE** – An organisation which aims to guarantee that the producer of goods such as foodstuffs and clothing gets a fair price for their goods.

**Faults** – Major cracks in rocks caused by the Earth's movements.

**Fetch** – The distance a wave travels over open sea.

**Fjords** – Deep-water sea inlets in the coastline of countries that have been **eroded** by ice.

**Flood plain** – The flat area of land either side of a river.

**Floodways** – Artificial channels built to divert the flow of a river.

**Flows** – The movement of a substance from one **store** to another (for example, the ways in which water moves in the **water cycle**).

**Food air miles** – How far the food has been transported to get from producer to consumer.

**Foreign exchange** – The way in which countries earn money from abroad (for example, by the sale of **exports** or by attracting foreign tourists).

**Formal occupations** – Jobs that receive a regular wage and which are recognised and controlled by the state.

**Formal sector** – That part of the economy in which workers have a contract which gives them some rights.

**Free trade** – When countries trade without any limits to the amount of goods that can be **exported** and **imported**.

## G

**Gender inequality** – Differences in income or **quality of life** that exist between men and women.

**Geographical Information System (GIS)** – Geographical data that is stored digitally and can be analysed by creating a map.

**Global warming** – The slight rise in average temperature of the Earth's atmosphere that is a sign of **climate change**.

**Globalisation** – Flows of people, ideas, money and goods are making an increasingly complex global web that links people and places from distant continents together.

**Gorge** – A steep-sided, narrow valley. Gorges are often found below a **waterfall**.

**Greenhouse gases (GGs)** – Gases such as carbon dioxide and methane that are able to trap heat in the atmosphere.

**Gross National Income (GNI) per person** – The average income in a country. It is also known as Gross National Product (GNP) per person.

**Ground surface** – A **store** in the **water cycle**, the boundary between the soil and atmosphere.

**Groundwater flow** – The **flow** of water through rocks.

**Groundwater stores** – Water in the ground below the water table.

**Groyne** – A type of coastal defence scheme consisting of low walls built into the sea. Groynes trap the **sediment** that is being moved by **longshore drift**.

## H

**High pressure** – Values of air pressure between 1020 and 1040 millibars (mb). High-pressure systems are known as **anticyclones** and bring periods of dry, settled weather.

**High-tech industries** – The use of advanced technology in manufacturing such as defence systems and medical equipment.

**Housing tenure** – The legal right to live in a house.

**Hurricane** – A tropical storm caused by a **low pressure** system involving strong winds more than 119 km per hour.

**Hydraulic action** – **Erosion** caused when water and air are forced into gaps in rock or soil.

**Hydro-electric power (HEP)** – Electricity generated by water flowing through turbines.

**Hydrological cycle** – The continuous **flow** of water between the Earth's surface and the atmosphere – more commonly known as the **water cycle**.

**Hydrograph** – A line graph showing **discharge** over time.

**Hypothesis** – A statement that can be proved or disproved using the available evidence.

## I

**Impermeable** – Soil or rock which does not allow water to pass through it, such as clay.

**Import duty** – A tax placed on goods brought into a country to make them more expensive.

**Imports** – The purchase of goods from another country.

**Indigenous peoples** – People who are native to a particular place.

**Indirect benefit** – An advantage that has come as a result of the investment by a business but not within the business itself. For example, an indirect benefit of a new company opening a factory in a region is work for other local businesses.

**Infant mortality rate (IMR)** – The number of children who die before the age of one for every 1,000 that are born.

**Infiltrate** – When rain water seeps down into the ground.

**Infiltration** – The movement of water from the **ground surface** into the soil.

**Informal sector** – The sector of the economy that includes many types of irregular jobs as well as types of work such as household chores, childcare and studying.

**Informal settlements** – Homes where the householders have no legal rights to the land, that is, they do not have legal **housing tenure**. Informal settlements are commonly known as shanty towns and squatter settlements.

**Infrastructure** – The systems needed to make a region work efficiently. These include paved roads, communication facilities, power supply, water supplies and sewers.

**Inner urban** – The central, and usually older, part of a city.

**Intercept** – When water is prevented from falling directly to the ground. For example, the **canopy** of leaves in a forest intercepts rainfall.

**Interdependence** – The complex patterns of trade, communication and aid, which link different countries together.

**Irrigation** – Supplying crops with water on a farm.

**Isolines** – Lines of equal amount on a map. For example, isotherms are lines of equal temperature and isobars are lines of equal pressure.

## J

**Joints** – Cracks that form lines of weaknesses running through rock.

## K

**Key services** – The way in which **ecosystems** provide benefits for people. For example, **mangrove forests** act as coastal buffers, soaking up wave energy during a storm and reducing the risk of erosion and flooding.

**Knowledge economy** – Jobs which require high levels of education or training.

**Knowledge Intensive Service (KIS)** – Industries such as finance and education.

**Kyoto Protocol** – An international agreement made in Kyoto, Japan in 1997 to limit the emission of **greenhouse gases**.

## L

**Labour intensive** – Work that is still done by hand rather than using labour-saving machines.

**Lagoon** – A shallow pond of salt water.

**Leaching** – The removal of **nutrients** from the soil by rainwater washing them away.

**Leeward side** – The side of a barrier (for example, a hill or hedgerow) that is sheltered from the wind.

**Less Economically Developed Countries (LEDCs)** – The countries that are to the south of the Brandt Line in Central and South America, Africa and parts of Asia. Most LEDCs have lower incomes than **More Economically Developed Countries (MEDCs)**.

**Life expectancy** – The average age to which people can expect to live.

**Linear** – A geographical distribution in which the places described fall along a line.

**Load** – The **sediment** carried by a river.

**Longline fishing** – A fishing technique in which fish are caught on hooks on extremely long lines. The technique is criticised by conservationists for killing many species of unwanted fish as well as sea birds, turtles and sharks.

**Longshore drift** – A process by which beach material is moved along the coast.

**Long-term benefits** – Advantages that will have an impact for years to come.

**Low pressure** – Values of air pressure below 1000 millibars (mb). Low-pressure systems are known as **cyclones** and bring periods of unsettled **weather** with strong winds and rain.

## M

**Mangrove forests** – A tropical forest that grows in coastal regions.

**Manufactured goods** – Goods which have been produced in a factory or workshop.

**Manufacturing** – The production of goods and processed materials by the **secondary sector** of the economy.

**Maritime climate** – The climatic condition of land close to sea. The sea moderates temperatures meaning that there are only small variations in temperature.

**Meander** – A sweeping curve or bend in the river's course.

**Mechanisation** – The increased use of machines to replace human labour.

**Meltwater** – Water flowing from a melting glacier. Meltwater rivers are seasonal with very low **discharges** in winter and very high discharges in summer.

**Micro-credit** – Small loans given to businessmen and women who are too poor to qualify for traditional bank loans.

**Millennium Development Goals (MDG)** – Development targets set by the United Nations with aims to meet by 2015.

**More Economically Developed Countries (MEDCs)** – The countries that are to the north of the Brandt Line in North America, Europe, northern Asia and parts of Oceania. Most MEDCs have higher incomes than **Less Economically Developed Countries (LEDCs)**.

**Monsoon** – A **climate** type experienced in South Asia in which a seasonal pattern of wind brings a distinct wet season.

**Mouth** – The point at which a river enters a lake or the sea.

**Multi-lateral aid** – Aid that involves many donor countries.

**Multi-national companies** – Large businesses, such as Sony, Microsoft and McDonald's, which have branches in several countries. Multi-national companies are also known as **trans-national companies**.

## N

**Natural increase** – A population increase which is due to there being more births than deaths.

**Negative multiplier effect** – A downward spiral of decline in the economy. Negative multipliers may be triggered by the closure of a large employer.

**Net in-migration** – When more people move into the region than leave it.

**Net out-migration** – When more people leave the region than move in.

**Non-Governmental Organisations (NGOs)** – Non-profit-making organisations, such as Oxfam, ActionAid or WaterAid, which are independent of the government.

**Nutrient flows** – The movement of minerals from one **store** to another.

**Nutrient stores** – A part of an **ecosystem** in which nutrients are kept.

**Nutrients** – Minerals containing nitrogen and phosphates.

## O

**Oceans** – The major **store** in the **water cycle**.

**Off-grid electricity** – Electricity supplied by using car batteries or photovoltaic cells and which is not connected to the national electricity network.

**Over-abstraction** – When water is abstracted at a faster rate than it is recharged, leading to a **store** of water decreasing in size.

**Overland flow** – The **flow** of water across the **ground surface**.

**Overseas Development Aid (ODA)** – Government funding given to many different long-term development projects abroad.

## P

**Pastoral farmers** – Farmers who keep grazing animals such as cattle or goats.

**Percolation** – A **flow** in the **water cycle**. The movement of water out of the soil and into the rocks below.

**Permafrost** – Soil or rock that has remained frozen for at least two consecutive years. Permafrost is common in the Arctic region.

**Permeable** – A rock which allows water to pass through it, such as limestone.

**Plant** – A factory, office or laboratory.

**Plunge pool** – The pool of water found at the base of a **waterfall**.

**Population density** – The number of people per square kilometre ($km^2$).

**Porous** – A rock which has many tiny gaps within it (pores) that allow it to **store** water, such as chalk and sandstone.

**Positive multiplier** – A positive chain of events triggered by the creation of new jobs in a region.

**Poverty line** – A level of income. If someone earns less than this amount they are said to be poor.

**Precipitation** – The movement of water from the atmosphere to the ground. Precipitation may be in many forms including rain, snow and hail.

**Prevailing wind** – The direction in which the wind most often blows.

**Primary commodities** – Raw materials which have not been processed. Coal, minerals and unprocessed foodstuffs are all examples.

**Primary enrolment** – The percentage of children of primary school age who regularly attend primary school.

**Primary sector** – The part of the economy that produces raw materials such as a foodstuffs, timber or minerals.

**Private sector** – People who are either **self-employed** or work for a larger company or organisation that is not controlled by the government.

**Public sector** – People employed by the national, regional or local government.

**Pull factors** – Reasons that attract migrants to move to a new home.

**Push factors** – Reasons that force people to move away from their existing home.

## Q

**Quality of life** – A measure of the happiness and contentment of an individual or family.

**Quotas** – Restrictions on the amount of particular goods that can be **imported** each year.

## R

**Rain shadow** – A **climate** effect causing an area located on the **leeward side** of a mountain to have low rainfall.

**Rainwater harvesting** – The collection of rainwater. For example, the collection and use of rainwater from the roof of a house.

**Random** – Where geographical features are scattered at irregular distances from each other.

**Recharge** – Water that enters an **aquifer** and refills a **groundwater store**.

**Refugees** – People who are in danger and who leave their homes for their own safety. Refugees may move because of a natural disaster such as a volcanic eruption or because of conflict.

**Regular** – Where geographical features are equally spaced.

**Remittances** – The return of money sent by migrant workers to support their families who have remained at home.

**Remote sensing** – Collecting geographical data from a distance. For example, satellites orbiting the Earth are used to collect data about **weather** systems.

**Renewable resource** – Something useful to people that is capable of replacing itself. Water, forests and wind energy are all examples of renewable resources.

**Respiration** – The biological process of breathing in which living things take in the oxygen that is needed for life and expel waste gases such as carbon dioxide.

**Revetments** – Structures that reduce the **erosion** of coastlines and river banks.

**Right-to-buy schemes** – Scheme giving the tenants of local authority housing the right to buy their council house.

**Rotational cliff slumping** – A process where soft cliffs collapse towards the sea.

**Rural depopulation** – When the population of a rural region decreases.

## S

**Sahel** – The semi-arid region of North Africa to the south of the Sahara desert. The word means 'shore' in Arabic.

**Saltation** – A process of river **transport** where **sediment** bounces along the bed of the river.

**Sanitation** – The safe disposal and treatment of sewage and waste water.

**Savanna** – An **ecosystem** of grasslands with scattered trees and bushes, and which has a seasonal wet/dry **climate**.

**Second homes** – Houses which are used only for holidays or at weekends. Also called holiday cottages.

**Secondary sector** – The secondary sector is the part of the economy which is involved in processing and manufacturing.

**Security of tenure** – Where people have the legal right to live in their home and not be evicted indiscriminately.

**Sediment** – Material carried by a river or wave in the sea. Sediment varies in size from large particles such as boulders through gravel and sand down to silt and mud.

**Self-employed** – People who work for themselves.

**Self-help** – Improvement projects carried out by ordinary people rather than by businesses or governments. Many homes in **informal settlements** are improved in this way.

**Short-term benefits** – Advantages that will have an impact over the next few months.

**Social housing** – Homes that are rented from a not-for-profit organisation such as a housing association or the local authority.

**Social premium** – A small payment made by **FAIRTRADE** companies to their suppliers, which is then used to fund community projects such as wells.

**Socio-economic** – A combination of social and economic factors.

**Socio-economic group** – A group of people who have similar social and economic characteristics. For example, school leavers who have been unable to find a job and are therefore claiming benefit are members of one socio-economic group.

**Soft engineering** – Alternative method of reducing floods by planting trees or allowing areas to flood naturally.

**Soil store** – **Store** in the **water cycle** between the **ground surface** and rock, composed of minerals, organic matter, air and water.

**Solar footprint** – The amount of the Sun's energy that heats each square metre ($m^2$) of the Earth.

**Solution** – A type of river **transport** where dissolved **sediment** is carried in river water. Solution is also a way in which rainwater is able to wear away certain rocks, especially chalk and limestone.

**Source** – The place where a river starts to flow.

**Spit** – A coastal landform formed by the **deposition** of **sediment** in a low mound where the coastline changes direction, for example, at the **mouth** of a river.

**Stack** – An **erosional** landform, a pillar of rock that remains when a headland recedes.

**Standard of living** – A measure of the relative wealth of individuals or families.

**Stem flow** – Rainwater that falls onto vegetation and then trickles down branches and stems.

**Stewardship** – The concept that humans should care for the environment so that future generations can also enjoy it.

**Store** – A place where something remains for a period of time (for example, within the **water cycle** or **carbon cycle**).

**Stump** – A low pillar of rock that is left behind when a stack has been eroded.

**Sub-Saharan Africa** – Africa South of the Sahara.

**Subsidy** – A payment which a country makes to its own farmers and businesses so that their goods can be sold at a lower price to consumers.

**Subsistence** – A type of economic activity where very little money is used. In subsistence farming the farmer produces only enough food to feed the family. There is very little surplus that can be sold for cash.

**Suburban sprawl** – When a city expands into the neighbouring countryside. Greenfield sites are used to build new **urban** homes, offices and retail parks at the edge of the city.

**Surface stores** – Places where water is found on the surface such as lakes and rivers.

**Suspension** – A process of river **transport** where **sediment** is lifted and carried by the flow of water.

**Sustainable development** – Making changes that improve the **quality of life** for people today but without damaging the environment so that future generations will also be able to have a reasonable quality of life.

## T

**Tele-working** – Jobs where most of the working week is spent working from home. Tele-working (or tele-cottaging) has been made more widely available by the use of personal computers, mobile technology and the internet.

**Tertiary sector** – This part of the economy provides services to other industries or to individual consumers like you and me. Retailing, health and education are all examples of the tertiary sector.

**Therapeutic food** – Food high in protein and fat that is given as part of an **emergency aid** package to treat malnourished children.

**Thermal** – A column of warm rising air.

**Throughflow** – The **flow** of water through the soil. Part of the **water cycle**.

**Tombolo** – A coastal landform made by **deposition** of **sediment** joining the coast to an island.

**Total annual rainfall** – The sum of all the rainfall over a period of a year.

**Traction** – A process of river **transport** where **sediment** is pushed along the riverbed by the **flow** of water.

**Trade blocs** – Trading partnerships between different countries. The European Union is one example.

**Trans-boundary conflicts** – Disputes between neighbouring regions or countries. Conflicts can be caused by the use of water from a river that flows from one country to another.

**Trans-national companies (TNCs)** – Large businesses, such as Sony, Microsoft and McDonald's, which have branches in several countries. Trans-national companies are also known as **multi-national companies**.

**Transpiration** – Water loss from plants though pores in the leaves.

**Transport** – The movement of material through the landscape.

**Tundra** – An **ecosystem** largely found in the Arctic region. The tundra is treeless because the growing season is short and the average monthly temperature is below 10°C.

## U

**Undercutting** – **Erosion** at the base of a river cliff, sea cliff or **waterfall**.

**Unemployment** – The percentage of people who do not have a paid job.

**Unsustainable** – At a rate that cannot be maintained.

**Unsustainable development** – Improving the lives of people but in a way that is using up too many natural resources and/or is polluting the environment so badly that future generations will have a lower **quality of life**.

**Urban** – Larger towns and cities. The United Nations definition is that urban settlements have more than 20,000 inhabitants.

**Urban heat island** – When a city has temperatures that are warmer than in the surrounding rural area.

**Urban microclimate** – The small-scale, local climate of a large city which is influenced by its buildings and traffic.

**Urban population** – The percentage of a country's population that lives in settlements greater than 20,000 people.

**Urbanisation** – The physical and human growth of cities.

## V

**Vegetation store** – Water stored in plants. Part of the **water cycle**.

## W

**Water cycle** – The continuous **flow** of water between the Earth's surface and the atmosphere – also called the **hydrological cycle**.

**Watershed** – The boundary of a **drainage basin**.

**Wave-cut notch** – **Undercut** slot cut into the bottom of a cliff by wave action.

**Wave-cut platform** – A rocky shelf in front of a cliff. The wave-cut platform is caused by **erosion** and left by the retreat of the cliff.

**Weather** – Our day-to-day experience of temperature, wind, **precipitation** and sunshine.

**Weather hazards** – **Weather** conditions that could potentially result in harmful or damaging effects.

**Weathering** – The breaking up of rock by the effects of the **weather** such as rainfall and temperature change.

**Wetlands** – **Ecosystems** which are naturally saturated with water.

**Wilderness** – Areas that have been left in a wild state. Wilderness regions are uninhabited and are not farmed. Large parts of Iceland can be described as wilderness.

**Wildlife corridor** – Strips of habitat which allow wild animals to migrate from one **ecosystem** to another. For example, wildlife corridors can be created by planting hedgerows and trees to connect remaining fragments of forest together.

**Wing dikes** – Walls built into the river channel to increase river flow and thereby to deepen the river channel.

# Index